Reversible Polymeric Gels
and Related Systems

ACS SYMPOSIUM SERIES **350**

Reversible Polymeric Gels and Related Systems

Paul S. Russo, EDITOR

Louisiana State University

Developed from a symposium sponsored by
the Division of Polymer Chemistry, Inc.
at the 191st Meeting
of the American Chemical Society,
New York, New York,
April 13–18, 1986

American Chemical Society, Washington, DC 1987

Library of Congress Cataloging-in-Publication Data

Reversible polymeric gels and related systems/Paul S.
Russo, editor.
   p.   cm.—(ACS symposium series, ISSN
0097-6156; 350)

   "Developed from a symposium sponsored by the
Division of Polymer Chemistry, Inc., at the 191st
meeting of the American Chemical Society, New York,
N.Y., April 13-18, 1986."

   Includes bibliographies and indexes.

ISBN 0-8412-1415-8

   1. Colloids—Congresses. 2. Polymers and
polymerization—Congresses.

   I. Russo, Paul S., 1954-   . II. American Chemical
Society. Division of Polymer Chemistry. III. American
Chemical Society. Meeting (191st: 1986: New York,
N.Y.) IV. Series.

QD549.R46   1987   87-20305
551.3'451—dc19   CIP

ACS Symposium Series

M. Joan Comstock, *Series Editor*

1987 Advisory Board

Foreword

The ACS SYMPOSIUM SERIES was founded in 1974 to provide a medium for publishing symposia quickly in book form. The format of the Series parallels that of the continuing ADVANCES IN CHEMISTRY SERIES except that, in order to save time, the papers are not typeset but are reproduced as they are submitted by the authors in camera-ready form. Papers are reviewed under the supervision of the Editors with the assistance of the Series Advisory Board and are selected to maintain the integrity of the symposia; however, verbatim reproductions of previously published papers are not accepted. Both reviews and reports of research are acceptable, because symposia may embrace both types of presentation.

Contents

Preface..ix

1. A Perspective on Reversible Gels and Related Systems...................1
   Paul S. Russo

2. Viscoelastic Behavior of Ultra High Molecular Weight Polyethylene
   Pseudogels...22
   B. Chung and A. E. Zachariades

3. Dynamic Light Scattering and Transient Electric Birefringence Study
   of Poly(vinyl chloride) Microgels...................................33
   S. J. Candau, Y. Dormoy, E. Hirsch, P. H. Mutin, and J. M. Guenet

4. Concentration Dependence of the Polymer Diffusion Coefficient..........46
   Wender Wan and Scott L. Whittenburg

5. Effects of Aggregation and Solvent Quality on the Viscosity
   of Semidilute Poly(vinylbutyral) Solutions............................57
   C. W. Paul and P. M. Cotts

6. Reversible Polymer Complexes Stabilized Through Hydrogen Bonds.......72
   Ilias Iliopoulos, Roland Audebert, and Claude Quivoron

7. Association and Gelation of Polystyrenes via Terminal Sulfonate Groups...87
   Martin Möller, Jürgen Omeis, and Elke Mühleisen

8. Solvent Mobility in Atactic Polystyrene–Toluene Systems...............107
   Frank D. Blum and Byaporn naNagara

9. Physical Gelation of a Steroid–Cyclohexane System: Kinetic
   Phenomenological Approach.......................................115
   P. Terech

10. Nematic Solutions of Rodlike Polymers: Light Scattering from Nematic
    Solutions with Complex Texture and Phase Separation in Poor Solvents...129
    Kazunori Se and G. C. Berry

11. Gelation of Poly(γ-benzyl-α,L-glutamate)............................152
    Paul S. Russo, Paul Magestro, and Wilmer G. Miller

12. Structure Formation and Phase Transformations in Solutions of a Rigid
    Polymer..181
    Yachin Cohen, Herbert H. Frost, and Edwin L. Thomas

13. Ordering and Gelation in DNA Solutions............................199
    Victor A. Bloomfield

14. Thermally Reversible Gelation of the Gelatin–Water System.............211
    Madeleine Djabourov and Jacques Leblond

15. In Vitro Polymerization of Complex Cytoplasmic Gels................224
    Ralph Nossal

16. **Thermally Reversible Hydrogels: Swelling Characteristics and Activities of Copoly(*N*-isopropylacrylamide–acrylamide) Gels Containing Immobilized Asparaginase**..........................236
   Liang Chang Dong and Allan S. Hoffman

17. ***N*-Isopropylacrylamide and *N*-Acryloxysuccinimide Copolymer: A Thermally Reversible, Water-Soluble, Activated Polymer for Protein Conjugation**...245
   Carol-Ann Cole, Sigrid M. Schreiner, John H. Priest, Nobuo Monji, and Allan S. Hoffman

18. **Lower Critical Solution Temperatures of Aqueous Copolymers of *N*-Isopropylacrylamide and Other *N*-Substituted Acrylamides**........255
   John H. Priest, Sheryl L. Murray, R. John Nelson, and Allan S. Hoffman

19. **Polymer Network Studies Using Paramagnetic Probes: Cu(II) in Cross-Linked Polyacrylamide Gels**..........................265
   Gary C. Rex and Shulamith Schlick

INDEXES

Author Index...284

Affiliation Index...284

Subject Index..284

Preface

ONE OF THE UNIQUE CHARACTERISTICS of macromolecules is the physical control they can exert upon less complex systems such as simple fluids. Nowhere is this more evident than in gels, where a macromolecular component, usually present in minor amounts, solidifies a liquid system. This remarkable transformation is only achieved by molecules or assemblies that possess a great span *and* a mechanism of associating with similar molecules to produce a three-dimensional, space-filling structure. The associations may be covalent (chemical gels) or reversible (physical gels). The structures and underlying mechanisms of reversible gelation are varied and not fully understood in most cases. However, substantial progress is being made, in part due to powerful techniques such as cold-stage electron microscopy, video-enhanced optical microscopy, and rheo-optical methods. Greater sophistication in data analysis and theoretical interpretation permits conventional methods, such as dynamic light scattering, to make greater contributions than were once possible. The resurgent interest in reversible gelation is evident among scientists of practically every discipline. Even as biologists display increased interest in the elegant reversible gels that nature has employed for eons, chemists and engineers dealing with synthetic polymers have come to realize the opportunities afforded by reversibly gelling systems for novel materials and devices.

The symposium from which this book was developed brought together a diverse group of researchers involved in reversible polymer gels. During the preparation of the symposium, it became evident that not only reversible gels, but also related systems such as transient gels, semidilute solutions, and permanent gels, were of interest to some researchers planning to attend. Speakers included physical and organic chemists, theoretical physicists, biochemists and biophysical chemists, and materials scientists and engineers from industrial and academic laboratories. The diversity in the audience was even greater. It is a testimony to the need for cross-disciplinary approaches and thought processes in gel research that most participants attended from start to finish, even though the symposium—like the book—was arranged approximately by subdiscipline, and despite strong competing symposia.

This book should appeal to scientists who, like most gel researchers, have no formal training in gels per se but encounter them as interesting extensions of more traditional systems. The book has a reservoir of good ideas and techniques from a variety of disciplines and will be a success if it enhances the interchange of ideas from one subdiscipline to another. The overview chapter, Chapter 1, looks at the nature of gels in general and reversible gels in particular. References, a solid definition of the term "gel", a proposed gel classification scheme, and a prospectus for future research appear in this chapter. We hope that this chapter will be useful to the newcomer while providing fresh viewpoints and information for the veteran gel researcher. Chapters 2–8 concern synthetic systems in nonaqueous media. Subjects run the gamut from fundamental science in support of an important commercial gel process to theory, experiments involving semidilute solutions, and new information about other important systems. Chapter 9 is a thorough and fascinating study of a small molecule that assembles into structures large enough to gel. Chapters 10–12 focus on gels made from rodlike polymers. A clearer understanding of gelation phenomena will be required to perfect high-performance materials and superstructures made from such macromolecules. Chapters 13 and 14 give clear accounts of the state of knowledge about gelation of two important biomolecules that are also rather stiff chains: DNA, which displays some extraordinary transitions that may be related to its recently discovered reversible gelation, and gelatin, the classic reversible gel. These chapters mark the transition to aqueous systems. Chapter 15 presents kinetic theory pertaining to one of nature's most elegant networks, the cytoskeleton. It is encouraging that such a complex system can be modeled in tractable form. Chapters 16–18 deal with a promising copolymer for biomedical applications. Chapter 19 demonstrates the use of spin resonance for determination of ionic and water environments in gel systems.

I was fortunate to have many helpers while I arranged the symposium and edited this book. In particular, I thank Juanita Miller for her efficient and organized handling of the considerable correspondence associated with both the symposium and this book. My cochair of the symposium, Paul Dubin of Indiana–Purdue University at Indianapolis, was a vital source of helpful suggestions and advice. I thank all the reviewers for their careful, prompt, and constructive evaluations of the articles. Finally, I thank all the contributors for their patience, cooperation, and attention to detail.

PAUL S. RUSSO
Department of Chemistry
Louisiana State University
Baton Rouge, LA 70803–1804

June 3, 1987

Chapter 1

A Perspective on Reversible Gels and Related Systems

Paul S. Russo

Macromolecular Studies Group, Department of Chemistry, Louisiana State University, Baton Rouge, LA 70803-1804

The features common to reversible polymer gels of many types are identified and discussed. The nature of the gel state is carefully defined, and a novel classification scheme based on morphology, rather than chemical or mechanistic considerations, is proposed. The article also serves as an overview to some of the more commonly used techniques used in the study of gels, and as an introduction to some of the current trends in reversible gel research. Some speculations regarding future trends in reversible gel research are presented.

Of all the physical states, there is something especially elusive about gels. Systems which gel reversibly are particularly difficult to understand, for the requirement is that an enormous transformation of physical state must occur, usually involving only a small portion of the system. Yet an astounding variety of mechanisms can result in reversible gelation, and it seems that a general understanding of reversible gels will not soon be achieved. Perhaps the greatest universality is presently found in the objectives of gel researchers and the obstacles to meeting them (1). The would-be gel researcher must first confirm positively that the system is a gel. Even this isn't always trivial. Next, the conditions under which reversible gelation occurs must be carefully mapped out. Recent controversies show that this matter is often complex, too. After these preliminaries, a structural analysis of the gel is appropriate. Next, it is often of considerable interest to undertake the kinetic study of how the structure forms during gelation--a question which is often the most difficult of all. Finally, we may add such practical concerns as the commercial utility or biological function of the gel.

0097-6156/87/0350-0001$06.25/0
© 1987 American Chemical Society

Several factors conspire against research into the above
issues.   The viscoelastic nature of gels can exhibit long-term
and sample history effects.   It is often necessary to account for
the delicate interplay between non-equilibrium phenomena and
seemingly equilibrium structure.   Conveniently measureable
transitions--such as visual clearing--may or may not be actually
connected to true melting.   Weak optical contrast can impede
conventional optical microscopy for morphological analysis, even
in systems where the structural elements are otherwise large
enough.   Also, unlike many conventional solids, the mechanical
weakness of gels can complicate electron microscopic
investigations.   Accordingly, gel structure and its development
can often only be inferred from indirect observations.

The foregoing problems surface as central themes for the
many diverse studies in this collection.   However, each study has
its own "flavor", derived in part from the system itself but also
from the traditions and lore of a specific scientific discipline,
there being no science devoted exclusively to the study of gels.
It is interesting to consider the backgrounds of our
contributors.   Included are polymer/colloid physical chemists,
biophysical chemists, physicists, materials scientists and
engineers, and at least part-time synthetic chemists.   On a
global scale, the field is even more diverse.   Most are led to
gel problems, not as a primary area of interest, but as an
extension of other efforts.   Occasionally, this diversity of
interests and backgrounds seems to have led to misunderstandings,
as workers with different objectives and training have paid more
or less attention to particular aspects of a given problem.   For
example, much of the current interest in polyethylene gels
derives from gel spinning operations for the production of
commercially important ultrahigh modulus fibers ($\underline{2},\underline{3}$).   Perhaps
it was the focus on fiber spinning which led to the belief ($\underline{4}$)
that stirring was a prerequisite for gelation.   Exhaustive
studies have now shown that this is not the case ($\underline{5}$).
Occasionally, problems of language can interfere with a clear
picture.   For example, terms such as " 'adsorption entanglement'
(gel)" are probably best avoided.   In this paper, we shall
endeavor to be as precise about the term "gel" as possible.

Turning to a more general view of the interplay between
various areas of research, we find synthetic polymer gel problems
being attacked on at least two fronts.   A battalion of
researchers with roots in the dilute solution characterization of
polymers and colloids using methods such as light scattering,
dynamic birefringence, sedimentation, viscosity, etc., ($\underline{6}$) is
allied with materials scientists and engineers, armed with
electron microscopes, rheological equipment, dynamic mechanical
testers, and the like.   Since the target gel objectives of this
battle are neither conventional dilute solutions nor materials in
the usual sense, measurement techniques are often stretched to
their limits.   Little wonder that clever new adaptations are so
actively sought ($\underline{7}$).   In the biological theater, cytologists are
allied with chemists, biochemists, and physicists in an assault
on difficult structure/function problems.   The added dimension of
performing "in vivo" experiments has resulted in powerful,
noninvasive and sensitive techniques, such as video microscopy

(see below). Also, it is in the biological sciences, where gel
electrophoresis is so widespread, that gels serve as a research
tool. As a result, preparative techniques for making the
(covalently crosslinked) acrylamide gels are very highly refined,
and this has enabled beautifully clever and reproducible
experiments on the thermodynamic nature of the gel state (8-13).
Much of what is learned should carry over to reversible gels, and
it seems that the opportunities for new devices (14) based on gel
transitions abound. In sum, the study of reversible gels and
related systems exemplifies interdisciplinary science at its
best, uniting as it does individuals with true expertise in
diverse specialty areas.

The remainder of this chapter is devoted first to
elaborating on the terminology and common issues of reversible
gel research, secondly to identifying and comparing some of the
strategies that contributors from diverse fields have found
successful, and lastly to speculate about future trends of
research in reversible gels and related systems.

Fundamental Considerations

The Ferry Definition. Abuse of the word "gel" is a persistent
problem, despite the clarifying efforts of prominent authors
(15,16). A particularly common error is the reference to any
highly viscous solution as a gel. Thus, it will be convenient to
begin with a precise statement of what a gel is. A satisfactory
and succinct definition was given by Ferry many years ago (16):

A gel "is a substantially diluted system which
exhibits no steady state flow".

Implicit in this simple definition are some important
limitations. For example, gels are restricted to liquid-bearing
colloidal systems--dispersions of one ultrafine material in a
liquid. Thus, frozen solutions, or even frozen gels (defined as
a gel where the liquid component has solidified on the molecular
scale), are not gels. Neither, for our purposes, are dried gels,
even if the drying is accomplished without perturbing the network
structure. The Ferry definition clearly identifies the gel state
as a macroscopic solid, but difficult issues of time and physical
scale are required to make this judgement. For example, in order
to determine whether a solution is a gel, one might turn it on
its side and observe whether it flows. But how long should one
be prepared to wait? How large must the sample be? Certainly,
large enough that capillarity could not account for any observed
lack of flow, but not so large that the gel structure would
disintegrate under its own weight.

Analogous problems exist for practically every conceivable
alternative test. In the commonly used "ball drop" method
(17), a chemically inert sphere is placed on top of the gel, and
its motion under gravitational influence observed. But for how
long? How large must the sphere be? Large enough that it is
retained by the reticular gel structure, but not so large that
its weight destroys the gel. Many workers would agree that
rheological measurement is the soundest method for identifying

gels. For example, if we place a dilute suspension suspected to
be a gel between two horizontal parallel plates and apply a weak
static shear strain by displacing the upper plate a small and
fixed distance while holding the lower plate still, we expect the
true gel to exert a counterbalancing force. Ideally, the force
required of us to maintain the displacement would be constant,
but how long are we willing to wait to ensure that it is?   And
how small must the shear displacement be to ensure that the gel
structure is not perturbed by the measurement? The difficulty of
these questions is emphasized by the results of studies on
covalently crosslinked networks (18).   In such systems, long-time
relaxation processes associated with entanglement release are
often found, but a residual force associated with the elasticity
of chain segments between covalent crosslinks does remain almost
indefinitely. The temporary force associated with the release of
entanglements demonstrates that even these gels, which are
undoubtedly permanent on any chemically significant time scale,
have some temporary character, which can be perturbed by the
measurement itself. Thus, rheological measurement substitutes
the human sense of vision used in simple "flow" or "ball-drop"
experiments, which might be augmented by a microscope,
cathetometer, or other motion-sensing mechanism, with the sense
of touch, as enhanced by the rheometer. Nevertheless, the
potential for ambiguity remains.

Comparison to More Common Physical States. From the foregoing,
one may deduce that restraint in the rigorous application of any
definition of the gel state is appropriate. In fact, there is
nothing new about this. The same problems exist in
characterizing liquids and solids. Ordinary glass is thought to
be a fluid on the appropriate time scale, but tossing a rock at a
windowpane has a distinctly different result from dropping one
into a lake, which in turn is rather different from skimming a
stone across a smooth pond. Similarly, ice is both solid enough
to skate upon, and liquid enough to form glacial "rivers" ,
depending on physical scale (19). The only new feature of
gelling systems is that we are less accustomed to "typical" time
and physical scales. We require a standard.
     Lack of steady flow of a liquid-bearing colloidal solution
requires the existence of a space-filling, three-dimensional
structure. As we might select a perfect crystal as a canonical
solid, or liquid argon as a prototypical liquid, we can choose
the covalently crosslinked network, without any entanglements, to
represent the ideal gel state. Then an appropriate time scale
for reversible gels would be the lifetime of a typical crosslink
bond: if subjected to conditions that would cause flow in a pure
liquid but which at the same time do not disrupt the gel
structure, a permanent gel should not exhibit steady flow over a
period of several years. Regarding physical scale, the system
should be large enough that capillary forces would not impede
flow but small enough to avoid collapse. Where these time and
physical scales are inapplicable or inconvenient (i.e., for gels
in vivo) it can be tested, at least in principle, whether a
portion (the structural portion) of the system is immobile on a
time scale appropriate for the system and research at hand.

When discussing a new gel it is exceedingly important that full details of the observation that led to describing the system as a gel be given, including: physical scale; method of determining flow, and, especially, duration of the observation.

When is the gel formed? As if it were not difficult enough to decide whether a system is a true gel under just one set of conditions, it is often valuable to determine a map ("phase diagram" is not always appropriate, implying as it does equilibrium structure) showing how conditions may be varied and gelation still be obtained. Some of the major factors are concentration, temperature, and chain length. For ionic gels, pH, ionic strength, even ion type, can be important. Biopolymer gels often involve several components, and their mutual synergism must be charted (20). The detailed sample history is sometimes important, certainly more often for gels than for most simpler colloidal solutions. For example, in order for the spinodal decomposition mechanism of phase separation (21,22), which has been considered as a potential gelation mechanism (23, and references therein), to dominate over nucleation and growth, very rapid quenching may be required for any solution away from the critical composition.

A Classification Scheme for Gels: Fishnet & Lattice Gels

Provided that gelation has been confirmed and properly mapped, it is appropriate to turn to morphological considerations. General and excellent schemes for classifying gels have been proposed (15,24). These classification schemes are based on the chemical nature and interactions of the building blocks making up various types of gels. For example, stereoregular homopolymers may fall into one category; covalently bonded gels into another, etc. This is a very useful approach, and what follows is not meant to replace it so much as to offer a different viewpoint. In the present scheme, there are two very broad categories of structure--"fishnet" and "lattice", which can, in fact, be achieved by a variety of mechanisms. Thus, the viewpoint offered below is strongly tied to the end structure of the gel, and only indirectly to chemical properties which produce them. The various structures are defined in the text, but use is also made of simple drawings. It is hoped that others will adopt the wider use of simple pictorial diagrams for the description of gel structures.
      Some consideration of the mechanisms which can lead to the various structures is appropriate, even though this is not the basis of the classification scheme. In this connection, it may be noted that mechanisms are often the least-known aspect of gelation. Accordingly, in this paper we will not just limit discussion to the most commonly considered mechanisms, but will also include reasonable hypothesized ones, for which there may be little experimental evidence so far.

Fishnet Gels. By analogy with typical covalent gels, reversible gel structures are frequently discussed in terms of "crosslinks" which join "network strands". In reversible gels, the crosslinks must be the result of molecular association, but the details vary. The necessary condition is that a polymer chain, on average, pass through two or more "domains of association", resulting in a network. The structure within these domains-- i.e., within the crosslink--depends primarily on the crystallizability of the polymer and is the subject of much current interest. The simplest case is that of easily crystallizable stereoregular chains where the relationship between gelation and crystallization has been documented thoroughly and a plausible mechanism of gelation has been put forth (5,24).

Polymers that are not crystallizable in the bulk phase, or only very weakly crystallizable, are not so well understood. This category includes such polymers as atactic polystyrene (25-29) or poly(vinylchloride) (30,31 and references therein). A closely related problem is the gelation of non-block copolymers (5), which share with atactic polymers the feature that chemically and conformationally homogeneous sequences may be relatively short, so that when two or more chains interact, large crystalline domains are prevented from forming.

Let us explore just two noncrystalline systems, in order to gauge the complexity of the situation. For example, in poly(vinylchloride) it has been proposed that gelation occurs by molecular entanglement and hydrogen bonding, while crystal formation occurs only later (30). This result is based on: determinations of the heat of gelation via the Eldridge-Ferry relationship (32) in various solvents with different H-bonding character; partially on the observed difference between the temperature of melting as measured by falling ball methods and the temperature of a thermodynamic transition associated with crystal melting, as measured by differential scanning calorimetry (DSC); and, finally, on the observation that DSC melting endotherms were absent (or undetectably weak) in young gels, appearing slowly over a period of several hours, well after gelation. Before generalizing these these results, it should be remembered that poly(vinylchloride) samples differ from source to source.

A rather different picture emerges from the extensive studies of ethylene copolymer gels, where DSC endotherms are coincident with the ball drop melting temperatures (5). It is argued that this shows that crystallization is a requirement for gelation. Indeed, it is unlikely that the agreement between the DSC and "ball drop" melting temperatures in (5) is fortuitous--i.e., that the some supposed initial, non-crystalline gel structure and the final crystallite structure have identical melting points. Thus, is likely that, in the ethylene copolymer gels, the equilibrium gel has a crystalline crosslink. However, this does not prove that crystallization is a necessary condition for gelation. There remains the possibility that the gel is first established by another mechanism, such as aggregation, and only later converts to a form stabilized by crystalline junctions (27), perhaps at the expense of the initial gel structure, thereby rendering its earlier existence undetectable in a ball drop or DSC melting experiment.

In the two systems just considered, gelation is taken to occur from a one-phase solution. However, under some circumstances, there is the possibility that liquid-liquid phase separation precedes crystallization, and that a gel forms as a result of this process. A crystallization process may or may not be superimposed on this phase separation at a later time, and the crystals may or may not further stabilize the gel.   One may surmise that the detailed nature of the crosslink is sometimes a very difficult problem. The crosslink may be a well-formed crystallite, or it may be a much more nebulous "aggregate", or it may even transform from the latter to the former. One tactic which may help in these complex systems is to focus on microgel particles, using the powerful tools of dilute solution analysis. An interesting example of this approach appears in this book (31). However, it is not necessary for a classification scheme to dwell excessively these details.

The fundamental feature shared by all the above systems is the very existence of crosslinks--nevermind their structure-- which are separated by flexible polymer strands. The crosslink is the "strong point" of the structure, with the strand providing the elasticity, quite like typical covalent gels. ALL networks of this type, whether reversible or covalent, will be referred to as fishnet gels. These systems obviously bear some structural resemblence to typical rubberlike networks, especially when the crosslink occupies a relatively small portion of the available volume. As a striking example of the utility of this relationship, the maximum draw ratio of polyethylene films prepared by drying gels has been successfully accounted for by modifying the classical rubberlike theory to account for the initial solvent content (3).

Lattice Gels. The customary division of gel structure into strong crosslink and loose strand is often too restrictive. The requirement for gelation is more fundamentally that a permanent, space filling structure exist. The familiar concepts of "crosslinks" and "strands" are supplemental, not basic. We shall refer to those space-filling structures in which a clean division of structure into crosslinks and strands is inappropriate as "lattice gels". For example, a lattice structure could be evolved during an attempt, perhaps incomplete, by the system to separate into two phases, especially by a nucleation-free mechanism (spinodal decomposition). Although a crystallization process may be superimposed upon the spinodal decomposition, this is not really necessary, as sometimes supposed (24). For example, the creation of a polymer-rich phase might generate regions containing entanglements of sufficiently long lifetime to qualify as a gel structure, or even "glassy" regions. This hypothesis is discussed relative to rodlike polymer gels elsewhere in this book (23). Lattice gels might also be made by the assembly of small subunits, involving specific or non-specific interactions between the structural components, and it is possible that spinodal decomposition might occur as a prelude to this sort of process (96; see below). Lastly, we place all gels made from rigid fibrillar structures into this category, including covalently linked gels of rodlike polymers (33). Lattice gels obviously do not bear the formal resemblence

to rubberlike networks that fishnet gels do. Conspicuously
absent is a proper mechanical/viscoelastic treatment for such
systems.

Macroscopic Examples. It is helpful to consider larger, more
tangible analogs of these basic types of structure. A fishnet or
volleyball net, especially when not under any tension, is a
two-dimensional example of a "fishnet gel". Anyone who has had
the misfortune of getting tangled up in seaweed while swimming
has had a frightening encounter with a three-dimensional,
macroscopic analog of a fishnet gel. Large lattice structures
are slightly more obscure. Figure 1 shows two kinds of lattice
structures. Geologically slow "phase separation", brought about
by convection of a mud-stone "solution", has produced a
two-dimensional lattice structure at Spitsbergen, Figure 1a.
This figure may be compared to Figure 7a of Ref. 23 and, perhaps,
to Figure 5 of Ref. 34. More coordinated growth processes may
also lead to lattice structures, as exemplified by a venerable
crape myrtle (Lagerstroemia indica) on the campus of Louisiana
State University, Figure 1b, which may be compared to Figures 3
and 4 of the article by Terech (this book), and Figure 1b of Ref.
35. In both the "spongy" lattice of Figure 1a and the fibrillar
lattice of Figure 1b, the structure is continuous, and the
mechanical distinction between crosslinks and strands is obscure.
Certainly, it would not be easy to evaluate the relative strength
or resiliency of the various parts of the structure without
additional information. Yet the structures are space-filling (in
the appropriate dimension) and, like fishnet gels, would even be
viscoelastic in an appropriate limit (36).

Transient Gels. A transient gel is any in which the structure is
not "permanent", as defined on the time scale already proposed.
As discussed elsewhere (15, 18: pp. 537-8), this sort of gel can
occur when the structural elements are in sufficiently rapid
dynamic equilibrium with the sol fraction and/or other structural
components, as may occur in gels stabilized by ionic
complexation, hydrogen bonds, or other weak attractions. Gels of
this type may eventually "heal" if fractured. However, the
transient gels currently receiving the most attention are those
solutions in which polymer overlap leads to temporary crosslinks
by chain entanglement (37-39). These "complex solutions" are a
convenient bridge between the well-understood properties of
dilute solutions and more complex systems such as gels, swollen
polymers and melts. For perturbations of time $t < t_r$, where t_r
is the time required to remove the topological constraint by the
motions of the polymers, the system behaves as a gel. Yet one
would not usually speak in terms of fracturing these solutions,
and only the very impatient would grow tired waiting for a
typical entangled solution to exhibit flow, so they are not
properly considered as permanent gels, EXCEPT in case $t_r \longrightarrow \infty$
(i.e., when a glass transition has been reached). In the scheme
proposed above, entangled solutions of random coil polymers would
be transient fishnet gels, while entangled rods would be
transient lattice gels. It should be noted that the

simple picture of topological constraint by entanglement is
coming under increased scrutiny where solutions are involved,
since the forces of constraint are actually transmitted via
hydrodynamic interaction (40-42, 97). Despite the differences in
the physical structure of permanent and transient gels, it is
fitting to consider transient gel systems in this collection; to
assert otherwise would be to deny the importance of short-time
perturbation on permanent gels. Additionally, it seems that
reduction of entanglement by crystallization (leading to
gelation) plays an important role in enhancing drawability for
the production of high-modulus fibers (2-4). The importance of
entanglements in network dynamics may be gauged by the
observation that it is actually easier to draw fibers from the
crystallites.

Pictorial Representation. The essence of the foregoing is
represented pictorially in Figure 2, which shows fishnet and
lattice structures made from random coil, rigid rod and globular
molecules. Each structure is named according to certain key
words (legend). The symbol $\rightleftharpoons$ implies significant dynamic
equilibrium between transient "structural" elements and free
components. The symbol NNN in structure F3C indicates
well-formed crystalline crosslinks which may, in in the case of
easily crystallized polymers, occupy a substantial portion of the
available volume. The structures ⊗ in F2C may indicate small
and/or poorly formed crystalline crosslinks, "micellar"
junctions, or completely amorphous crosslinks that result from
aggregation. The difference between L2G and L3G is that the
former is a structure evolved from spinodal decomposition, while
the latter is stabilized either chemically or physically (denoted
by darkening of the circular structural elements). It is, of
course, NOT necessary for L2G to precede L3G, nor must L3G have a
"spongy" lattice structure resembling spinodal decomposition, as
shown here; a fibrillar L3G is easily imagined. Although not
shown, it is possible that some similar form of stabilization
could occur for L2C and L2R--e.g., crystalline or
microcrystalline domains could evolve within the polymer-rich
regions. However, such highly organized domains are not
prerequisite to gelation, any more than a simple solid is
required to be crystalline. It is also possible that L2C, L2R
and L3G could be very long-lived, metastable intermediate states.

Present Strategies and Future Outlook

This section is devoted to certain patterns of current
gel research and a difficult extrapolation to future prospects.
Both subjects place the author at some risk. Presentation of
selected approaches in a limited space will inevitably leave some
important work unmentioned. Since no attempt has been made at an
exhaustive literature review, which would unduly slow the
publication of this symposium, it is hoped that those whose work
was excluded will not take offense. At the same time, the
rapidly expanding horizons of gel research imply that future
trends could come from totally unforeseen developments.

a

Figure 1. Macroscopic lattice structures. (a) Rock lattice
generated by convective currents in the soil of Spitsbergen.
A two-dimensional space-filling structure is obviously present
but is not easily discussed in terms of "strands" and "crosslinks." Continued on next page.

b

c

Figure 1. <u>Continued</u>. Lattice structure in crape myrtle (Lagerstroemia indica) occurs as branches of this thin-barked shrub merge and grow together. The branches are almost rigid, but the points of intersection ("crosslinks") can be either weak (b) or relatively strong (c). (Courtesy of Bernard Hallet, Quaternary Research Center, University of Washington, Seattle, WA 98105.)

CHEMICAL

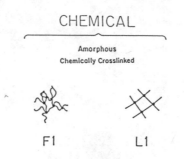

REVERSIBLE

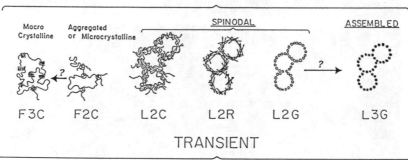

TRANSIENT

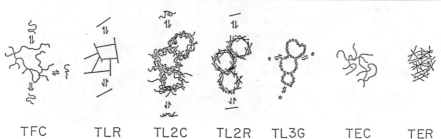

Figure 2.   Structural classification scheme for polymer gels and related systems.   Key: F = fishnet; L = lattice; T = transient; E = entangled; C = coil; R = rod; G = globular.

A major driving force in scientific endeavor has been the desire to "see" the invisible; be it stars or micro-organisms, a very substantial fraction of scientific effort can be described as expansion of the "visible" horizon. It is hardly surprising that microscopes and telescopes were among the earliest tools of scientific exploration. When these would no longer suffice, indirect methods such as spectroscopy, diffraction, scattering, radio-astronomy, and chemical and thermal analysis were introduced. Thus, the structure of graphite, as just one example, was hardly in doubt even prior to its recent visualization at atomic resolution by scanning tunnelling microscopy (43). Still, "seeing is believing", and the recent successful efforts to "see" at the atomic level are offering new details of surface morphology that might otherwise have gone unnoticed. As do many other colloidal/polymeric solutions, gels lie in a "twilight zone" where direct visualization may be "almost possible". At the present time, indirect methods still predominate, attesting to the complexity, delicacy, and dynamic nature of the relatively large structural elements found in polymers and gels. Nevertheless, the value of direct visualization methods--newly revealed in the application of scanning tunnelling microscopy to solid materials--should not be lost on gel researchers.

Direct Methods.

Visible Microscopy: The small size and low optical contrast usually renders the internal structure of gels invisible by light microscopy, except in the case of large crystallites which are easily visible between crossed polars. However, various contrast improvement techniques promise to make visualization possible in at least some other cases. Some hint of the potential for such methods appears in this collection (23) and in related work (34). Progress in this area may be most rapid in biological systems (44-47), as the appropriate dyes, image processing equipment, and trained personnel are most commonly found in association with the biological sciences. It may be noted that long cylindrical

o

fibrils with diameters as small as 250A have now been "seen"--live, no less--by analog and digitally contrast-enhanced optical microscopy (45). These developments are sometimes received skeptically, because conventional thought places the resolution limit of the optical microscope at about a factor of ten larger. However, there is no arguing with the reasonableness of the blurry images reported, and we conclude that video vision can significantly extend the range of the optical microscope. Even though the images are fuzzy, they are quite adequate for observing changes, including especially cellular functions. While even relatively simple techniques can dramatically improve contrast (48), perhaps it is the exotic new methods, such as those for producing "live" stereoscopic images at near-micron resolution (49,50), or the Allen Video Enhanced Contrast system (44,45), which typify the explosive growth in the ancient science of visible microscopy. Although the focus has been on biosystems, there is no reason why these technologies cannot be

imported to a wider variety of problems. Of some importance to
gels, optical microscopy is essentially non-perturbing and
dynamic evolution of structure may be visible in some
circumstances (34). Image analysis methods (51) enable
quantitation of the subjective impressions from video optical
microscopy. It is difficult to imagine that this method will not
have substantial impact on gel research, especially for systems
having structures in the 0.05 - 1 μm size range, just as it has
begun to on the study of less structured colloidal solutions
(52,53). The new optical microscopy emphatically will not
supplant other, less direct, methods, but it may help guide them
and improve the reliability of their interpretation.

Nonvisible microscopy: Even in its recently improved form,
optical microscopy does not begin to approach the ultimate
resolution of electron or x-ray microscopy. Nor does any
analogue for electron diffraction or x-ray backscattering
measurements for molecular-level structure exist. Thus, with
appropriate care during preparation of the delicate gel
structures, visualization by electron microscopy is an extremely
powerful tool (24,30,35,55-62). Specifically, ultra-fast
freeze-fracture methods and cold stage microscopy (61) warrant
further attention. As gel is defined here, the latter is the
only method for truly direct visualization by electron
microscopy. Even when the macroscopic gel collapses during
preparation for visualization, the resolution is such that one
may still observe by electron microscopy the fine structure of
the collapsed structural elements. Unfortunately, the electron
microscope is poorly suited for studies of evolution of
structure, requiring that the gelation somehow be stopped in a
controlled fashion. Recently discovered x-ray microscopy should
enable visualization of wet gels, but not real time during
gelation, at least as presently configured. To the author's
knowledge, this promising method has not yet been applied to gels
per se', but "network" structures have been observed within live
human platelets (54).

Indirect methods.

Scattering: Scattering methods, whether based on visible light
(63-65), neutrons (66-68), or x-rays (69), continue to be widely
applied for the determination of gels and related structures.
Owing to the rapid growth of quasielastic light scattering
methods, we must distinguish between "static" (63,64,69-72) and
"dynamic" (65) scattering. In static scattering a size parameter
is obtained from the angular dependence of scattered intensity.
Also, such information as the mean square average of contrast
fluctuations (e.g., refractive index fluctuations for visible
light scattering) and interfacial area between phases may be
obtained. These indirect results are far less satisfactory than
visualization would be, but static scattering retains many
advantages. Usually, scattering "averages" over many structural
elements in a way that is not easily achieved by direct
visualization methods. It is usually completely non-perturbing.

Additionally, the signal is often strong enough that even rapidly evolving systems can be followed "live". This feature is especially helpful when the entire angular range can be simultaneously scanned. Low-angle neutron and x-ray facilities often have real-time multi-angle capabilities as do some low-angle light scattering devices designed for polymer films (73,74). Recently, such a device was applied to the study of a lower critical phenomenon in solutions of hydroxypropyl-cellulose (75). By casual observation, this reversible phase transition results in a gel or gel-like material. Ironically, real-time multi-angle measurement is absent from even the most sophisticated high-angle light scattering devices designed for solution measurement (76), even though visible optics and detection are far simpler than their x-ray and neutron counterparts. Several research groups and at least two commercial ventures are known to be building a real-time multi-angle light scattering device, which could be of great value in studying gelation kinetics. With some combination of light, neutron, and x-ray sources it is now possible to study a very wide range of structure size, ca. 1 nm – 10 μm. Looking ahead, the increasing availability of synchrotron radiation may make it easier to span a wide range of scattering vectors, while at the same time providing sufficiently high intensity for real-time kinetic studies (77,78). Small superconducting storage rings designed primarily for x-ray lithography but also suitable as a source of soft x-rays for low-angle scattering should become commercially available at reasonable cost in 1988 (79).

   In the dynamic light scattering method (65), one monitors the rate of scattered intensity fluctuations, which occur as a result of the motion of the scatterers. One then tries to infer the properties of the scatterers from their motion. Thus, dynamic light scattering is even one more step further removed from direct structure visualization than is static light scattering, a problem often compensated by its wider range of application and high precision. As pointed out long ago (80,81), intensity fluctuations are naturally present in the light scattered from intact soft gels, and are related to the elastic modulus and network friction coefficient. For recent applications of this method and a review, see (82–85). A somewhat similar situation applies in the case of transient gels made of random coil polymers (86). The main value of dynamic light scattering, however, is its adeptness in dilute solution, where it enables wide-ranging measurements of mutual diffusion coefficients, hydrodynamic radii and inferred particle size, shape, etc. A research tactic that should gain momentum is the study of relatively dilute systems in the pregel state, or even microgel particles which have been further diluted by addition of solvent, using dynamic light scattering or other powerful solution methods (31,87). The bet is that the the structure of the microgel particles can be better determined from the well-developed methods for polymer analysis than could that of the intact gel itself. The precision of modern dilute solution techniques, combined with the rapid pace of interpretive methods for particle analysis (88,89), makes this a legitimate gamble. Implicit is the assumption that the microgel particle shares

common features with the intact gel. Dynamic light scattering
has also been applied for the determination of the very existence
of a gel structure by a rather novel technique, where static
light scattering failed (90).

Dynamic probe methods: Another indirect strategy for analysis of
gel structure is the measurement of the mobility of dynamic
probes whose sizes are well characterized. For example, dynamic
light scattering or any other method for diffusivity
determination (for examples, see 37) can be used to measure the
motions, through a gel matrix, of a series of spherically shaped
particles with varying sizes. To oversimplify greatly, if, as
probe size is raised, a dramatic decrease in diffusivity is
found, then the "mesh" size of the polymer gel may be estimated.
    Relatively few probe measurements have been carried out in
permanent, reversible gels. Recently, a light scattering study
of hemoglobin gels concluded that those hemoglobin molecules not
involved in the permanent network diffused about as fast as they
do in dilute solution (91). Sellen and coworkers studied
diffusion of dextran fragments in agarose and calcium alginate
gels (92-94). They were able to measure the mass per unit length
of the gel "fibers" in both cases, obtaining strikingly different
values. By a technique similar to that employed to follow the
progress of gelation in DNA (90), the relative concentration of
mobile diffusers was also determined. Fluorescence recovery
methods have been applied to the transport of latex spheres in
covalent polyacrylamide gels (95). Recently, probe motion was
used to follow the very initial steps of gelation of agarose, and
a nucleation-free sol-sol transition--a spinodal decomposition
(22,23)--was suggested to precede finalization of gelation (96).
    A related problem, which has received much more attention
(40-42,97), is the diffusion of probes through transient gels.
It is found empirically that a stretched exponential form,

$D = D^O \exp(-\alpha c^{\upsilon})$, where D is the diffusion, D^O represents the
zero-concentration limit, c is the concentration, α and υ are
parameters, fits the data from a wide variety of probes and
matrix polymers (40). Several theoretical justifications for
this behavior have been presented (97-101), but it is not
possible to tell yet which, if any, is uniquely correct. The
treatments range from simple physical considerations (98) to
treatments of hydrodynamical interaction of probe and matrix
(97,99). Other more complex and general treatments (100) do not
explicitly arrive at the stretched exponential form, but do
closely fit the available data. Much more work needs to be done
on probe diffusion in such transient networks. Beyond enhancing
the arsenal of gel characterization, the problem is quite
fundamental to a number of other important processes.
    In addition to the mobility of colloidal-sized probes, there
is considerable interest in monitoring the motion of small
molecules, including the solvent itself and also dye molecules.
Once again, more is known about such mobilities in the case of
transient gels, where it is now certain that "monomer segment
mobility" effects are prerequisite to a correct dynamical
interpretation (102-105). Several papers in the present volume

attest, however, to the utility of equivalent measurements in
true gels, and also to the value of "local motion" measurements,
such as spin-lattice and spin-spin relaxation times (106-108).

Rheology: Not very many of the studies this collection rely on
rheological methods primarily (109,110). Without equivocation,
rheological techniques are the final arbiter in defining gel-like
behavior and can be extremely useful in making comparisons of
poorly understood gels to better-understood systems (111). When
a well-established theory like the classical theory of rubberlike
elasticity is appropriate, rheology can quantitatively provide
microstructural details that are not easily obtained otherwise.
However, without such a foundation, as with most lattice gels,
the macroscopic nature of the usual rheological measurement
places it at some disadvantage for determination of absolute
structure and its kinetic development. This has led to the
development of rheo-optical techniques (109,110) with enormous
potential for relating the essential features of the gel
phenomenon--macroscopic lack of flow--to microscopic structure.
Surely, more of the rheo-optical methods now developed for solid
polymers (112,113) will be adapted for gels and complex
solutions.

Acknowledgment

The author expresses his gratitude to Wilmer Miller who
introduced him to the interesting world of gelation phenomena.
The generous financial support of the NSF (DMR-8520027) during
the preparation of this manuscript is gratefully acknowledged.

Literature Cited

1.   It is this belief which made the symposium and this
     collection possible.
2.   Lemstra, P. J.; Smith, P. Brit. Polym. J. 1980, 20, 212.
3.   Smith, P.; Lemstra, P. J.; Booij, H. C. J. Polym. Sci.,
     Polym. Phys. Ed. 1981, 19, 877.
4.   Barham, P. J.; Keller, A. J. Mat. Sci. 1985, 20, 2281.
5.   Domszy, R.C.; Alamo, R.; Edwards, C.O. and Mandelkern, L.
     Macromolecules 1986, 19, 310.
6.   Most contributors in this book fall into this category.
7.   New methods for analysis and their combined application to
     complex systems, such as reversible gels, is especially to
     be encouraged. An inspiring statement along these lines
     appears in the conclusion of Ref. 95.
8.   Ricka, J.; Tanaka, T. Macromolecules, 1985, 18, 83.
9.   Nicoli, D.; Young, C.; Tanaka, T.; Pollak, A.;
     Whitesides G. Macromolecules 1983, 16, 887.
10. Katayama, S.; Yoshitsugo, H.; Tanaka, T. Macromolecules
     1984, 17, 2641.
11. Ricka, J.; Tanaka, T. Macromolecules 1984, 17, 2916.
12. Ohmine, I.; Tanaka, T. J. Chem. Phys. 1982, 77, 5725.
13. Tanaka, T. Science 1982, 218, 467.

14. See for example, Irie, M. Macromolecules 1986, 19, 2890.
15. Flory, P.J. Disc. Farad. Soc. 1974, 57, 7.
16. Ferry, J.D., Viscoelastic Properties of Polymers; Wiley:
     New York, 1961; p 391. The definition of gels has survived
     through 3 editions (1970; p 557; 1980; p 529).
17. Takahashi, A.; Sakai, M.; Kato, T. Polym J. (Tokyo) 1980,
     12, 335.
18. Ferry, J. D. Viscoelastic Properties of Polymers, 3rd
     ed., Wiley: New York, 1980; pp 537-539.
19. Admittedly, flow of glaciers depends upon melting at the
     bottom and break/up. However, the net result is that these
     large ice masses do flow.
20. Nossal, R., this book.
21. Cahn, J.W. J. Chem. Phys. 1965, 42, 93.
22. Cahn, J.W.; Hillard, J.E. J. Chem. Phys. 1959, 31, 668.
23. Russo, P. S., Magestro, P.; Miller, W. G., this book.
24. Mandelkern, L. In Microdomains in Polymer Solutions;
     Dubin, P. L., Ed.; Plenum: New York, 1985.
25. Tan, H.; Moet, A.; Hiltner, A.; Baer, E. Macromolecules
     1983, 16, 28.
26. Koltisko, B.; Keller, A.; Litt, M.; Baer, E.; Hiltner, A.
     Macromolecules 1986, 19, 1207.
27. Hiltner, A.; Baer, E. ACS Polym. Prepr. 1986, 27(1), 207.
28. Clark, J.; Wellinghoff, S. T.; Miller, W. G. ACS Polym.
     Prepr. 1983, 24(2), 86.
29. Blum, F. D.; naNagara, B., this book.
30. Yang, Y. S.; Geil, P. H. J. Macromol. Sci.--Phys. 1983,
     B22, 463.
31. Candau, S. J.; Dormoy, Y.; Hirsch, E.; Mutin, P. H.;
     Guenet, J. M., this book.
32. Eldridge, J. E.; Ferry, J. D. J. Phys. Chem. 58, 992
     (1954).
33. Green, M. (Brooklyn Polytechnic); personal communication.
34. Russo, P. S.; Siripanyo, S.; Saunders, M. J.; Karasz, F. E.
     Macromolecules 1986, 19, 2856.
35. Tohyama, K.; Miller, W.G. Nature 1981, 289, 813.
36. Earthquake or hurricane, respectively.
37. Tirrell, M. Rubber Chem. and Tech. 1984, 57, 522.
38. Graessley, W.W. Adv. Polym. Sci. 1982, 47, 67.
39. DeGennes, P.G., Leger, L. Ann. Rev. Phys. Chem. 1982,
     33, 49.
40. Phillies, G. D. J.; Ullmann, G. S.; Ullmann, K., Lin, T.-H.
     J. Chem. Phys. 1985, 82, 5242.
41. Lodge, T. P.; Wheeler, L. M. Macromolecules 1986, 19, 2983.
42. Kim, H.; Chang, T.; Yohanan, J. M.; Wang, L.; Yu, H.
     Macromolecules 1986, 19, 2737.
43. Quate, C. F. Physics Today 1986, 39(8), 26.
44. Allen, R.D. Ann. Rev. Biophys. Chem. 1985, 14, 265.
45. Allen, R.D. Scientific American 1987, 256(2), 42
46. Arndt-Jovin, D.J.; Robert-Nicoud, M.; Kaufman, S.J.; Jovin,
     T.M. Science 1985, 230, 4723.
47. DiGuiseppi, J.; Inman, R.; Ishihara, A.; Jacobsen, K:,
     Herman, B. Biotechniques 1985, 3, 394.
48. Kachar, B. Science 1985, 227, 766.
49. Lewin, R. Science 1985, 230, 1258.

50. Boyde, A. Science 1985, 230, 1270.
51. Inouye, S. Video Microscopy; Plenum: New York, 1986.
52. Kachar, B.; Evans, D. F.; Ninham, B.W. J. Coll. Int. Sci. 1984, 99, 593.
53. Evans, D. F.; Brady, J.; Kachar, B.; Ninham, B. W. J. Solution Chem. 1985, 14, 141.
54. Feder, R.; Banton, V.; Sayre, D.; Costa, J.; Baldini, M.; Kim, B. Science 1985, 227, 63.
55. Bale, M. D.; Muller, M. F.; Ferry, J. D. Biopolymers 1985, 24, 461.
56. Muller M. F.; Ris, H.; Ferry, J. D. J. Mol. Biol. 1984, 174, 369.
57. Zasadzinski, J. A. N.; Chu, A.; Prud'homme, R. K. Macromolecules 1986, 19, 2960.
58. Terech, P., this book.
59. Cohen, Y.; Thomas, E. L., this book.
60. Djabourov, M.; LeBlonde, J., this book.
61. Thomas, E.L.; Cohen, Y.; slides shown during discussion at this symposium.
62. Newkome, G. R.; Baker, G. R.; Saunders, M. J.; Russo, P. S.; Gupta, V. K., Yao, Z.; Miller, J. E.; Bouillon, K. J. Chem. Soc., Chem. Commun. 1986, 752.
63. Light Scattering from Polymer Solutions; Huglin, M. B., Ed.; Academic Press: New York, 1972.
64. Kerker, M., "The Scattering of Light and Other Electromagnetic Radiation"; Academic Press: New York, 1972.
65. Dynamic Light Scattering; Pecora, R., Ed.; Plenum: New York, 1985.
66. Stein, R. S.; Han, C. C. Phys. Today 1985, 38(1), 74.
67. Picot, C. In Static and Dynamic Properties of the Polymeric Solid State; Pethric, R. A.; Richards, R. W., Eds. Reidel: Norwell, Massachusetts, 1982.
68. Benoit, H. Decker, D.; Duplessix, R.; Picot, C.; Rempp, P.; Cotton, J. P.; Farnoux, B.; Jannink, G.; Ober, R. J. Polym. Sci., Polym. Phys. Ed. 1976, 14, 2119.
69. Small Angle X-ray Scattering; Glatter, O.; Kratky, H. C., Eds.; Academic Press: New York, 1982.
70. Debye, P.; Bueche, A. M. J. Appl. Phys. 1949, 20, 518.
71. Debye, P.; Anderson, H. R.; Brumberger, H. J. Appl. Phys. 1957, 28, 679.
72. Goebel, K. D.; Berry, G. C. J. Polym. Sci.-Polym. Phys. Ed. 1977, 15, 555.
73. Wasiak, A.; Peiffer, D.; Stein, R. S. J. Polym. Sci.--Polym. Lett. Ed. 1976, 14, 381.
74. Han, C. C., (U. S. Nat'l. Bureau of Standards), to appear.
75. Mukherjee, P. and Kyu, T. ACS Polym. Prepr. 1987, 28(1), 361.
76. Haller, H. R.; Destor, C.; Cannell, D. S. Rev. Sci. Instrum. 1983, 54, 974.
77. Elsner, G.; Riekel, C.; Zachmann, H. G. Adv. Polym. Sci. 1985, 67, 1.
78. Perez-Grau, L.; Bordas, J.; Koch, M. H. J. Nucleic Acids Res., 1984, 12, 2987.
79. Saile, V. (HASYLAB, Hamburg, Germany); personal communication. Estimated cost is $5 million.

80.   Tanaka, T.; Hocker, L. O.; Benedek, G. B. J. Chem. Phys. 1973, 59, 5151.
81.   Wun, K.L.; Carlson, F. D. Macromolecules 1975, 8, 190.
82.   Nossal, R. Macromolecules 1985, 18, 49.
83.   Hwang, J. S.; Cummins, H. Z. J. Chem. Phys. 1983, 79, 5188.
84.   Geissler, E.; Hecht, A. M.; Duplessix, R. J. Polym. Sci., Polym. Phys. Ed. 1982, 20, 225.
85.   Tanaka, T. In Dynamic Light Scattering; Pecora, R., Ed.; Plenum: New York, 1985.
86.   Schaeffer, D. W.; Han, C. In Dynamic Light Scattering; Pecora, R., Ed.; Plenum: New York, 1985.
87.   Mutin, P. H.; Guenet, J. M. Polymer 1986, 27, 1098.
88.   Burchard, W.; Bantle, S.; Muller, M.; Reiner, A. Pure and Appl. Chem. 1981, 53, 1519.
89.   Burchard, W.; Schmidt, M.; Stockmayer, W. H. Macromolecules 1980, 13, 1265.
90.   Bloomfield, V. A., this book
91.   Kam, Z.; Hofrichter, J. Biophys. J. 1986, 50, 1015.
92.   Key, P. Y.; Sellen, D. B. J. Polym. Sci., Polym. Phys. Ed. 1982, 20, 659.
93.   Mackie, W.; Sellen, D. B.; Sutcliffe, J. J. Polym. Sci., Polym. Symp. 1977, 61, 191.
94.   Mackie, W.; Sellen, D. B.; Sutcliffe, J. Polymer 1978, 19, 9.
95.   Ware, B. R.; Cyr, D.; Gorti, S.; Lanni, F. In Measurement of Suspended Particles by Quasielastic Light Scattering; Dahneke, B. E., Ed.; Wiley: New York, 1983.
96.   San Biagio, P. L.; Newman, J.; Madonia, F.; Palma, M. U. Biomolecular Stereodynamics 1986, 3, 277. (Proceedings of the fourth Conversation in the Discipline Biomolecular Stereodynamics; Adenine Press: Schenectady, New York).
97.   Phillies, G. D. J., Macromolecules 1987, 20, 558.
98.   Ogston, A. G.; Preston, B. N.; Wells, J. D.; Snowden, J. Proc. Roy. Soc. (London) 1973, A333, 297.
99.   Cukier, R. I. Macromolecules 1984, 17, 252.
100.   Altenberger, A. R.; Tirrell, M.; Dahler, J. S. J. Chem. Phys. 1986, 84, 5122.
101.   Langevin, D.; Rondelez, F. Polymer 1978, 14, 875.
102.   Chen, S. P.; Ferry, J. D. Macromolecules 1968, 1, 270.
103.   von Meerwall, E. D.; Amis, E. J.; Ferry, J. D. Macromolecules 1985, 18, 260.
104.   Gesscke, D.; Fleischer, G.; Straube, E. Polymer 1986, 27, 1091.
105.   Nemoto, N.; Landry, M. R.; Noh, I.; Kitano, T.; Wesson, J. A.; Yu, H. Macromolecules 1985, 18, 308.
106.   Blum, F. D., naNagara, B., this book.
107.   Rex, G. C., Schlick, S., this book.
108.   Djabourov, M.; LeBlonde, J., this book.
109.   Chung, B.; Zachariades, A. E., this book.
110.   As an example relevant to this symposium: see Heeger, A. J.; Kapitulnik, A.; Casalnuovo, S. A.; Spiegel, D. ACS Polym. Prepr. 1986, 27(1), 226.

111.   Miller, W. G.; Chakrabarti, S.; Seibel, K. M. In
       <u>Microdomains in Polymer Solutions</u>; Dubin, P. L., Ed.;
       Plenum: New York, 1985.
112.   Siesler, H. W. <u>Advances in Polymer Science</u> 1984, <u>65</u>, 2.
113.   Stein, R. S. <u>Polymer Journal</u> 1985, <u>17</u>, 289.

RECEIVED July 14, 1987

Chapter 2

Viscoelastic Behavior of Ultra High Molecular Weight Polyethylene Pseudogels

B. Chung[1] and A. E. Zachariades[2]

[1]Research Division, Gen Corporation, 2990 Gilchrist Road, Akron, OH 44305
[2]Almaden Research Center, IBM, San Jose, CA 95120

The viscoelastic behavior of ultra-high molecular weight polyethylene (UHMWPE) gel-like system in paraffin oil (2-5% w/w concentration) has been studied by rheological and rheo-optical characterization techniques and was found to be significantly different from the true gels of covalent bonded molecular networks. The dynamic moduli of the UHMWPE gel-like systems exhibit shear history, temperature and frequency dependence and a remarkable hysteresis effect during thermal cycling in which the original modulus value cannot be recovered.

Ultra-high molecular weight polyethylene (UHMWPE) "gels" have been processed into high modulus/strength fibers by dissolving and spinning at elevated temperatures ($\sim200°C$) and subsequently quenching the spun fiber, removing the solvent and stretching to some high draw ratio (1-3). Whereas the effects of processing and preparation conditions on the mechanical properties of spun-drawn fibers have been investigated to a considerable extent (1-4), the viscoelastic behavior of the UHMWPE "gels" have been examined recently (5). Rheo-optical and rheological studies with UHMWPE/paraffin oil (2-5% w/w) systems indicate that these are not true gels like the covalent bonded molecular networks, and their viscoelastic properties, e.g., dynamic moduli (G' and G"), are frequency and temperature dependent.

Various diverse systems qualify as gels if one assumes that in these systems the common features are the solid-like behavior and the presence of a continuous structure of macroscopic nature (6,7). For the purpose of the discussion in this paper, we describe a gel as a colloidal system comprised of a dispersed component and a dispersion medium both of which the junction points are formed by covalent bonds, secondary valence bonds, or long range attractive forces that cause association between segments of polymer chains or formation of crystalline regions which have essentially infinite life time (8).

Systems such as the concentrated solution of the UHMWPE in paraffin oil (2-8% w/w) contain a three-dimensional molecular network in which the junction points are produced by secondary valence bonds which cause crystalline regions and by physical entanglements of different life times. Entanglements that are trapped between crystallites have, like the crystallites, essentially infinite life times.

Entanglements that are not trapped have transistory existence (and will be referred to as "temporary" entanglements). Since the dynamic moduli of these systems depend on the frequency, temperature and shear history of the system, we shall refer to such system as a gel-like or pseudo-gel in contrast to a true gel. A schematic diagram of the pseudo-gel structure is shown in Figure 1.

Experimental

Sample Preparation. The UHMWPE used in this study was a HiFax 1900 (Himont, Inc.) with an average molecular weight of $2-8 \times 10^6$. The UHMWPE was added to paraffin oil to concentrations from 2 to 5% w/w. To avoid polymer degradation at high temperatures, the polymer was stabilized with approximately 0.5% of BHT antioxidant. The mixture was stirred at 150°C. A solution was obtained that was clear until it was cooled to about 120°C when it became opaque and transformed into a gel-like or pseudo-gel.

Rheo-Optical Observations. The rheo-optical observations were made with a WILD stereoscope equipped with a custom made rotary optical stage using polarized light. The rotary optical stage described in detail elsewhere (9) was used for both the steady state shear and dynamic test conditions.

Rheological Properties Measurements. The viscoelastic behavior of the UHMWPE gel-like systems was studied using the Rheometric Mechanical Spectrometer (RMS 705). A cone and plate fixture (radius: 1.25 cm; cone angle: 9.85×10^{-2} radian) was used for the dynamic frequency sweep, and the steady state shear rate sweep measurements. In order to minimize the error caused by gap thickness change during the temperature sweep, the parallel plates fixture (radius: 1.25 cm; gap: 1.5 mm) was used for the dynamic temperature sweep measurements.

Results

Study of the Crystalline Regions. According to our morphological studies, the crystalline structure of UHMWPE pseudo-gel was different under different sample preparations. For example, spherulites and lamellar single crystal stacks were observed when the pseudo-gel was prepared under quiescent conditions, shish-kebab crystals under stirring conditions, and a mixture of single and shish-kebab crystals under uncontrolled conditions (10).

Rheological observations of the UHMWPE pseudo-gels of different concentrations under oscillatory shear conditions at different temperatures showed that these systems exhibit considerable drawability at temperatures above ambient. The deformation of the crystalline phase of the gel-like system is not reversible and, as shown in the sequence of photographs Figure 2, for a pseudo-gel of 4% concentration, it was greater when the sample was sheared under the same oscillatory conditions at higher temperatures. The displaced crystals of the UHMWPE pseudo-gel showed remarkable dimensional stability after shear cessation and removal of any compression load in the optical rotary stage.

Both the fresh gel and the gels after dynamic measurements were examined by X-ray. As shown in Figure 3, there are two intensity maxima peaks at 2θ angles about 21.5 and 24 degree; also, these two crystal peaks become sharper after the dynamic measurements. Furthermore, the DSC analysis showed that the 4% fresh

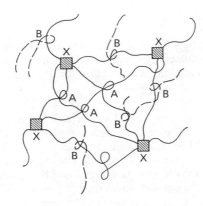

X :   crystals – essentially infinite life time

A :   "trapped" entanglements between crystals – essentially
       infinite life time

B :   "temporary" entanglements – transitory existence

Figure 1. Schematic diagram of the UHMWPE pseudo-gel structure.

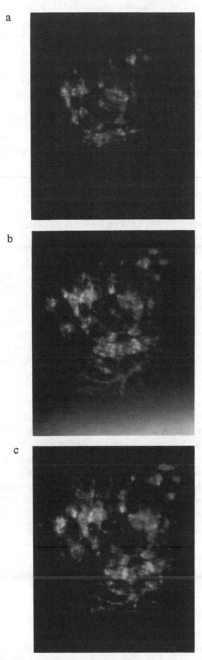

Figure 2. Deformability of 4% w/w UHMWPE pseudo-gel sample under oscillatory shear force at different temperatures: (a) 25 °C, (b) 30 °C, and (c) 40 °C.

gel has a ΔHm of 8.42 J/g and a Tm at about 116°C; after the dynamic frequency sweep, the ΔHm increased to 15 J/g but the Tm remained the same. Both the X-ray and DSC results suggest that the crystallinity of pseudo-gels increases under the hydrodynamic shearing force.

Study of Viscoelastic Behavior. The dynamic storage shear modulus, G', and loss modulus, G", of the UHMWPE pseudo-gels were measured at different temperatures in the frequency range from 10^{-2} sec^{-1} to 10 sec^{-1}. A plot of the G' versus the oscillation frequency is shown for the UHMWPE pseudo-gel of 4% concentration in Figure 4. The G' decreased in the low frequency range and approached a plateau in the intermediate frequency range, and then increased rapidly as the frequency increased above 10 sec^{-1}. When the sample was tested for a number of consecutive runs, the G' decreased in each run and approached to an equilibrium value, i.e., the plateau region at a low frequency. Similar is the loss modulus (G") variation with frequency but, as shown in Figure 5, is less sensitive to the shear history of the sample. Furthermore, as shown in Figures 6 and 7, the shear history dependence of the viscoelastic properties, G' and G", was less pronounced at lower temperatures, e.g., at 0°C. A similar behavior was observed for the other UHMWPE gel concentrations.

Dynamic temperature sweep measurements carried out at different frequencies from -20°C to about 100°C indicate that the G' of the UHMWPE pseudo-gels decreased significantly with increasing temperature. As shown in the Arrhenius plot of Figure 8, the variation is not monotonic and a transition was observed which corresponds to the change of the slope. Similar was the variation of the loss modulus with temperature. Most important, the shear modulus dependence on temperature was not reversible. As indicated in Figure 8, for the UHMWPE pseudo-gel of 3% concentration, the G' value at any particular temperature is higher in the heating part of thermal cycle between -20°C and 100°C at a frequency of 100 sec^{-1}. The storage modulus assumes a somewhat lower value on cooling at the beginning of the cooling cycle; on further cooling, it decreased to a minimum and then increased as the temperature decreased further but never recovered its original value (at the beginning of the heating cycle). As shown in Figure 9, similar was the variation of G" with temperature; however, the hysteresis phenomenon was less pronounced.

The viscoelastic response of the UHMWPE pseudo-gels depends also on the solution concentration. As shown in Figure 10, the G' increased with concentration at frequency 50 sec^{-1} over the temperature range from -20°C to 100°C. This is probably due to the higher entanglement density and/or higher crystallinity in the higher concentration solution.

Steady state shear viscosity measurements indicate a power-law type relation for the variation of the shear viscosity with shear rate even in the lower shear rate range between 10^{-1} to 1 sec^{-1}. The results at higher shear rates were questionable due to the slip between the sample and cone and plate fixtures.

Discussion

UHMWPE gels have been studied mainly for their processability into high modulus/strength products. The viscoelastic behavior of this polymer/solvent system, as well as others which are capable of forming a gel-like state at some suitable concentration, has received little attention. Previous studies have been carried out by Ferry et al. (6,7) with gel systems of cellulose derivatives and polyvinychloride

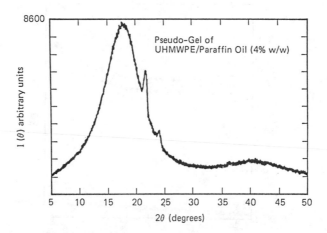

Figure 3. X-ray scan of UHMWPE pseudo-gel.

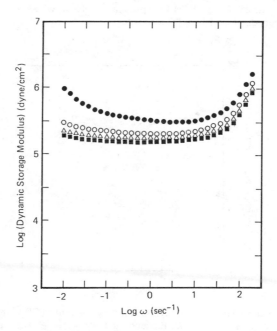

Figure 4. The variation of the dynamic storage modulus (G') with oscillation frequency at 25°C for UHMWPE pseudo-gel (4% w/w); ● first run, o second run, △ third run, ■ fourth run.

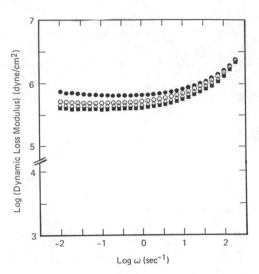

Figure 5. The variation of the dynamic loss modulus (G") with oscillation frequency at 25 °C for UHMWPE pseudo-gel (4% w/w); ●, first run; ○, second run; Δ, third run; ■, fourth run.

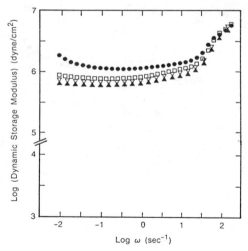

Figure 6. The variation of the dynamic storage modulus (G') with oscillation frequency at 0 °C for UHMWPE pseudo-gel (4% w/w); ●, first run; □, second run; ∇, third run; ▲, fourth run.

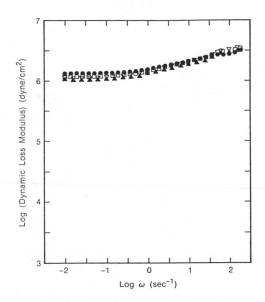

Figure 7. The variation of the dynamic loss modulus (G") with oscillation frequency at 0°C for UHMWPE pseudo-gel (4% w/w); ● first run, □ second run, ∇ third run, ▲ fourth run.

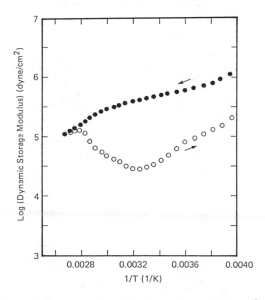

Figure 8. The variation of dynamic storage modulus (G') of UHMWPE pseudo-gel (3% w/w) with temperature at $\omega=100$ sec^{-1}; ● heating cycle, o cooling cycle.

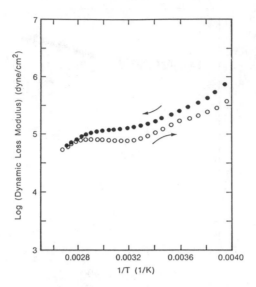

Figure 9. The variation of the dynamic loss modulus (G") of UHMWPE pseudo-gel (3% w/w) with temperature at $\omega=100$ sec^{-1}; ● heating cycle, o cooling cycle.

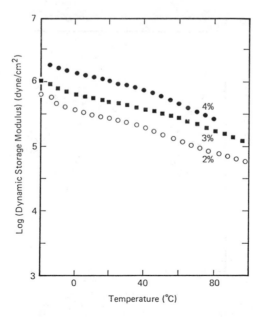

Figure 10. The variation of the dynamic storage modulus (G') of UHMWPE pseudo-gels of different concentration (w/w) with temperature at $\omega=50$ sec^{-1}.

assuming a cross-linked molecular network structure in which the cross-linking was provided by the crystalline regions in the gel. However, in their studies, they did not elaborate on the effects of temperature and shear history on the stability of the gels under hydrodynamic shear forces. This subject is important particularly in view of recent observations of polymer/solvent systems which may have different crystalline morphologies of considerable fraction that may vary significantly with the preparation and processing conditions (10).

The gel-like structure of the UHMWPE/paraffin oil system, as shown in Figure 1, associates with the presence of the crystals which act as permanent cross-links at temperatures below their melting point, the trapped entanglements between the crystals and the temporary entanglements which have a short lifetime in comparison to the other two types of junction points. The effect of the entanglements with short lifetime on the viscoelastic behavior of the UHMWPE pseudo-gels is shown in Figure 4 by the initial decrease of G' in the low frequency region, and by the overall decrease of the plateau G' in each consecutive run. The effect of shear history becomes less pronounced when the temperature is decreased because of the reduced mobility of the molecular chains. The plateau region in Figure 4 is due to the presence of the crystals and the trapped entanglements between them. However, as shown in Figure 4, this is not a true equilibrium state because the G' diminishes in each consecutive run. The fact that the equilibrium region extends into the lower frequency region after each run indicates a tendency of the system to approach a pseudo-equilibrium state. Although this pseudo-equilibrium plateau of G' is similar to what is observed in a covalent cross-linked gel, e.g., elastomeric gel, it depends strongly on the shear history, temperature, and gel concentration.

As shown in Figure 8, the G' of the UHMWPE pseudo-gel decreases with increasing temperature. The behavior is contrary to the behavior of a cross-linked gel system, in which the G' usually does not change with temperature. This presumably associates with the reduced rigidity of the crystals and simultaneous loss of the trapped entanglements which will disentangle and behave like the temporary entanglements as temperature increases under the hydrodynamic shear force. This is documented by the enhanced drawabilty of the crystals in photos in Figure 2. This behavior is more like the viscoelastic behavior of a polymer melt, however, the G' decrease is less drastic as the temperature decreases.

The hysteresis phenomenon during the thermal cycle between -20° to 100°C can be explained by considering the relative effects of the crystals, trapped entanglements, and temporary entanglements on the G' at the different temperature regions of the thermal cycle. The initial sharp decrease in G' up to about -10°C is due to the increasing mobility of the temporary entanglements, whereas the subsequent monotonic decrease with increasing temperature is mainly due to the reduction also by the rheo-optical observations. The sharp G' decrease above 60°C associates with the deformability of the crystals which enhances further the reduction of trapped entanglements. Thus, the UHMWPE pseudo-gel has fewer trapped entanglements at the end of heating cycle. For most polymer systems, the G' usually increases during cooling due to the decreasing chain mobility; but the UHMWPE pseudo-gel behaves quite different. On cooling, as shown in Figure 9, the G' of this system initially tends to change with temperature along the path of the heating cycle. However, at the high temperature range, the number of trapped entanglements continues to decrease, and apparently offsets the cooling effect which increases the G'. As a result, the G' soon assumes lower values. The sharp decrease of G' at lower temperatures reflects the disentanglement effect of trapped entanglements while the crystals are still deformable. As the temperature decreases below 40°C the crystals become less deformable and a larger fraction of entanglements remain trapped. This process alone will prevent the further decrease of the G' value. However, at this lower temperature range chain mobility is considerably hindered and, therefore, the storage modulus increases as the temperature decreases to -20°C. Since some of the trapped entanglements were lost permanently during the thermal cycle the original G' value cannot be recovered.

Conclusion

Rheo-optical and rheological strudies of concentrated solutions of UHMWPE/paraffin oil (2-5% w/w concentration) systems indicate that these are pseudo-gels unlike the covalent bonded molecular networks which exhibit a true gel behavior. The viscoelastic properties of the UHMWPE/paraffin oil pseudo-gels, i.e., dynamic shear moduli G' and G" are frequency and temperature dependent. Furthermore, the dynamic shear moduli depend on the concentration and shear history of the pseudo-gel and exhibit a hysteresis behavior during thermal cycling in which the original modulus value cannot be recovered.

Acknowledgments

The authors would like to thank Mr. R. Siemens and Miss G. Lim for their technical assistance in the DSC and X-ray measurements.

References

1.   Smith, P.; Lemstra, P. J. J. Mater. Sci. 1980, 15, 505.
2.   Smith, P.; Lemstra, P. J.; Booij, H. C. J. Polym. Sci., Polym. Phys. Ed. 1981, 19, 877.
3.   Smook, J.; Flinterman, M.; Pennings, A. J. Polym. Bulletin 1980, 2, 775.
4.   Barham, P. J. Polymer 1982, 23, 112.
5.   Chung, B.; Zachariades, A. E. ACS Polymer Preprints 1986, Vol. 5, 195.
6.   Nizomiya, K.; Ferry, J. D.; J. Polym. Sci. 1967, Part A-2, Vol. 5, 195.
7.   Birnboim, M. H.; Ferry, J. D. J. Appl. Phys. 1961, Vol. 32, No. 11, 235.
8.   Smith, T. L. Mechanical Properties of Gels and Thixotropic Substances, Inst. of Phys. Handbook, Margo Hill Book Co., New York, 1963.
9.   Zachariades, A. E.; Logan, J. A. Polym. Eng. Sci. 1983, 15, 797.
10. Zachariades, A. E. J. Appl. Polym. Sci., 1986, 32, 4277.

RECEIVED February 27, 1987

Chapter 3

Dynamic Light Scattering and Transient Electric Birefringence Study of Poly(vinyl chloride) Microgels

S. J. Candau[1], Y. Dormoy[1], E. Hirsch[1,3], P. H. Mutin[2], and J. M. Guenet[2]

[1]**Laboratoire de Spectrométrie et d'Imagerie Ultrasonores, Unité Associée au Centre National de la Recherche Scientifique, Université Louis Pasteur 4, rue Blaise Pascal, 67070 Strasbourg Cedex, France**
[2]**Institut Charles Sadron (Centre de Recherches sur les Macromolecules—Ecole d'Applications Hauts Polymères) 6, rue Boussingault, 67083 Strasbourg Cedex, France**

In order to gain information on the gelation mechanism of PVC in diethylmalonate, investigation of dilute solutions as a function of temperature and quenching concentration has been achieved through the use of transient electric birefringence and dynamic light scattering. The results show that the crosslinked aggregates formed at a quenching concentration $C_q = 0.5\ 10^{-2}\ g\ cm^{-3}$ are thermally stable while those obtained by quenching at higher concentration ($C_q = 1.6\ 10^{-2} g\ cm^{-3}$) break up upon heating. These observations suggest that the PVC gelation involves two kinds of crosslinks in agreement with previous DSC experiments.

Thermoreversible gelation of PVC solutions has long been associated with crystallization of the chain syndiotactic portions (1). On the basis of X-ray experiments performed on stretched and subsequently dried gels, Guerrero and Keller have suggested that the interchain bridging is due to the formation of tiny crystals of fringed-micellar type. The melting range of these crystals in the gel was 50 – 80°C depending on the solvent and the polymer concentration (2).

Recently, Yang and Geil have shown by DSC experiments that no melting endotherm is detectable on freshly-prepared gels (3). They therefore suggest that gelation arises from hydrogen bondings between chain and correspondingly that the junctions are rather point-like. These conflicting conclusions are inherent to the difficulties encountered in the investigation of systems out of equilibrium characterized by ageing effects. These effects are drastically reduced when studying small aggregates formed by quenching dilute PVC solutions. Recent experiments performed by light scattering, quasi-

[3]Current address: Laboratoire des Sciences de l'Image et de la Télédétection, Unité Associée au Centre National de la Recherche Scientifique, ENSPS, Université Louis Pasteur 7, rue de l'Université, 67000 Strasbourg, France

elastic light scattering, viscometry, transient electric birefringence and flow birefringence have been carried out on dilute PVC solutions (obtained by quenching a $C_q = 0.5\ 10^{-2}$ g cm^{-3} solution and subsequently diluting it (4)(5)). The results show that quenching dilute PVC solutions leads to the formation of crosslinked aggregates, stable upon dilution, optically inhomogeneous, with a permanent electrical dipole. Both the optical inhomogeneous structure showed by light scattering experiments and permanent dipole are consistent with a model of crosslinked aggregates where crosslinks are made of small syndiotactic crystallites.

In this study, has been investigated by means of quasi-elastic light scattering and transient electric birefringence the effect of the quenching concentration on the structure of the PVC aggregates as well as the thermal stability of these aggregates.

EXPERIMENTAL

MATERIALS

A PVC of commercial origin (Rhône Poulenc S.A.) has been used without further purification. This polymer has been synthesized at 50°C and is therefore mainly atactic. Tacticity characterization by ^{13}C NMR in cyclohexanone solutions has given the following values for the triades :

$$s = 0.33 \qquad h = 0.49 \qquad i = 0.18$$

Molecular weights determination has been achieved by GPC in THF at room temperature leading to :

$$M_w = 1.2\ 10^5 \qquad \text{and} \qquad M_w/M_n = 2.3$$

Freshly distilled diethylmalonate (DEM) was used as a solvent.

SAMPLE PREPARATION

Solutions at concentration $C_q = 0.5$, 1.2 and 1.6 10^{-2} g cm^{-3} were prepared under vigorous stirring at 150°C and then cooled down at 23°C. It was checked by NMR and infrared experiments that no alteration nor chemical modification had occured (4). After quenching, the intensity scattered by the solutions was recorded as a function of time. After approximately 36 h, no variation was detected for the sample $C_q = 0.5\ 10^{-2}$ g cm^{-3} while a slow linear increase of scattered intensity with time was detected for the two other samples. In this study, the solutions were allowed to stay at room temperature for three days and then diluted at the concentration $C = 10^{-3}$g cm^{-3}.

TRANSIENT ELECTRIC BIREFRINGENCE

Theory. In the general case where rigid revolution ellipsoidal particles in solution possess both a permanent and an induced dipolar moment colinear with the particle optical axis,the theory derived by Tinoco predicts the following behaviour of the solution birefringence $\Delta n(t)$ in the limit of weak electric field (6).

- The rise of the birefringence following the setting-up of the electric field is given by :

$$\Delta n(t) = \Delta n_o \left[1 - \frac{3P/Q}{2(P/Q+1)} e^{-2D_R t} + \frac{P/Q-2}{2(P/Q+1)} e^{-6D_R t} \right] \quad (1)$$

where Δn_o is the value of the steady-state birefringence, D_R is the rotational diffusion constant of the particle and :

$$P = \mu^2/k_B^2 T^2$$
$$Q = (\alpha_1 - \alpha_2)/k_B T \quad (2)$$

μ is the permanent dipolar moment,
α_1 and α_2 are the electrical polarizabilities of the particle parallel and perpendicular to the revolution axis respectively
k_B is the Boltzman constant and T the absolute temperature.
- The transient regime following electric field inversion allows more precise determination of the P/Q ratio to be achieved. If the particle does not possess any permanent dipole (P/Q = 0) the birefringence remains stationary upon field inversion. If there is a contribution of permanent dipole, then Δn reaches a minimum Δn_{min} related at low fields with P/Q according to :

$$\frac{P}{Q} = \frac{1 - \dfrac{\Delta n_{min}}{\Delta n_o}}{0,1547 + \dfrac{\Delta n_{min}}{\Delta n_o}} \quad (3)$$

- The birefringence decay following the removal of the field is exponential and reads (7) :

$$\Delta n(t) = \Delta n_o e^{-6D_R t} \quad (4)$$

- Information about absolute values of electrical and optical parameters of the particle are provided by the behaviour of the steady state birefringence Δn_o versus the square of the electric field E: Δn_o is given by (8) :

$$\frac{\Delta n_o}{\psi} = \frac{2\pi}{n} (g_1 - g_2)\phi \left[P/Q , (P+Q)E^2 \right] \quad (5)$$

where ψ is the volume fraction of polymer, $(g_1 - g_2)$ is the optical anisotropy factor , the indices 1 and 2 refering to the revolution axis and transverse axis respectively : ϕ is the orientation function.
In the limit of weak electric fields Eq.(9) reduces to :

$$\frac{\Delta n_o}{\psi} = n k_{sp} E^2 \quad (6)$$

where k_{sp} is the Kerr constant given by :

$$k_{sp} = \frac{2\pi}{15} \frac{g_1 - g_2}{n^2} (P + Q) \tag{7}$$

Setup. A He-Ne laser beam ($\lambda = 632.8$ nm) polarized at $3\pi/4$ to the vertical propagates parallel to the surface of two vertical flat "inox" electrodes immersed in the solution to be studied. The spacing between the electrodes is 2.5 mm and their length 40 mm. High voltage rectangular pulses are applied to the electrodes, with adjustable duration (from 10 μs to 10 ms, rise and decay times < 0.2 μs) and adjustable amplitude (up to 500 V for a single pulse and 250 V for a sequence of a positive pulse and a negative one). The inversion of the field takes place in less than 1 μs. The light beam emerging from the Kerr cell passes through a quarter wave plate whose slow axis at $3\pi/4$ is parallel to the polarisation direction, and through an analyser, before detection by a photodiode. The output signal is digitized by a transient recorder DATALAB DL 922 (8 bits, 2 koctets memory, 20 MHz maximum sampling rate) together with the high voltage electric pulse applied to the cell. The digital signals are sent to a HP 86 computer to be processed. Several recordings for each experimental condition are stored for further analysis.

QUASIELASTIC LIGHT SCATTERING

Experiments were performed by using either an argon ion laser ($\lambda = 488$ nm) or a helium-neon laser ($\lambda = 632.8$ nm) in conjunction with a 72-channel clipped digital autocorrelator for measuring the autocorrelation function of the scattered light intensity in the homodyne regime. The scattering angle was varied from 15° to 135°. The temperature was held constant to within ± 0.01°C.

Intensity correlation data were routinely processed, using the method of cumulants to provide the average decay rate <Γ> and the variance v (9)(10). The latter parameter is a measure of the width of the distribution of decay rates and is given by :

$$v = (<\Gamma^2> - <\Gamma>^2)/<\Gamma>^2 \tag{8}$$

In the case of homogeneous particles the diffusion coefficient D is given by the first reduced cumulant $<\Gamma>/2K^2$. The magnitude of the scattering vector K is given by :

$$K = \left[4\pi n \sin(\theta/2)\right]/\lambda \tag{9}$$

where θ is the scattering angle, λ is the wave-length of the incident light in a vacuum and n is the refractive index of the scattering medium.

EXPERIMENTAL RESULTS

TRANSIENT ELECTRIC BIREFRINGENCE

Dynamic behaviour. Time dependent curves of the birefringence $\Delta n(t)$ induced by applying successively a positive and a negative electric

field pulse to solutions of PVC at C = 10^{-3} g cm^{-3} have been recorded
(Fig.1) for the following starting concentrations C_q : 0.5 % and 1.2%
at 25°C ; 1.6 % at 25°C, 40°C and 60°C.

From the values of Δn_{min} measured at the electric field reversing, and using "Equation 3", the P/Q ratios reported in Table I are
obtained. We note that the PVC particles possess both a permanent and
an induced electric dipole moment ; the P/Q ratio depends on the quenching concentration of the solution as well as on the temperature.

A single exponential curve (cf. "Equation 4") has been fitted
to the birefringence decay curve after removal of the electric field;
the agreement is good for C_q = 0.5 % at 25°C (Fig.1) and moderately
good for C_q = 1.6 % at 60°C (Fig.2 b). The fits lead to the relaxation
times τ_R = 1/6 D_R reported in Table I. As to the other cases, the
agreement is very poor (Fig.2a) ; a two exponential curve is then
necessary to describe the decay curves behaviour. The two-time constants are reported in Table I.

The theoretical curve described by "Equation 1" has been fitted
to the experimental rise curve of the birefringence only when the decay curve is single-exponential ; the agreement is then found to be
very good, the rotational diffusion constant D_R and the P/Q ratio
obtained from the best fit being very close to the values of these
parameters deduced from birefringence behaviour at removal and at
reversing of the electric field respectively. Since the rise curve
is already described by a sum of two exponentials "Equation 1" for a
single relaxation process, it was not attempted to fit this curve
when the decay curve cannot be described by a single exponential.

Size of the particle. Assuming a spherical shape, the value of the
rotational diffusion constant D_R can provide an average radius using
the following relationship :

$$\tau_R = \frac{1}{6D_R} = \frac{4\pi\eta_o R^3}{3 k_B T} \qquad (10)$$

where η_o is the solvent viscosity.

The values of R are reported in Table I. When the decay curve of
birefringence is characterized by two relaxation processes, a radius
is attributed to each time constant.

An increase of the particle radius is observed at 25°C (the
smaller one in the case of a two exponentials fit) as the starting
concentration is increased. Furthermore, for C_q = 1.2 % and 1.6 %,
a second species of particles appears with a radius about twice larger. These two kinds of particles seem to coexist with no change of
size distribution as the temperature is increased from 25°C to 40°C
for a starting concentration of 1.6 %. Yet, at 60°C, only the smaller particle species remain in solution.

Steady-state birefringence. The investigation of the steady-state
birefringence variation versus the squared electric field leads to
the knowledge of the Kerr constant k_{SP}, the electrical parameters
of the particle μ and $\alpha_1 - \alpha_2$, and its optical anisotropy $g_1 - g_2$.
As this variation is close to linearity in the whole electric field
range investigated the P/Q ratio deduced from the birefringence

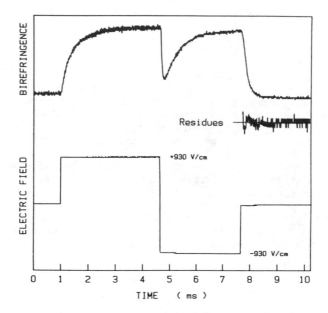

Figure 1.   Time dependence of the birefringence signal under the action of a reversing electric pulse of a PVC solution at C = 10^{-3} g cm^{-3} and T = 25°C. The quenching concentration was 0.5 10^{-2} g cm^{-3}. The single exponential curve (dotted line) deduced from the best fit of "Equation 8" to birefringence decay curve is indistinguishable from the experimental curve. Residues (i.e. difference between theoretical and experimental curve) are plotted below the birefringence curve.

Table I. Transient electric birefringence parameters for PVC solutions at $C = 10^{-3}$ g.cm^{-3}

Quenching Concentration (10^{-2} g cm^{-3})	Temperature °C	P/Q (Reversing pulse)	Birefringence Decay		Steady State Birefringence		
			τ_R (μs)	R (Å)	k_{SP} 10^{16} (m^2.V^{-2})	μ 10^{26} (m.c)	10^5 (g_1-g_2)
0.5	23	1.82	126	400	1.05	3.51	0.44
1.2	23	1.49	227/1384*	487/890*	3.30	4.35	0.82
	23	0.75	571/4134*	662/1281*	9.50	4.09	1.92
1.6	40	0.95	387/2659*	643/1223*	4.88	3.71	1.36
	60	1.01	274	645	0.89	3.62	0.27

* The two values correspond to a two exponential fit (cf. text).

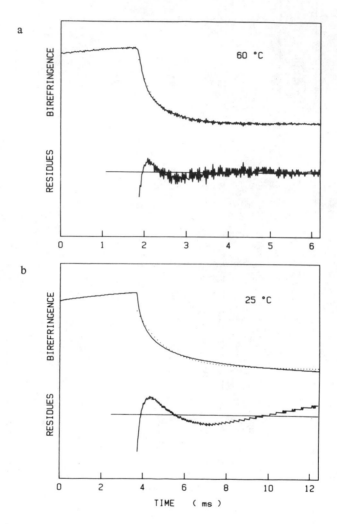

Figure 2. Time dependence of the birefringence decay signal, at
the removal of the electric field, of a PVC solution at C = 10^{-3}
g cm^{-3} and for a quenching concentration of 1.6 10^{-2}g cm^{-3}. Temperatures are T = 25°C (Fig.2a) and T = 60°C (Fig.2b). Dotted
lines represent the single exponential curves deduced from the
best fit of "Equation 8" to the experimental curves. Residues
(i.e. difference between these two curves) are plotted below.

behaviour at the reversing pulse (see above) is imposed in order to
reduce the number of adjustable parameters in the fit of "Equation 5"
to the experimental values.

The values of permanent dipole moment μ, optical anisotropy
$g_1 - g_2$ and Kerr constant k_{SP} are reported in Table I. We note that
the k_{SP} and $g_1 - g_2$ values increase at 25°C as the starting concentration of the solution increases.Increasing temperature from 25°C
to 60°C for the C_q = 1.6 % solution results in lowering these two parameters down to values near those found in the 0.5 % solution at
25°C.

QUASI-ELASTIC LIGHT SCATTERING

Fig.3 shows the wavevector dependence of the first reduced cumulant
for the three samples. At given K, $<\Gamma>/2K^2$ decreases as the starting
concentration C_q increases. The variance measured in the high K limit increases   with C_q from 0.1 to 0.2, to 0.25 for C_q = 0.5, 1.2
and 1.6 10^{-2} g cm^{-3} respectively. This result suggest that PVC molecules form aggregates whose size and polydispersity increase with
the starting concentration. The K dependence of $<\Gamma>/2K^2$, observed
for the sample quenched at C_q = 1.6 10^{-2} g cm^{-3} is characteristic of
deformable or/and polydisperse particles in the limit $K\overline{R}$ < 1 ($\overline{R}$,
average radius or radius of gyration of the particles). Extrapola-
tion to zero K provides D_o, the z average translational diffusion
coefficient. In addition, the curves relative to the two other samples exhibit an anomalous increase in the low K range. So far, such
a behaviour has been only observed for latex particles of large size
(Radius > 200 nm) at moderately high volume fractions ($\Psi > 10^{-2}$) and
has been attributed to short-range ordering of the scattering particles (9)(10). Yet this interpretation is not consistent with the persistence of the effect upon dilution (4)(5). An anomalous static
structure factor has also been observed in classical light scattering
experiment (4)(5). The static scattered intensity increases with K
in the range K where $<\Gamma>/2K^2$ decreases and goes through a small maximum. Such an anomalous behaviour has been previously observed for
other polymers liable to also forming physical crosslinks and was
attributed to long range order (11)(12). This interpretation cannot
be retained in the present case, since the effect is unaffected by
dilution (4). Therefore, it is concluded that the particles should
be optically inhomogeneous and a tentative explanation is put forward on the basis of a "correlation hole" effect (13) arising from
the presence of crosslinks of crystalline nature which could act as
strong scatterers.

The anomalous static structure factor of the aggregates associated with a relatively small size polydispersity could produce the observed behaviour of $<\Gamma>/2K^2$. The latter parameter is given by :

$$<\Gamma>/2K^2 = \sum_i N_i \, f_i^2 \, D_{oi} / \sum_i N_i \, f_i^2$$

where N_i is the number of particules of species i with diffusion
coefficient D_{oi} and scattering amplitude f_i.

If the scattered amplitude f_i is a function of K, then $<\Gamma>/2K^2$
is K dependent through the polydispersity effect, even though D_{oi}'s
are independent on K. Such an effect has been investigated in detail

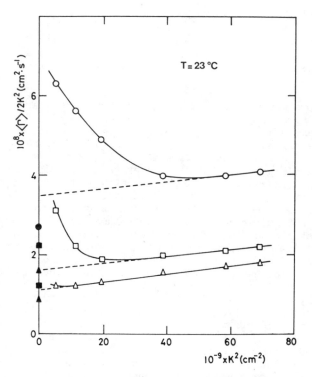

Figure 3. Variations of $<\Gamma>/2K^2$ versus K. The symbols refer to quenching concentrations (in $10^{-2}g\ cm^{-3}$) o (0.5) ; ◻ (1.2) ; Δ (1.6). The filled symbols correspond to the D_O values calculated from the transient electric birefringence results (cf. text).

by Pusey in the case of particles large enough such that the first
minimum of the static structure factor lies in the investigated K range (14).This cannot be invoked here, since aggregates with radius as
low as 400 Å also exhibit anomalous K dependence . In addition,if
the structure factor of each scattering particle has a K dependent
maximum, then, obviously $<\Gamma>/K^2$ can vary any way with K. Small polydispersities could produce large effect on $<\Gamma>/2K^2$ if $f_i(K)$ is very
sensitive to the size and the internal structure of the particle.Al-
ternatively, large polydispersities would average out the effect.This
is what probably occurs for $C_q = 1.6 \ 10^{-2}$ g cm^{-3}.

We have also reported on the ordinate axis of Fig.3 the values
of the translational diffusion coefficient D_o calculated from radius
values measured by transient electric birefringence, using :

$$D_o = \frac{k_B T}{6 \pi \eta_o R}$$

For $C_q = 1.6 \ 10^{-2}$ g cm^{-3} and $C_q = 1.2 \ 10^{-2}$ g cm^{-3} the extrapolation at zero K of the values of $<\Gamma>/2K^2$ obtained by a cumulant
analysis lies in between the two values of D_o determined from the
two exponential fit of the decay curve of the transient birefringence. In this respect, it must be remarked that a bimodal relaxation
curve is much easier to analyse in transient electric birefringence
experiments since the relaxation times vary as R^{-3} whereas in QELS
they are inversely proportional to R.For the sample $C_q = 0.5 \ 10^{-2}$g cm^{-3}
the effect of the curve rise at the low K prevents to extrapolate
with reasonable accuracy. Yet, one can notice that the D_o value obtained from transient electric birefringence is consistent with quasielastic light scattering data.

The figures 4 and 5 illustrate the effect of temperature on the
first reduced cumulant. The data have been normalized to take into
account the temperature dependence of the viscosity.

For the sample $C_q = 0.5 \ 10^{-2}$g cm^{-3} there is very little change
in the K dependences of $<\Gamma>/2K^2$. The data of Fig.4 relative to the
two extreme temperatures investigated i.e. 23°C and 62°C nearly su-
perimpose, mainly in the high K range. The variance also remains
constant with temperature.

Alternatively, the effect of temperature is quite important for
samples prepared at high quenching concentration. As seen in Fig.5,
upon increasing temperature, the normalized first cumulant increases
and the anomalous increase in the low K range appears. Again, it must
be noticed that the extrapolation of $<\Gamma>/2K^2$ to zero K from the high
K range coïncides with the value of D_o calculated from transient
electric birefringence.

DISCUSSION

The results presented above show that the structure of the aggregates
formed by the quenching of PVC solutions depends on the starting concentration. If the starting concentration is low enough ($C_q = 0.5$
10^{-2} g cm^{-3}) the particles are characterized by an average radius
$R \simeq 400$ Å and a small size polydispersity that are quite independent
of temperature in the range 23°C - 62°C. The anomalous static structure factor and the existence of a permanent dipole moment strongly

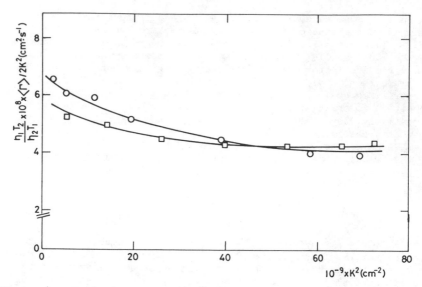

Figure 4. Variations of $<\Gamma>/2K^2$ versus K for sample C_q = 0.5
10^{-2} g cm^{-3}. T = 23°C (o) ; T = 62°C (□).
η_1 and η_2 represent the viscosity of the solvent at the reference
temperature T_1 = 23°C and the temperature of the measurement T_2
respectively.

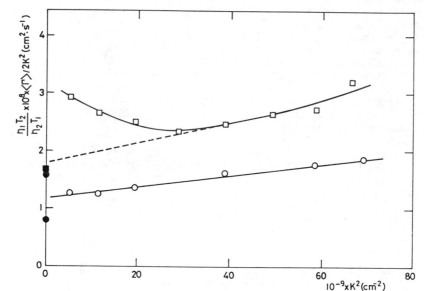

Figure 5. Variations of $<\Gamma>/2K^2$ versus K for sample C_q = 1.6
10^{-2} g cm^{-3}. T = 23°C (o) ; T = 62°C (□).
η_1 and η_2 represent the viscosity of the solvent at the reference
temperature T_1 = 23°C and the temperature of the measurement T_2
respectively.

support the presence in the aggregate of small crystallites acting as crosslinks. The anomalous dynamical structure factor likely associated with a distribution of peak shaped static structure factors is not significantly modified by an increase of temperature. Kinetics studies that will be reported elsewhere show that the crosslinks responsible of the aggregation form quite instantaneously after quenching.

Higher starting concentrations result in the formation of larger and more polydisperse aggregates. In that case the anomalous effect on the dynamical structure factor is smeared out. Heating these samples produce a breaking up of the aggregates with a trend to form particles similar to those obtained at lower starting concentration, characterized by smaller size, polydispersity, Kerr constant and optical anisotropy (cf. Table). These results suggest that a second kind of crosslinks unstable upon temperature rise is present in the aggregates. Kinetic studies show that these crosslinks form slowly after quenching.

These observations complement results of DSC experiments performed on macroscopic gels which show no melting endotherm for the primary crosslinks found in the initial stage of the gelation. DSC peaks appear only when significant time has elapsed after quenching.

Literature Cited

1. Alfrey, T.; Wiederhorn, N.; Stein, R.; Tobolsky, A. Ind. Eng. Chem. 1949, 41, 70.
2. Guerrero, S.J.; Keller, A. J. Polym. Sci. Polym. Phys. Ed. 1980, 18, 1533.
3. Yang, Y.S.; Geil, P.H. J. Macromol. Sci. Phys. 1983, B 22 (3), 463.
4. Mutin, P.H.; Guenet, J.M. Polymer 1986, 27, 1098.
5. Candau, S.J.; Dormoy, Y.; Mutin, P.H.; Debeauvais, F.; Guenet, J.M. Polymer, submitted for publication.
6. Tinoco, I.; Yamaoko, K. J. Phys. Chem. 1959, 63, 423.
7. Benoit, H. Ann. Phys. 12e Série, 1951, 6, 1.
8. O'Konski, C.T.; Yoshioka, K.; Orttung, W.H. J. Amer. Chem. Soc. 1959, 63, 1558.
9. Fijnaut, H.M.; Pathmamanoharan, C.; Nieuwenhuis, E.A.; Vrij, A. Chem. Phys. Lett. 1978, 59, 351.
10. Fijnaut, H.M.; Dhont, J.K.G.; Nieuwenhuis, E.A. Advances in Colloid and Interface Science 1982, 16, 161.
11. Burchard, W. Polymer 1969, 10, 29.
12. Mrkvickova, L.; Konak, C.; Sedlacek, B. In Physical Optics of Dynamic Phenomena and Processes in Macromolecular Systems; Sedlacek, B., Ed.; W. de Gruyter : Berlin, 1985; p.353.
13. De Gennes, P.G. Scaling Concepts in Polymer Physics; Cornell Univ. Press : Ithaca (N.Y.), 1979.
14. Pusey, P.N.; Van Megen, W. J. Chem. Phys. 1984, 80, 3513.

RECEIVED January 24, 1987

Chapter 4

Concentration Dependence of the Polymer Diffusion Coefficient

Wender Wan[1] and Scott L. Whittenburg

Department of Chemistry, University of New Orleans, New Orleans, LA 70148

A theoretical expression for the concentration dependence of the polymer diffusion coefficient is derived. The final result is shown to describe experimental results for polystyrene at theta conditions within experimental errors without adjustable parameters. The basic theoretical expression is applied to theta solvents and good solvents and to polymer gels and polyelectrolytes.

One measure of the dynamics of motion of polymers is the rate of diffusion of the polymer. Due to the complex nature of the polymer molecule the dynamic phase diagram is also complex. The rate of diffusion depends on the concentration of the polymer, the temperature, the polymer-solvent interaction and the characteristic length associated with the experiment. To understand the concept of the characteristic length of the measurement consider a typical quasi-elastic light scattering (QELS) experiment. The intensity of the light scattered by the polymer is analyzed as a function of angle between the incident laser beam and the scattered direction which is determined by two pinholes. Using the scattering angle, θ, the scattered wavevector, q, is calculated via $q = (4\pi n/\lambda)\sin\theta/2$, where n is the index of refraction of the scattering medium and λ is the wavelength of the laser line. Thus, the experimenter chooses a particular value of q by a suitable choice of scattering angle. The characteristic length of the experiment is q^{-1}, which can be seen by dimensional analysis. For large q the characteristic length is very small, corresponding to the motion of individual segments. This regime is termed the internal motion regime (I). For smaller values of q the correlated motions of more and more segments are sampled until the experiment can be interpreted as probing the motion of entire polymer molecules. This transition occurs at $q\xi = 1$, where ξ is the correlation length. The nature of the system in the macroscopic regime is determined by the ratio, q/q^{+}, where $q^{+} = (\tau_r D_g)^{-1/2}$

[1]Current address: Department of Chemistry, Brown University, Providence, RI 02914

where τ_r is the relaxation time for knots in the gel entanglement network and D_g is the gel diffusion coefficient. Below this curve the polymer system has a liquid- like (L) response to perturbations, while above this curve the response is gel-like (G). These different dynamic regimes are shown in the dynamic phase diagram shown below.

The form of the concentration dependence of the polymer diffusion depends on the concentration of the polymer relative to the crossover concentration, c^*, between the dilute and semidulute regimes. At concentrations below c^* and below q^ξ =1 the diffusion is of a single polymer molecule. At concentrations above c^* the polymer chains entangle and the diffusing species again becomes the segments of the polymer molecule. These concentration regimes are shown in Figure 1. As the polymer concentration is increased the friction coefficient is increased, thus leading to a slowing down of the motion of individual molecules. A measure of the rate of diffusion is the diffusion coefficient. The decrease in the rate of diffusion as the the concentration is increased below c^* is marked by a decrease in the diffusion coefficient, D. A microscopic, hydrodynamic theory explains this behavior quite adequately (1). As the polymer concentration approaches c* the diffusion coefficient versus concentration curve flattens out and, at concentrations above c* but still in the semidilute regime, the diffusion coefficient becomes a linearly increasing function of the polymer concentration(2-5). This behaviour is shown in Figure 2 for polystyrene of various molecular weights as a function of concentration in cyclohexane at the theta temperature, $34.5^\circ C$, and in cyclopentane at its theta point, $20.4^\circ C$.

Typically, scaling approaches are employed to explain the behavior in the semidilute regime. By examining static correlations near the temperature, Daoud and Jannick(6) have expressed the density–density correlation function in terms of a correlation length that is inversely proportional to concentration. Since the diffusion coefficient is inversely proportional to the correlation length it is directly proportional to the concentration.

Combining the above descriptions leads to a picture that describes the experimentally observed concentration dependence of the polymer diffusion coefficient. At low concentrations the decrease of the translational diffusion coefficient is due to hydrodynamic interactions that increase the friction coefficient and thereby slow down the motion of the polymer chain. At high concentrations the system becomes an entangled network. The cooperative diffusion of the chains becomes a cooperative process, and the diffusion of the chains increases with increasing polymer concentration. This description requires two different expressions in the two concentration regimes. A microscopic, hydrodynamic theory should be capable of explaining the observed behavior at all concentrations.

Theory

The diffusion coefficient is related to a microscopic variable through a Green–Kubo relation

$$D = (1/3) \int_0^\infty dt <A(t)A^+(0)> \tag{1}$$

where for diffusion the microscopic variable is the flux of the number of particles through an imaginary plane of unit area in the fluid. Thus, for diffusion $A(t) = (dx/dN)\dot{N}(t)$, where $\dot{N}(t)$ is the flux of the number of particles through the plane at time t. Equation 1 is a general expression for the diffusion coefficient. A diffusion coefficient may describe either cooperative or non-cooperative processes. For non-cooperative processes the chemical species that we are following with our experiment moves in the average force field of the instantaneous structure of the fluid at its instantaneous position. The average force is usually expressed in terms of some average property of the fluid, typically the vis-

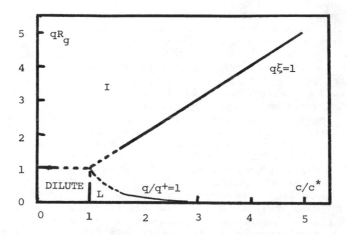

Figure 1.   The different dynamic regimes for a polmer system. The notation for the regimes is given in the text. (Reproduced from Ref. 20. Copyright   1985 American Chemical Society.)

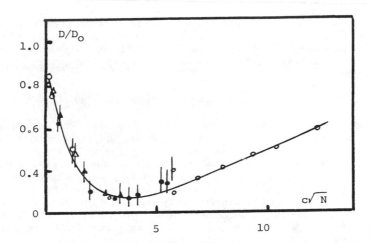

Figure 2. Concentration dependence of the diffusion coefficient for polystyrene in two solvents at the theta point for various molecular weights. The line is the theoretical curve. (Reproduced from Ref. 12. Copyright 1983 American Chemical Society.)

cosity of the fluid. For non-cooperative diffusion we may visualize
an experiment in which we tag one of the particles in the fluid and
observe its diffusion thorugh the fluid. This is referred to a
self-diffusion and is approximated in scattering experiments in
which a dye molecule is embedded into a polymer matrix. Alternatively, if we do not label any of the molecules in the fluid, then
we can only measure the rate at which molecules move past each
other. This is referred to as mutual diffusion. In experiments in
which non-labelled particles are employed the measured quantitity is
D_{mut}. Depending on the experimental conditions it is possible that
the motion of one chemical species is driven by the motion of other
species. This would be the case of the diffusion of polymer segments in an entangled network. The diffusion of a single chain must
push other segments out of the way. The is referred to as cooperative diffusion. Equation 1 describes self, mutual and cooperative
diffusion because of the generality of the dynamic variable, $\overset{\circ}{N}(t)$.
$\overset{\circ}{N}(t)$ is a phase-space variable; that is, the flux will depend on
both the positions and velocities of the polymer segments. Therefore, we can expand it in the variables (x_i, p_i) and, using Equation
1, obtain

$$D = \int_0^\infty dt \; \langle v_i(t)v_i(0)\rangle + \int_0^\infty dt \; (dx_i/dN)^2 (dN/dp_i)^2 \langle F_i(t)F_i(0)\rangle \quad (2)$$

where we have used the repeated index convention. For isotropic
systems we could write each of the terms on the right hand side of
Equation 2 as one-third of the component of the velocity or force in
each direction. Noting that the velocities of the individual segments add up to the overall polymer velocity, we see that the first
term in Equation 2 gives simply the relation between the polymer
diffusion coefficient and the velocity-velocity correlation
function. A microscopic approach yields the Einstein relation(3) D =
$k_bT/f_0(1 + k_sc)$, where k_b is Boltzmann's constant, T is the absolute
temperature, f_0, is the friction coefficient at infinite dilution,
k_s, is a constant, and c is the polymer concentration. Because the
forces on the individual segments are not additive, the second term
in Equation 2 must be left in terms of segment variables. It is
clear that the first term on the right hand side of Equation 2
describes the self diffusion coefficient. We are following the
velocity of an individual particle as a function of time and the
contribution of its neighbors in the fricitional drag expressed
through the viscosity of the fluid. The second term on the right
hand side of Equation 2 decribes the contribution of both mutual
diffusion and cooperative diffusion.
    Following Ferrell(8), the second term in Equation 2 can be
expressed as a Green-Kubo integral over a flux-flux correlation
function. The transport is due to a velocity perturbation caused by
two driving forces, the Brownian force and frictional force. The
transport coefficient due to the segment-segment interaction can be
calculated from the Kubo formula(9)

$$\lambda = (1/k_bT)\iiint_0^\infty dr_1 dr_2 d(t_2-t_1) \; J(r_2,t_2)J(r_1,t_1) \quad (3)$$

where $J(r,t) = S(r,t)V(r,t)$ and the transport coefficient λ is
related to the diffusion coefficient through $\lambda = 3(V/k_BT)^2 D$. $S(r,t)$
is the density fluctuation, and $V(r,t)$ is the local velocity of the

segment in the polymer solution. For simplicity(8), we define the equal time density correlation function $G(r)$

$$G(r_{12}) = <S(r_1,0)S(r_2,0)> \tag{4}$$

and the time-integrated velocity correlation tensor $A_{ij}(r)$

$$A_{ij}(r_{12}) = \int_0^\infty dt <V_i(r_1,t)V_j(r_2,0)> \tag{5}$$

Substituting $G(r)$ and $A_{ij}(r)$ into Equation 3, we have

$$\lambda = (1/k_bT) \quad \iiint dr_1 \, dr_2 dt \; S(r_2,t)V(r_2,t)S(r_1,0)V(r_1,0) \tag{6}$$

which simplifies to

$$\lambda = (1/k_bT)\iiint dr_1 \, dr_2 dt \; G(r_{12})V(r_2,t)V(r_1,0)$$

$$\lambda = (1/k_bT) \iint G(r_{12})A(r_{12})dr_1 \, dr_2 = (V/k_bT) \int G(r)A(r) \, dr$$

where $A(r)$ is the trace of A_{ij} and V is the volume of the system. The diffusion coefficient can be obtained by Equation 1, that is, the flux divided by the thermodynamic driving force via

$$D = (1/3) \; k_bT/ \; V \int G(r)A(r) \; dr \; = (1/3) \; <A> \tag{7}$$

Such a decomposition of the diffusion coefficient has previously been noted by Pattle et al.(10) Now we must evaluate $<A>$. The time-integrated velocity correlation function A_{ij} is due to the hydrodynamic interaction and can be described by the Oseen tensor. The Oseen tensor is related to the velocity perturbation caused by the hydrodynamic force, F. By checking units, we see that A is the Oseen tensor times the energy term, k_bT, or

$$A_{ij}(r) = (k_bT/8\pi\eta)(\delta_{ij}/r + r_ir_j/r^3) \tag{8}$$

where δ_{ij} is the Kronecker delta. Obviously, the trace of $A_{ij}(r)$ is

$$A(r) \quad = \quad k_bT/(2\pi\eta r) \tag{9}$$

For now, we restrict our discussion to the θ point, where the polymers in solution have a random coil distribution. Therefore, it is reasonable to say that in the semidilute regime at the θ point the distribution of the segments in the solution is spherical. With this concept, the velocity of the diffusing segments at the θ condition can be expressed as

$$V_i(t)(4\pi <R_{ij}>^3/3) = \int_{r<(R_{ij})} dr \; V(r,t) \tag{10}$$

Then the diffusion coefficient due to the hydrodynamic interaction between the segments in the polymer solution, that is, the mutual diffusion coefficient, is given by

$$D_{mut} = (1/3) \int \; dt \sum_{ij} <V_i(t)V_j(0)> \tag{11}$$

$$= (1/3)\iiint dt \; dr_1 \, dr_2 \; (3/4\pi R_{ij}^3)^2 \; k_bT/2\pi\eta R_{ij}$$

$$D = (1/3)[k_bT/(2\,\pi\eta<R_{ij}>)] = (k_bT/6\pi\eta)\ <R_{ij}^{-1}>$$

where we have used Equation 9 and Equation 10 and $<R_{ij}^{-1}>$ is the inverse average distance between any two segments in the solution. Although the notation is perhaps misleading, we have chosesn to write the expression in this form to correspond to the notation of Imai(11). Equation 11 is the contribution to the diffusion coefficient due to mutual or cooperative diffusion. This can be seen by realizing that it arises from the force-force correlation function or, from Equation 11, the velocity-velocity correlation function of different particles. Thus, the dynamic variable is the velocity of two particles relative to each other. This describes mutual diffusion. Combining the expressions for the self and mutual diffusion coefficients yields the following expression for the polymer diffusion coefficient

$$D = k_bT/f_0(1 + k_s c) + k_bT/6\pi\eta_0)<R_{ij}^{-1}> \qquad (12)$$

Typically the experimental data on the diffusion coefficient are normalized relative to the diffusion coefficient at infinite dilution, $D_0 = k_bT/f_0$, so that Equation 12 will be most useful as

$$D/D_0 = (1 + k_s c)^{-1} + R_H<R_{ij}^{-1}> \qquad (13)$$

where the hydrodynamic radius $R_H = f_0/6\pi\eta_0$. Equation 13 is the general result of this chapter.

Application to Theta Solvents

The term $<R_{ij}>$ has been evaluated by Imai for hydrodynamic interactions at the θ point(11). The transport is due to a velocity perturbation caused by some driving force. Diffusion of the segments is a result of the hydrodynamic force that can be described in terms of the Oseen tensor (11) with the solvent modeled as a continuum with viscosity, η_0. Thus, Imai has shown that the second term in Equation 13 can be written as the energy, k_bT, times the trace over the Oseen tensor. Averaging over the distribution of segment positions yields

$$<R_{ij}^{-1}>=(1/6\pi\eta_0)<T_{ij}> = (\pi Nb^2/9)c \qquad (14)$$

where N is the number of segments and b is the segment bond length. Combining Equation 13 and Equation 14 with the experimental result for the hydrodynamic radius, $R_H = R_H'M^{1/2}$, where R_H' is a constant for a given polymer-solvent system, yields our final result, which is specific for θ conditions.

$$D/D_0 = (1 + k_s c)^{-1} + 2.10124 \times 10^{15} R_H' b^2 N^{1/2} c_w/m^{1/2} \qquad (15)$$

where c is expressed as a weight concentration (g/cm^3), $c_w = c\sqrt{M}/m$, where m is the molecular weight of each segment and the bond length is given in angstroms.

We compare our theoretical expression with the experimentally measured values for the diffusion coefficient of polystyrene. The diffusion coefficient has been measured for polystyrene of various molecular weights in cyclohexane, using light scattering, by Munch, et al.(12). This study examined the concentration dependence of the diffusion coefficient over a wide range of molecular weights and at concentrations spanning the dilute-semidilute regimes. For polystyrene the hydrodynamic radius is given(13,14) by $R_H = 0.228M^{1/2}$ A^o and the bond length is 3.124 A^o.

The constant k_s is given by $k_s = (2mNA_2 - k_f - \bar{v})$, where A_2 is the second virial coefficient, k_f is the frictional hydrodynamic interaction parameter, and v is the specific volume. $\bar{v}$ is negligible compared to k_f. For polystyrene at the θ point k_s is 1.45 cm^3/g (13). The fit to the experimental points is given in Figure 2.

As can be seen in Figure 2, the microscopic expression for the diffusion coefficient, Equation 15, correctly describes the shape of the diffusion coefficient curve over the dilute and semidilute concentration regimes. It is important to note that Equation 15 contains no adjustable parameters. All of the constants in our microscopic expression have been independently measured by various experimental techniques. Thus, the description of the concentration dependence of the diffusion coefficient does not require a microscopic theory in the dilute regime and a scaling argument in the semidulute regime. A single microscopic approach is capable of explaining the observed behavior in both concentration regimes. It should also be stressed that even though Equation 13 implies that both overall polymer and segmental diffusion contribute at all concentrations, except at concentrations near c*, one term or the other dominates. Indeed, at concentrations near the crossover concentration both types of diffusional motion contribute to the measured diffusion coefficient. Thus, there is no sharp dividing line along the concentration axis, to be identified with c*, that separates the different contributions to D/D_0. Equation 13 does yield an expression for a crossover concentration at which the two contributions are equal. Equating the two terms on the right-hand side of Equation 13, noting that, at c*, $k_s c \gg 1$, and solving for the concentration yield

$$c* = \langle R_{ij} \rangle / k_s R_H \tag{16}$$

The crossover concentration calculated for polystyrene with this expression is in the range of the reported values(12,15). Finally, the above discussion points out that c* is not a sharp dividing line. It is therefore not physically meaningful to scale the concentration axis in a plot of D/D_0 versus concentration divided by the crossover concentration. Equation 13 demonstrates that it is better to plot the relative diffusion coefficient vs. the weight concentration of the polymer, as was done by Munch et al. (12).

Application to Non-Theta Conditions

Equation 13 can be extended to non-θ conditions by multiplying $\langle R_{ij} \rangle$ by an expansion parameter. Since it is known that the expansion paramenter is greater than unity for good solvents and less than unity for poor solvents, Equation 13 would predict that the slope of the D/D_0 versus c_w line for $c_w > c*$ would decrease in good solvents and increase in poor solvents, in agreement with predictions from

scaling theory($\underline{16,17}$).   This is only superficial, since expansion
parameters are functions of the polymer concentration and, therefore, for non-θ solvents the diffusion coefficient curve at concentrations above the crossover concentration may no longer be linear
($\underline{18}$). These predictions are in agreement with the results on polystyrene in THF ($\underline{19}$) (Figure 3).

Application to the Ordinary-Extraordinary Transition

The above approach also can explain the ordinary-extraordinary transition observed in polyelectrolytes. The ordinary-extraordinary
transition in dilute solutions of mononucleosomal DNA fragments has
been studied by Bloomfield and the results reported in another
chapter in this monograph. Equation 2 shows that both the velocity-
velocity correlation function and the force-force correlation
function add to the measured diffusion coefficient, D. In the polyelectrolytes the force, F_i, is the coulombic force due to the charge
on the polymer. As the ionic strength of the solution is lowered
the apparent translation diffusion coefficient, D(c), increases due
to the lowered shielding of the repulsive polyelectrolyte interaction. At a sufficiently low salt concentration the velocity-
velocity correlation function begins to contribute to the measured
diffusion coefficient. Thus, at very low salt concentrations the
experimental correlation function should display two exponential
decays. One is due to F_i, is present at all ionic strengths, and is
therefore the ordinary contribution. The second is due to v_i, is
present only at low salt concentrations, and is the extraordinary
contribution. These assignments are in agreement with the suggestions of Bloomfield.

Application to Polymer Gels

A polymer gel consists of a cross-linked polymer network that gives
elasticity to the gel and a liquid occupying the space between the
network chains. The friction contribution of the liquid will give
the same contribution to the diffusion coefficient as in the liquid
regime discussed in the "Application to Theta Conditions" section
above. The elastic force between the knots in the gel network is
independent of the polymer concentration and will therefore contribute a non-zero intercept to the D(c) versus concentration curve (Figure 4). Thus, Equation 2 predicts that the D(c) versus concentration
in the gel regime should be linear with a slope equal to that of the
liquid regime, but with a positive intercept. This prediction is in
agreement with the measurements on polystyrene in the gel and liquid
regimes.

Summary

We have shown that the microscopic expression for the polymer diffusion coefficient, Equation 2, is the starting point for a discussion
of diffusion in a wide range of polymer systems. For the example
worked out, polymer diffusion at theta conditions, the resulting
expresssion describes the experimental data without adjustable parameters. It should be possible to derive expressions for diffusion

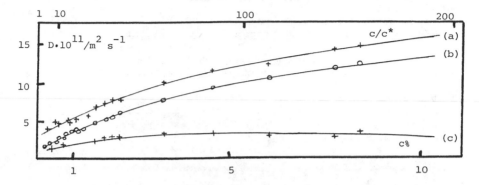

Figure 3. Concentration dependence of the diffusion coefficient of polystyrene in THF at 25°C. (a) collective modes, (b) cumulant values and classical gradient diffusion, (c) cooperative mode. (Reproduced   from Ref. 19. Copyright 1985 American Chemical Society.)

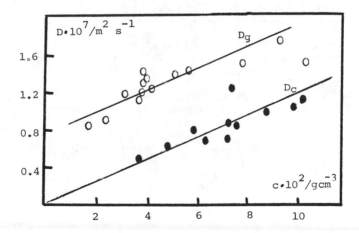

Figure 4. Concentration dependence of the liquid, D_c, gel, D_g, diffusion coefficients. The various symbols refer to different molecular weights. (Reproduced   from Ref. 20. Copyright 1985 American Chemical Society.)

in polymer gels and polyelectrolytes starting from Equation 2. We
are working in this direction.

Literature Cited

1. McQuarrie, D. A. Statistical Mechanics, 1st ed.; Harper and
    Row: New York, 1976.
2. Roots, J.; Nystrom, B. Polymer 1979, 20, 148.
3. Roots, J.; Nystrom, B. J. Macromol. Sci., Rev. Macromol. Chem.
    1980, C19,35.
4. Roots, J.; Nystrom, B. Macromolecules 1980, 13, 1595.
5. Roots, J.; Nystrom, B. J. Polym. Sci., Polym. Phys. Ed.
    1981, 19, 979.
6. Daoud, M.; Jannink, G. J. Phys. (Les Ulis, Fr.) 1976, 37, 973.
7. Brochard, F.; de Gennes, P.-G. Macromolecules 1977, 10, 1157.
8. Ferrell, R. Phys. Rev. Lett. 1970, 24, 1169.
9. Green, M. S. J. Chem. Phys. 1954, 22, 398.
10. Pattle, R. E.; Smith, P. J. A.; Hill, R. W. Trans. Faraday Soc.
    1967, 63, 2389.
11. Imai, S. J. Chem. Phys. 1970, 52, 4212.
12. Munch, J.-P.; Hild, G.; Candau, S. Macromolecules 1983, 16, 71.
13. Caroline, D.; Jones, G. In Light Scattering in Liquids and
    Macromolecular Solutions, Degiorgio, V., Corti, M., Giglio,
    M., Eds.; Plenum Press: New York, 1980.
14. Peterlin, A. J. Chem. Phys. 1955, 23, 2464.
15. Daoud, M.; Cotton, J. P.; Farnoux, B.; Jannink, G.; Sarma, G.;
    Benoit, H.; Duplessix, R.; Picot, C.; de Gennes, P.-G. Macro-
    molecules 1975, 8, 804.
16. Brochard, F.; Jouffroy, J.; Levinson, P. Macromolecules 1983,
    16, 1638.
17. de Gennes, P.-G. Scaling Concepts in Polymer Physics; Cornell
    University Press: Ithaca, NY, 1980.
18. Yamakawa, H. Modern Theory of Polymer Solutions; Harper and
    Row: New York, 1971.
19. Brown, W. Macromolecules 1985, 18, 1713.
20. Adam, M.; Delsanti, M. Macromolecules 1985, 18, 1760.

RECEIVED January 24, 1987

Chapter 5

Effects of Aggregation and Solvent Quality on the Viscosity of Semidilute Poly(vinylbutyral) Solutions

C. W. Paul[1] and P. M. Cotts

Almaden Research Center, IBM, San Jose, CA 95120-6099

The relative viscosities at 25°C of solutions containing 12% wt/vol poly(vinylbutyral) in pure methanol (MeOH), 1:1 methyl iso-butyl ketone (MIBK)/MeOH by volume and 9:1 MIBK/MeOH were in the ratio 1.0:0.9:4.3, respectively. The apparent activation energy for flow was 20 kcal/mol in the latter solution and only 8 kcal/mol in the former two. The dramatic influence of the solvent on the solution viscosity is attributed to the separate effects of solvent quality and polymer aggregation. Better solvents tend to reduce the viscosity while polymer aggregation tends to increase it. Aggregation is controlled not by solvent quality, but by solvent polarity and manifests itself as a hysteresis in plots of viscosity versus 1/T. Aggregates disperse and reform slowly--weeks may be required to reach equilibrium at room temperature. The thermodynamic quality of various solvents and solvent mixtures was determined by light scattering and intrinsic viscosity measurements. These data demonstrated that most mixtures of MIBK and MeOH are better solvents for PVB than either individual solvent.

It has been established (1) that solutions containing crystallizable polymers can form gels via the formation of microcrystallites. The gelation of noncrystallizable polymers is far less well understood (1,2). The polymer solutions investigated in this study do not conform to the strict definition of a gel in that they do not exhibit a yield stress (3). However, they do exhibit the tendency to form supramolecular structures or aggregates in a thermally reversible fashion. This tendency can lead (under proper conditions of temperature, concentration and solvent) to a true gel. Most investigations of the viscosity of semidilute polymer solutions have focused on the dependences on molecular weight, concentration and temperature; fewer have studied the effects of the solvent (4-14). The increase in intrinsic viscosity of a given

NOTE: This work has appeared largely in its present form in Reference 35.

[1]Current address: Allied–Signal, Columbia Road, Morristown, NJ 07960

0097–6156/87/0350–0057$06.00/0

flexible polymer in better solvents may be attributed to excluded volume effects, but these are expected to be minimal at higher concentrations. It has been reported that in the semidilute concentration range the relative viscosity of a polymer solution increases more rapidly with concentration using poor solvents (6), and that at sufficiently high concentrations the relative viscosity has been observed to be greater using poor solvents than with good ones, by up to more than an order of magnitude (8). This phenomenon has been observed with both polar polymers such as poly(methyl methacrylate) (8), ethylcellulose (9), poly(vinyl chloride-acetate) copolymers (10), as well as with poly(styrene) (8,13), and poly(α-methylstyrene) (14), nonpolar polymers. In some cases, enhanced viscosity in poor solvents has been attributed to clustering or aggregation of polymer segments which reduces the molecular mobility (7,8). Other studies (11,12) have found that the relative viscosity remains higher in the better solvent until relatively high concentrations (c~25%), where excluded volume effects are minimal, and η becomes independent of solvent quality. An increased η at a given concentration in the semidilute region for a poor solvent (12) was attributed to a larger concentration dependence of the friction coefficient for the poor solvent.

This study addresses two questions: 1) Is polymer aggregation in solutions directly related to solvent quality? 2) If not, does solvent quality exert an effect on the viscosity of semidilute solutions separate from the effect of aggregation? The copolymer poly(vinylbutyral) (PVB) was chosen for this investigation. PVB is known to aggregate in several solvents (15). Light scattering and intrinsic viscosity measurements were used to assess solvent quality. Viscosities were measured at one concentration in three solvents and temperatures from 25° to 55°C.

Equipment and Procedures

The solvents were MCB reagent-grade methyl iso-butyl ketone (MIBK) and glacial acetic acid, EM Science glass-distilled methanol (MeOH), and MCB Omni Solv glass-distilled tetrahydrofuran (THF) with 250 ppm BHT as a stabilizer. Poly(vinylbutyral) was purchased from Monsanto. It has the structure shown in Figure 1. The sample is polydisperse with $M_w/M_n \cong 2.9$ (by gel permeation chromatography), but uniform in functional group composition (15).

Light Scattering. The Rayleigh factor, R_θ, was measured using a Chromatix KMX-6 Low-Angle Light Scattering Photometer. The scattering equation for dilute polymer solutions is

$$Kc/R_\theta = \frac{1}{P(\theta)M_w} (1 + 2A_2M_wc + \cdots) \qquad (1a)$$

where K is the optical constant, c is the polymer concentration in g/ml, M_w is the polymer weight average molecular weight, $P^{-1}(\theta)$ is the particle scattering function, and A_2 is the second virial coefficient. Because the angle employed in the Chromatix KMX-6 is typically only ~4°, and light scattering measurements with Brookhaven light scattering goniometer for $30°<\theta<135°$ demonstrated that $P^{-1}(\theta)$ is unity at $\theta=4°$ within the limits of experimental determination, Equation 1a reduces to

$$\lim_{\theta \to 0} Kc/R_\theta = 1/M_w + 2A_2c \qquad (1b)$$

The optical constant, K, is given by known experimental parameters (see Ref. 35). Once K is evaluated for a given system, a plot of Kc/R_θ versus c yields $1/M_w$ from its c=0 intercept and A_2 from its initial slope.

Viscometry.   *Intrinsic viscosity.*   Kinematic viscosities ($\nu \equiv \eta/\rho$, where η is the viscosity) were measured in a Cannon-Ubbelohde capillary viscometer. At least four concentrations, covering the relative viscosity range ($\eta_r \equiv \nu/\nu_s$, where the subscript s denotes the solvent) from about 1.8 to 1.2 were used to construct Schulz-Blaschke plots. These plots of η_{sp}/c versus η_{sp}, where $\eta_{sp} \equiv \nu/\nu_s -1$, yield a slope of $k_{SB}[\eta]$ and an intercept of $[\eta]$ according to the Schulz-Blaschke Equation (18)

$$\eta_{sp}/c = [\eta] + k_{SB}[\eta]\eta_{sp} + \cdots \qquad (2)$$

Viscosity of 12% PVB solutions.   Solutions were prepared with $0.1185<c<0.1188$ g/ml at 25°C. Kinematic viscosities were measured in a size 400 Cannon-Zhukov viscometer. In this viscometer, the apparent shear rate at the wall, $\dot{\gamma}_w \equiv \tau_w/\eta$, ranged from 2.5 to 40 sec^{-1}. It is possible that non-Newtonian effects were present even at these low shear rates. However, such effects would only alter the data quantitatively--but not qualitatively--and the qualitative features of the data are the focus of this investigation. For further details about equipment and procedures, see Ref. 35.

Results

Light Scattering. Light scattering data were taken with the aim of ranking by quality the various solvents for PVB using the measured second virial coefficients, A_2. Scattering plots from PVB in MeOH are shown in Figure 2. According to Equation 1b, the c=0 intercept of these plots should yield $1/M_w$, while the slope in this limit is $2A_2$. Using the measurements obtained at ~24°C (O and □), neither of these quantities could be accurately determined due to the strong curvature as c→0. Such curvature is symptomatic of polymer aggregation in a poor solvent (20). Aggregation enhances the scattering (R_θ), thus reducing Kc/R_θ. PVB is known to aggregate in both poor solvents, such as MeOH and EtOH, as well as in THF, a fairly good solvent (15). The measurements at 50°C shown in Figure 2 (△) form a linear plot and allow a more accurate determination of the intercept, $1/M_w$. Apparently, heating these samples to 50°C removed some of this aggregation permanently. The scattering plot obtained at ~24°C a full three weeks after heating (□) lies well above that initially obtained at this temperature (O). If these solutions are considered largely nonaggregated

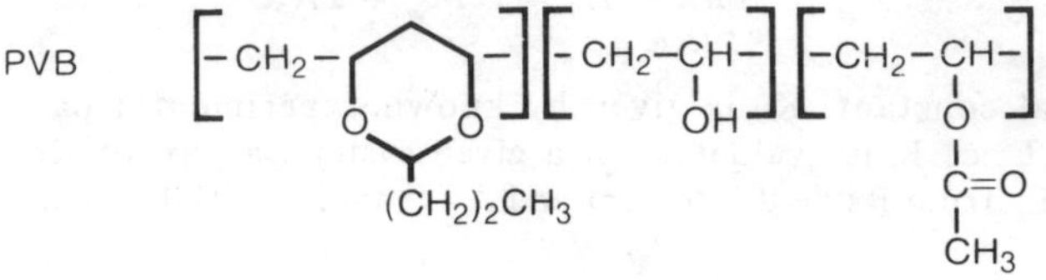

PVB $\left[-CH_2-\underset{\underset{(CH_2)_2CH_3}{\overset{\displaystyle O\;\;\;O}{\diagdown}}}{}-\right]\left[-CH_2-\underset{OH}{CH}-\right]\left[-CH_2-\underset{\underset{CH_3}{C=O}}{\overset{O}{|}}CH-\right]$

	Acetal	Alcohol	Acetate
mole%	55	43	2
wt%	79½	19	1½

Figure 1. Structure of poly(vinylbutyral) (PVB).

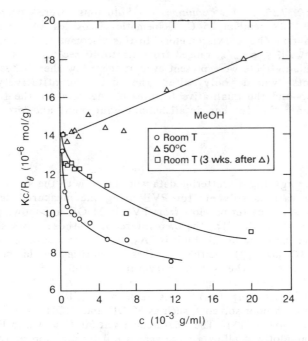

Figure 2. Light scattering plots for PVB in MeOH.

during the later readings at ~24°C, then the negative slope of this plot (negative A_2) is evidence that MeOH is a very poor solvent for PVB at this temperature.   Negative values of A_2 indicate very poor solvents, a slope of zero occurs in theta solvents, while in good solvents A_2 is strongly positive.

The best solvent we have found for PVB is acetic acid.   Scattering data, shown in Figure 3, obtained before (O) and after heating for two hours at 80°C (△) yield nearly identical plots.   Thus, there appears to be only a slight amount of aggregation in this solvent prior to heating.   The intercept is very close to that determined in MeOH at 50°C, and therefore most likely represents the true value of $1/M_w$ for our PVB sample.

Scattering measurements at 44°C in MIBK are also shown in Figure 3 (□).   The slope of this plot is nearly zero.   The intercept is well below that obtained in MeOH and acetic acid.   The value of M_w calculated from this intercept is almost three times larger than the true value, indicating that the solutions are strongly aggregated even at this elevated temperature.   Linear scattering plots which yield excessively high M_w values have been previously observed for PVB in several solvents and also have been attributed to aggregation (15).

Aggregation of PVB was also observed in a solvent mixture of 3:1 MIBK/MeOH by volume (see Figure 4 (O)).   Heating, cooling and then remeasuring the scattering yielded a curve (△) which is shifted upward and has a 27% greater slope.   After allowing these solutions to stand one month, additional scattering data (□) was taken which indicates that the most dilute solutions did not reaggregate.   More concentrated solutions reaggregated to an extent which increased with concentration.   Nonetheless, the strong positive slope of the plots in Figure 4 is evidence that the solvent mixture is an excellent one for PVB even though each solvent individually is a poor solvent.   Such systems are not uncommon (21) and are termed "cosolvents."

Scattering plots obtained after heating from PVB in various solvent mixtures of MIBK and MeOH are shown in Figure 5.   The intercepts of these plots may differ from $1/M_w$ due to polymer aggregation or selective adsorption of one of the two solvents by the polymer.   Aggregation can only lower the intercept below $1/M_w$.   If the plot for the 1:1 mixture is assumed to be unaffected by aggregation, then the intercept of this plot indicates a slight selective adsorption of MIBK by the PVB.   The intercept above $1/M_w$ obtained in the 3:1 MIBK/MeOH mixture can only be attributed to selective adsorption of MeOH.   Since MeOH is selectively adsorbed in the 3:1 MIBK/MeOH solvent, it is safe to assume it is even more strongly adsorbed in the 9:1 solvent mixture.   Therefore, the low intercept obtained in the 9:1 MIBK/MeOH solvent mixture cannot be attributed to selective adsorption.   Selective adsorption of MeOH raises the intercept.   Instead, the low intercept must be attributed to aggregation in this solvent.

The second virial coefficients measured in various solvents at room temperature after heating are given in Table I.   In the absence of aggregation and selective adsorption, a ranking by quality of solvents for PVB would follow the order of A_2 values.   The higher A_2, the better the solvent.   However, since these effects were not completely absent in the data used to construct Table I (particularly in the 9:1 solvent mixture), the solvent ranking given in this table must be considered tentative.

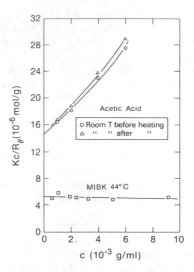

Figure 3. Light scattering plots for PVB in acetic acid and MIBK. Heating of the acetic acid solutions was for 2 hours at 80°C.

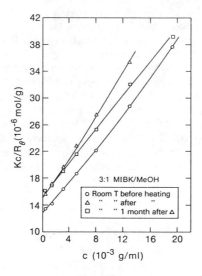

Figure 4. Light scattering plots for PVB in 3:1 MIBK/MeOH. Heating was for 4 hours at 55°C.

Table I. A_2 versus Solvent at Room T after Heating[a]

Solvent	$A_2(10^{-4}$ ml-mol/g^2)
Acetic acid, CH$_3$$\overset{\overset{\text{O}}{|}}{\text{C}}$-OH	10.4
3:1 MIBK/MeOH	7.9
1:1 MIBK/MeOH	7.8
9.1 MIBK/MeOH	1.6
MeOH	(-)[b]
MIBK, CH$_3$$\overset{\overset{\text{O}}{|}}{\text{C}}CH_2$CH(CH$_3$)$_2$	insoluble

[a]All data were taken on solutions which had been heated for at least two hours at no less than 50°C. For the 1:1 and 9:1 MIBK/MeOH solvents, only the most concentrated solution was heated. Immediately after cooling, the most concentrated solution was used to prepare the solutions of lower concentration by dilution.
[b]This scattering plot was too nonlinear for accurate determination of A_2. However, A_2 was negative.

Intrinsic Viscosity. Due to the complicating effects of aggregation and selective adsorption on the A_2 values determined by light scattering, another means was sought to characterize the quality of solvents for PVB. The alternate means chosen was intrinsic viscosity measurements. Theory relates the intrinsic viscosity to the polymer chain dimensions through the expression (24)

$$[\eta] = \Phi\left(<r^2>_0/M\right)^{3/2}M^{1/2}\alpha^3 \tag{3}$$

where Φ is a universal constant--the same for all polymer molecules, M is the polymer molecular weight, $<r^2>_0$ is the mean square end-to-end distance in the unperturbed or theta state and α is the expansion factor for the chains defined as $\alpha \equiv <r^2>^{1/2}/<r^2>_0^{1/2}$. For a given polymer, the larger α the better the solvent. If $<r^2>_0$ is assumed unaffected by the solvent, then $[\eta]$ varies only with α (Φ and M being constant), and therefore $[\eta]$ is a relative measure of solvent quality. $[\eta]$ and the Schulz-Blaschke constant, k_{SB}, were determined from Schulz-Blaschke plots.

A previous investigation (15) found that the presence of aggregates had no measurable effect on $[\eta]$ for PVB in THF. The same value of $[\eta]$ was obtained regardless of whether or not solutions were heated prior to measurement. The same heat treatment reduced the apparent molecular weight (from light scattering measurements) by ~30% and increased A_2 up to 50% (25). We made measurements on heated and unheated solutions of PVB in pure MeOH and 9:1 MIBK/MeOH and also found no effect on $[\eta]$. The lack of any effect of heat treatment on $[\eta]$ again supports the conclusion that aggregates have a minimal influence on the intrinsic viscosity. This conclusion has also been reached by other investigators studying different systems in which polymer aggregation occurs (26,27).

The intrinsic viscosity of PVB is shown as a function of solvent composition for various MIBK/MeOH mixtures in Figure 6. Since [η] increases with α (see Equation 8), the higher [η] the better the solvent. Apparently, most mixtures of MIBK and MeOH are better solvents for PVB than either pure solvent. Based on Figure 6, PVB should have a weak selective adsorption of MIBK in a 1:1 solvent mixture and weak adsorption of MeOH in a 3:1 MIBK/MeOH solvent mix. These predictions are in accord with light scattering data discussed previously. The intrinsic viscosity data is also consistent with the second virial coefficient data in Table II in indicating that the 1:1 and 3:1 MIBK/MeOH mixtures are nearly equally good solvents for PVB, the 9:1 mix is a worse solvent, but still better than pure MeOH.

Table II. Viscosity of 12% PVB Solutions (Summary of Figures 9-11)

Solvent	Solvent Quality Ranking	η at 25°C (cP)			E_A (kcal/mol)	
		Most Aggregated[a]	Least Aggregated[b]	% Diff.	Most Aggregated[a]	Least Aggregated[c]
MeOH	3	391.3	378.2	3.5	7.6	7.2
1:1 $\frac{\text{MIBK}}{\text{MeOH}}$	1	352.8	308.1	14.5	7.6	6.6
9:1 $\frac{\text{MIBK}}{\text{MeOH}}$	2	1674.3	1114.1	50.3	19.5	8.6
					E_A=2.19	pure MIBK
					2.57	pure MeOH

[a]Start of heating cycle.
[b]End of cooling cycle, immediately after temperature equilibration.
[c]Start of cooling cycle.

Viscosity of 12% PVB Solutions. The viscosity of 12% PVB solutions was measured at temperatures from 25° to 55°C using as solvents pure methanol, 1:1 MIBK/MeOH by volume and 9:1 MIBK/MeOH. The results are shown in Figures 7-9. There is some hysteresis in these plots; higher viscosities are obtained on the cycle of increasing temperature than on the decreasing temperature cycle. The extent of this hysteresis increases with the MIBK content of the solvent. In all plots, data indicated by open points were obtained once η had stabilized to the extent that it was changing less than ~1/2% per hour. No detectable change in η with time was observed in pure MeOH. In the 1:1 MIBK/MeOH solvent, changes were barely detectable except at 25°C on the cooling cycle where the increase in η with time was pronounced. In the solvent containing 9:1 MIBK/MeOH viscosity changes of

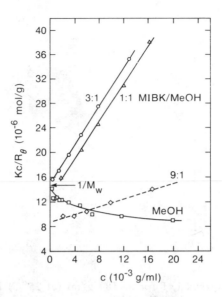

Figure 5. Light scattering plots for PVB in MIBK/MeOH mixtures at room temperature. All data were taken on solutions which had been heated for at least 2 hours at no less than 50°C. For the 1:1 and 9:1 MIBK/MeOH solvents, only the most concentrated solution was heated. Immediately after cooling, the most concentrated solution was used to prepare the solutions of lower concentration by dilution.

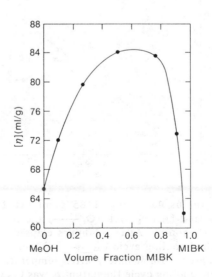

Figure 6. Intrinsic viscosity of PVB in MIBK/MeOH mixtures at 25°C.

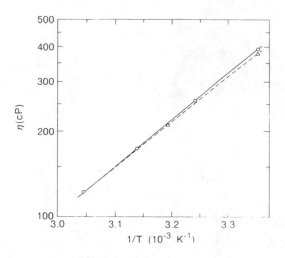

Figure 7. Log η versus 1/T for 0.1187 g/ml (at 25°C) PVB in MeOH on the heating (O, ——) and cooling ($\triangle$, - - -) cycles.

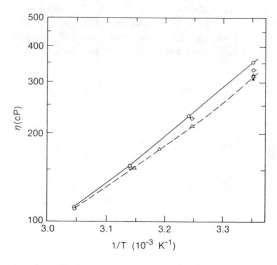

Figure 8. Log η versus 1/T for 0.1185 g/ml (at 25°C) PVB in 1:1 MIBK/MeOH. The first heating cycle (O, ——) and first cooling cycle ($\triangle$) were separated by 15 hours. After 72 hours elapsed, the second heating cycle (O–) and second cooling cycle ($\triangle\_$,- - -) were conducted, between which 15 hours elapsed. Immediately after temperature equilibration at the end of the second cooling cycle the datum $\blacktriangle$ was taken.

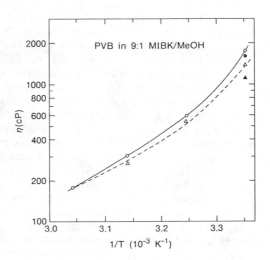

Figure 9.   Log η versus 1/T for 0.1188 g/ml (at 25°C) PVB in
9:1 MIBK/MeOH on the heating (O, ———) and cooling ($\triangle$, – – –) cycles.
The datum $\blacktriangle$ was taken immediately after temperature equilibration at the
end of the cooling cycle.   The datum $\bullet$ was taken 12 days later.

at least several percent were observed at each temperature and on both cycles before the viscosity stabilized. However, the viscosity was not affected by the measurement process. Repeated flow time measurements caused no detectable change in solution viscosity.

We attribute the hysteresis in Figures 7-9 to the presence of supramolecular structures or aggregates. The extent of aggregation is reduced upon heating, but increases slowly when cooled. Notice in Figure 9 that even 12 days after completing the cooling cycle the viscosity had not risen to its initial value. Eventually, however, it might have. Thus, with enough patience, the heating and cooling cycles might coincide.

The extent of aggregation is apparently affected far more by solvent polarity than solvent quality. A measure of aggregation is given in Table II. Here is shown the percentage difference between the "most aggregated" (initial) 25°C viscosity and the "least aggregated" 25°C viscosity (measured at the end of the cooling cycle immediately after temperature equilibration). This measure of the extent of aggregation increases with the MIBK content of the solvent. Based on the intrinsic viscosity data shown in Figure 6, pure MeOH is a poorer solvent than either solvent mixture, yet PVB aggregates the least in it. A 1:1 ratio of MIBK and MeOH is nearly the optimum solvent ratio for PVB, still aggregation occurs. It is in the solvent of intermediate quality, the 9:1 mixture, where aggregation is most severe. Aggregation increases with solvent nonpolarity, seemingly independent of solvent quality. This finding is consistent with our previous observation that filtration difficulties were more severe in solvents containing a greater percentage of the relatively nonpolar MIBK. We conclude that the polar alcohol groups in the PVB molecules (see Figure 1) are instrumental in aggregate formation. The better a solvent is for these highly polar alcohol units, the less tendency there is for the molecules to associate. Since these units, however, represent a relatively minor portion of the chains (weight fraction 19%), the best solvents for these polar units may be poor solvents for the chain overall. Aggregation phenomena which are not related to thermodynamic solvent quality have previously been reported (26,28). We believe that the combined measurements of dilute solution properties and concentrated solution viscosities for PVB in these solvents provide exceptionally strong evidence of this behavior.

The solvent composition affects not only the hysteresis or history dependence of the viscosity, but also its magnitude and temperature dependence. The viscosity was ~10% higher using pure MeOH as the solvent than when a 1:1 MIBK/MeOH mixture was used. However, the 9:1 solvent mixture produces the highest solution viscosity by more than a factor of four. (A solution using a 19:1 MIBK/MeOH solvent mixture was so viscous it would barely flow in the flask in which it was prepared.) The apparent activation energy for flow

$$E_A \equiv \partial \ell n \eta / \partial (1/RT) \qquad (4)$$

was also much higher using the 9:1 MIBK/MeOH solvent mixture, especially at the start of the heating cycle (most aggregated conditions). These effects cannot be attributed to differences in solvent viscosity as this property varies by only 1.3% amongst these mixtures, being lowest in the 1:1 mix. The activation energy for solvent flow was not measured, but should be similar for all three solvents as the values of E_A for pure MeOH (2.57 kcal/mol) and pure MIBK (2.19 kcal/mol) are very close (29).

A surprising feature of the results in Table II is that the best solvent (1:1 MIBK/MeOH) yields a lower solution viscosity than the worst solvent (MeOH) despite greater aggregation in the better solvent. The viscosity of a semidilute polymer solution may be expressed as the product of a structure factor F and friction factor ζ

$$\eta = F \cdot \zeta \tag{5}$$

The structure factor includes the effects of chain size and overlap. The friction factor accounts for all other contributions to η, the most important being the segmental mobility. At a given polymer concentration, F depends primarily on molecular weight, while ζ depends on temperature (5). Variation in η with solvent can arise through differences in ζ, or through changes in excluded volume interactions which increase the chain dimensions and hydrodynamic screening length, thus affecting F. The influence of the solvent on F depends on the degree of chain overlap. The concentration c^* where overlap begins is $c^* \cong 0.77/[\eta]$.(30) Thus, our solutions are all at $c \geq 10 c^*$, and the polymer coils strongly overlap. At such high concentration of polymer, the chain dimensions and therefore F should be nearly the same in all solvents (30). In any case, any residual influence of solvent quality would lower the ratio $F_{MeOH}/F_{1:1}$ below one, and therefore could not account for the observation $\eta_{MeOH}/\eta_{1:1} > 1$. Instead, the higher viscosity obtained with MeOH must be attributed to a larger value of ζ.

A higher relative viscosity (η/η_s) in poor solvents than in good ones has been reported with both polar polymers such as poly(methyl-methacrylate) (8), ethylcellulose (6), poly(vinylchloride-acetate) copolymers (10), as well as with the nonpolar poly(styrene) (8,13) and poly(α-methylstyrene) (14). In contrast, the steady-state compliance of poly(α-methylstyrene) solutions is independent of solvent quality (14,31,32). The above two observations led Isono and Nagasawa (14,33) to propose that solvent quality influences the solution viscosity through its effect on the strength of polymer entanglements rather than their number. Entanglements are stronger in poorer solvents. This explanation is consistent with our observation that the activation energy for flow (under least aggregated conditions) is higher in the poorer solvent MeOH (7.2 kcal/mol) than in the better 1:1 mixture (6.6 kcal/mol). The stronger the entanglements, the higher the activation energy for flow. It should be noted that this entanglement effect, must be separate from the aggregation phenomenon in PVB solutions since it follows solvent quality not solvent polarity. The viscosity is lower using the better 1:1 MIBK/MeOH solvent than in MeOH despite increased aggregation.

With the least polar solvent, 9:1 MIBK/MEOH, aggregation dominates the viscosity behavior. This solvent is of intermediate quality, between pure MeOH and the 1:1 mixture. Still, the viscosity is greatest using the 9:1 mix at all temperatures, by up to a factor of four. The effect of temperature on the aggregation in the 9:1 MIBK/MeOH solution is so large that the $\ell n \, \eta$ versus $1/T$ curve becomes significantly nonlinear. An apparent E_A determined when the solution is most highly aggregated is more than twice those measured in other solvents, and even at the highest temperature (55°C), the apparent E_A is still much larger than in the 1:1 mixture or in MeOH. Aggregation affects both the friction factor ζ and the structure factor F. It alters ζ through its effect on the segmental mobility and F through its effect on the apparent molecular weight. Association of portions of the chains results in a weak, reversible crosslinking, which raises the apparent molecular weight.

The nature in which the alcohol groups of PVB aggregate may be through simple hydrogen bonding through microcrystallization. Poly(vinyl alcohol) (PVOH) is a highly crystalline polymer (34). While bulk PVB is amorphous, this does not preclude the possibility that in solution, PVOH crystallites may form from the alcohol units of this copolymer (1). The slow increase in solution viscosity after heating and then cooling support crystallization as the mechanism of aggregation. Similar aging effects are observed with gels from crystallizable polymers (2).

Summary and Conclusions

The viscosity and its temperature dependence of semidilute (12% wt/vol) PVB solutions were strongly affected by the solvent. The viscosity in the poorer solvent MeOH was higher than in the good solvent 1:1 MeOH/MIBK despite greater aggregation in the latter solvent. This is due to a larger friction coefficient in MeOH, which it has been suggested may be due to tighter entanglements in this poorer solvent. This explanation is consistent with the observed higher activation energy for flow using this solvent. The solution viscosity using the 9:1 solvent mixture was dramatically higher, as was its temperature dependence due to severe aggregation. η versus $1/T$ curves were highly nonlinear in the 9:1 solvent, in contrast with MeOH and the 1:1 mixture, as the degree of aggregation decreased with increasing temperature. The intrinsic viscosity measured in these solvents was insensitive to the state of aggregation. It is concluded that aggregation is via the hydroxyl groups of PVB since aggregation did not decrease with solvent quality, but rather with solvent polarity. Aggregates dispersed and reformed slowly--weeks may be required to reach equilibrium at room temperature.

Literature Cited

1. Domszy, R. C.; Alamo, R.; Edwards, C. O.; Mandelkern, L. Macromolecules 1986, 19, 310.
2. Hiltner, A; Baer, E. Polym. Preprints 1986, 27, 207.
3. Flory, P. J. Disc. Farad. Soc. 1974, 57, 7.
4. Bohdanecky, M.; Kovar, J. "Viscosity of Polymer Solutions"; Elsevier: New York, 1982; p. 189.
5. Berry, G. C.; Fox, T. G. Adv. in Pol. Sci. 1968, 5, 261.
6. Simha, R.; Utracki, L. J. Polym. Sci. Part A-2 1967, 5, 853.
7. Simha, R.; Zakin, J. L. J. Colloid Sci. 1962, 17, 270.
8. Ghandi, K. S.; Williams, M. C. J. Polym. Sci. Part C 1971, 35, 211.

9. Spurlin, H. M.; Martin, A. F.; Tennent, H. G. J. Polym. Sci. 1946, 1, 63.
10. Janssen, A. G.; Caldwell, B. P. Polymer Bulletin 1945, 1, 120.
11. Berry, G. C.; Nakayasu, H.; Fox, T. G. J. Pol. Sci., Pol. Phys. Ed. 1979, 17, 1825.
12. Hager, B. L.; Berry, G. C. J. Pol. Sci., Pol. Phys. Ed. 1982, 20, 911.
13. Onogi, S.; Masuda, T.; Miyanaga, N.; Kimura, Y. J. Pol. Sci., Pol. Phys. Ed. 1967, 5, 899.
14. Isono, S.; Nagasawa, M. Macromolecules 1980, 13, 862.
15. Cotts, P. M.; Ouano, A. C., in "Microdomains in Polymer Solutions"; Dubin, P., Ed.; Plenum Press: New York, 1985.
16. The alcohol content was determined by Monsanto. The weight percent of acetal was determined by K. Sachdev, M. Khojasteh and S. Shear of IBM, East Fishkill, New York.
17. Elias, H. G., in Polymer Handbook, Brandrup, J.; Immergut, E. H., eds.; Wiley: New York, 1975; second edition, p. VII-23.
18. Ibrahim, F. W. J. Polym. Sci. Part A 1965, 3, 469.
19. Johnson, B. L.; Smith, J., in Light Scattering from Polymer Solutions, Huglin, M. B., Ed.; Academic: New York, 1972, p. 29.
20. Elias, H. G., in "Light Scattering from Polymer Solutions"; Huglin, M. B., Ed.; Academic: New York, 1972, p. 400.
21. Cowie, J. M. G.; McEwen, I. J. Macromolecules 1984, 17, 755.
22. Strazielle, C., in "Light Scattering from Polymer Solutions"; Huglin, M. D., Ed.; Academic: New York, 1972, p. 652.
23. Strazielle, C., in "Light Scattering from Polymer Solutions"; Huglin, M. B., Ed.; Academic: New York, 1972, p. 658.
24. Flory, P. J. "Principles of Polymer Chemistry"; Cornell University Press: Ithaca, New York, 1953, p. 611.
25. Ouano, A. C.; Cotts, P. M. IBM Research Report RJ3207 (39233), August 3, 1981.
26. Tanner, D. W.; Berry, G. C. J. Polym. Sci., Polym. Phys. Ed. 1974, 941.
27. Kratochvil, P., in "Light Scattering from Polymer Solutions"; Huglin, M. B., Ed.; Academic: New York, 1972, p. 371.
28. Elias, H.-G., in "Order in Polymer Solutions"; Solc, K., Ed.; Gordon and Breach Science Publishers: New York, 1976, p. 215.
29. Reid, R. C.; Prausnitz, J. M.; Sherwood, T. K. "The Properties of Gases and Liquids"; McGraw-Hill: New York, 1977, third edition, p. 629.
30. Graessley, W. Polymer 1980, 21, 258.
31. Kajiura, J.; Oshiyana, Y.; Fujimoto, T.; Nagasawa, M. Macromolecules 1978, 11, 894.
32. Isono, Y.; Fujimoto, T.; Kajiura, H.; Nagasawa, M. Polymer J. 1980, 12, 363.
33. Takahashi, Y.; Isono, Y.; Noda, I.; Nagawawa, M. Macromolecules 1985, 18, 1002.
34. Venney, J. F.; Willcockson, G. W. J. Polym. Sci. A-1 1966, 4, 679. 35. "Lange's Handbook of Chemistry"; Lange, N. A.; Forker, G. M., Eds.; McGraw-Hill: New York, 1967, tenth edition, p. 1403.
35. Paul, C. W. and Cotts, P. M. Macromolecules 1986, 19, 692.

RECEIVED February 26, 1987

Chapter 6

Reversible Polymer Complexes Stabilized Through Hydrogen Bonds

Ilias Iliopoulos, Roland Audebert, and Claude Quivoron

Laboratoire de Physico-Chimie Macromoléculaire, Université Pierre et Marie Curie,
Unité Associée au Centre National de la Recherche Scientifique No. 278, ESPCI 10,
rue Vauquelin, 75231 Paris Cedex 05, France

Polymer complex formation between polyacrylic acid
(PAA) and three polybases (polyoxyethylene (PEO),
polyvinylmethylether (PVME) and polyvinylpyrrolidone
(PVP), is examined for various degrees of neutralization of the polyacid and several concentrations of the
polybase. The effect of molecular weight of polymers
on complex formation is also discussed. Potentiometric
measurements show that the complex formation occurs
through hydrogen bonds and give information about
influence of nonactive groups (acrylate groups, COO^-)
on complex formation. Data relative to the structure
of the complex are obtained from viscometry
(macroscopic structure) and polarized luminescence
(local structure). The complex may exist in either a
compact form with a corresponding decrease in viscosity and polymer chain mobility, or a highly branched
structure, close to a gel, leading to a very high viscosity but not to a pronounced change in chain mobility. For instance, the viscosity of the PAA/PVP mixture may be 600 times higher than those of the
original polymer solutions.

The behaviour of ternary systems consisting of two polymers and a
solvent depends largely on the nature of interactions between components (1-4). Two types of limiting behaviour can be observed. The
first one occurs in non-polar systems, where polymer-polymer interactions are very low. In such systems a liquid-liquid phase separation is usually observed ; each liquid phase contains almost the
total quantity of one polymer species. The second type of behaviour
often occurs in aqueous polymer solutions. The polar or ionic water-
soluble polymers can interact to form macromolecular aggregates,
occasionally insoluble, called "polymer complexes". Examples are
polyanion-polycation couples stabilized through electrostatic interactions, or polyacid-polybase couples stabilized through hydrogen
bonds.

0097–6156/87/0350–0072$06.00/0
© 1987 American Chemical Society

It was reported that such systems exhibit cooperative stabilization of the complex, which means that the state and behaviour of every unit mainly depends on its interactions with neighboring units. Moreover, a minimal chain length is required for stable complex formation : a polybase, which forms a complex with a long chain of polyacid, must have a degree of polymerization larger than a critical number corresponding on the minimum chain length (5-7).

Most of the studies in aqueous solution have been devoted to interactions between homopolymers (5-10). In these systems the mean stoichiometry between interactive groups is close to 1:1. Only a few studies have been devoted to the behaviour of homopolymer/copolymer systems (11-14). Still a variation in copolymer composition leads to a modulation in the interpolymer interaction system. In a sense, inactive groups behave as structure defects.

In this work, we have chosen several systems stabilized through hydrogen bonds. The homopolymer is a polybase, i.e. PEO, PVME or PVP, and the copolymer is polyacrylic acid with various degrees of neutralization α, in which the acrylates are the non active groups. Complex formation is studied by potentiometry (because complexation induces a variation of the solution pH) and by viscometry and polarized luminescence which respectively give information about the macroscopic and local structure of the complex in solution. The influence of parameters such as the degree of neutralization of PAA α, the concentration ratio $r = [\text{polybase}]/[\text{PAA}]$, the concentration and the molecular weight of polymers is examined.

Experimental

The sources and molecular weights of polymers used in this study are given in Table I. The elimination of simple electrolyte residues from polymers was performed by ultrafiltration using a "Diaflo PM 10" (Amicon) membrane of 10 000 nominal molecular weight cut-off. Water was purified by a Milli-Q system (Millipore). All other reageants were of analytical grade.

The labelled polyacrylic acid PAA-M, used for polarized luminescence measurements, was prepared by grafting of 9-aminoacridine on the PAA-800 000 chain (15). The degree of derivatization of the polyacid (evaluated from the UV-vis spectra of PAA-M and 9-aminoacridine) is very low :

$$(-CH_2 - CH)_x - (CH_2 - CH-)_y$$

with $C = 0$, HN (9-aminoacridine) on the first unit and $C = 0$, OH on the second unit, and $\dfrac{x}{y} \approx \dfrac{1}{15\ 000}$

Since only one per fifteen thousand of acid monomer units is labelled, the properties of PAA remain unchanged. The resulting PAA-M was purified as described above.

Table I. Source, molecular weight and method of $\overline{M}_w$
determination of polymers

Sample and $\overline{M}_w$	Method of $\overline{M}_x$ determination	$\overline{M}_w/\overline{M}_n$	Source
PAA - 100 000	Light scattering	-	Polysciences
PAA - 670 000	"	-	"
PAA - 800 000	"	-	"
PEO - 20 000	GPC and viscometry	4,5	Touzart & Matignon
PEO - 100 000	"	2,9	Aldrich
PEO - 750 000	"	6,8	"
PVP - 55 000	GPC	2,4	Fluka
PVP - 900 000	"	2,5	"
PVME - 90 000	"	2,0	Polysciences

A Tacussel TAT-5 pH-meter was used with a glass-calomel unitu-
bular electrode. Both a Ubbelohde type viscometer and a "Low-Shear
30" apparatus (Contraves) were used to obtain viscosity values   in
the Newtonian plateau. A Fica 55-MK II spectrofluorimeter was used
with excitation and emission wave lengths of 351nm and 410nm respectively.

All the samples were prepared by mixing of concentrated solutions of the interacting components and were allowed to rest for   24
hours. Measurements were then performed at 30°C. For each series   of
experiments the PAA concentration was kept constant, and the polybase concentration varied in order to adjust the ratio τ =
[polybase]/[PAA] to the required value. The concentration of PAA is
0.02 or 0.1 unit mol/l as given in the figure captions. The polybase
concentration is obtained from [PAA] and τ values : [polybase] =
τ.[PAA].

Results and Discussion

Potentiometry. Polyacrylic acid in water solution is dissociated
according to the equilibrium :

$$- COOH \quad \underset{}{\overset{k_d}{\rightleftharpoons}} \quad - COO^- + H^+$$

The percentage of acrylate groups may be adjusted by addition of a
strong base, e.g. NaOH. In the presence of polybases such as PEO,
PVME and PVP, the following complexation equilibrium takes place :

$$- COOH + O\langle \quad \underset{}{\overset{k_d}{\rightleftharpoons}} \quad - COOH \ldots O\langle$$

Therefore, addition of a polybase in a PAA solution results in decrease of free COOH concentration and consequently increase of pH.

In Figure 1 the pH is plotted versus concentration ratio r, for the PAA-670 000 / PEO-100 000 system and for various degrees of neutralization of the PAA α, determined by the ammount of NaOH added. For all the experimental points the concentration of PAA in polymer units is constant and equal to 0.02 unit mol/l.

The increase in pH, characteristic of complexation, becomes more pronounced as α approaches zero. It becomes negligible when α is higher than 12%. Consequently small amounts of "defects" (acrylate groups) on PAA chains completely prevent the complex formation. It suggest that the introduction of some acrylate groups, prevents the complexation ability of an important part of carboxylic sites. Comparable patterns are obtained for the other molecular weights of PAA and PEO and also for systems involving PVME and PVP. The limit value of neutralization degree α_{lim} (for $\alpha > \alpha_{lim}$ no complexation occurs) is about 12% for PEO, 15% for PVME and higher than 20% for PVP.

From potentiometry results we can easily calculate the degree of complexation θ, which is the ratio of the concentration of complexed acid groups to the total concentration of PAA : θ = [-COOH...O<]/[PAA]. Details about the θ calculation are given in ref. 17. In Figure 2, θ is plotted versus r. The dashed line corresponds to the case of complete complexation of the polybase according to a 1:1 stoichiometry.

The effect on complex formation of structure defects, in our case the acrylate groups, is clearly shown in Figure 3. There is an exponential relation between degree of complexation θ, and acrylate ratio p : θ = exp(-A.p). The acrylate ratio p is the total concentration of COO$^-$ over the total concentration of PAA, so p is equal to α plus the quantity of acrylate groups due to polyacid dissociation. The constant A is characteristic to the system and always higher than zero. The higher the complexation power of polybase the lower the A value (Figure 3).

Figure 2 shows that for a polymer couple, even for a large excess of polybase, the fraction of carboxylic groups actually complexed (given by the compelxation degree θ) is always smaller than one and strongly depends on α (or on p, see Figure 3). This corresponds to a variable mean stoichiometry in contradiction with most of the previous papers, where a mean complex stoichiometry close to 1:1 is proposed (5-10), but in agreement with Morawetz's results (16).

The experimental points of each curve of figure 3 are obtained with polymer of various molecular weights. So, $\bar{M}_w$ - in the studied range - has no effect on θ.

Viscometry. It has been reported that complexation of two polymers leads to a decrease of the mixture viscosity and the minimum in viscosity corresponds to the mean stoichiometry of the complex (8-10). This was generally attributed to a compact structure for the complex. The hydrodynamic volume of the complex is small relative to the sum of hydrodynamic volumes of the original macromolecules.

In Figure 4, we plot the variation of specific viscosity of the mixture against the concentration ratio r. The polymers, their molecular weights and concentrations are the same as those of Figure 1 concerning potentiometric study.

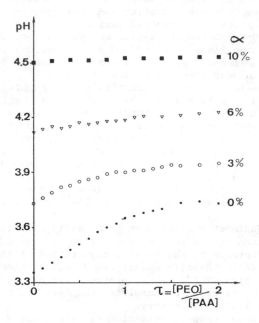

Figure 1. pH change versus concentration ratio, τ = [PEO]/[PAA], for various degrees of neutralization, α.
System PAA-670 000/PEO-100 000.
Concentration of PAA : 0.02 unit mol/l.

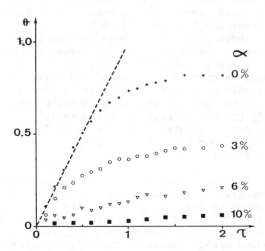

Figure 2. Degree of complexation, θ, versus concentration ratio. System, concentration and symbols as in figure 1.

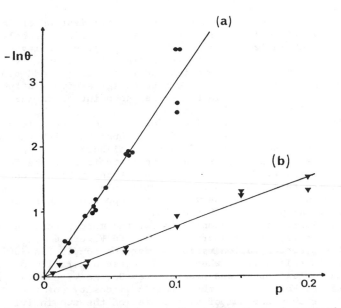

Figure 3. Variation of -lnθ as a function of acrylate ratio p = [COO⁻]/[PAA]. [PAA] = [polybase] = 0.02 unit mol/l. (a) PAA/PEO, A = 30 ; (b) PAA/PVP, A = 7.5.

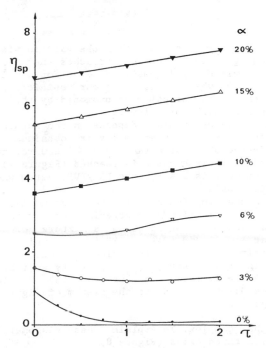

Figure 4. Specific viscosity of the PAA-670 000/PEO-100 000 system versus concentration ratio. [PAA] = 0.02 unit mol/l.

As expected, when the degree of neutralization of PAA is 0%, the specific viscosity falls rapidly with addition of polybase. For degrees of neutralization 3 and 6% we also get viscosity curves characteristic of a compact complex formation. For the values of α higher than 10% the linear variation is due to the addition of PEO without complex formation. These results agree with the potentiometric ones : for instance in both cases no point characteristic of a fixed stoichiometry is observed.

Similar curves are obtained for lower concentrations in polymers, but a very different behaviour is observed with the same system at higher concentration (five times higher), see Figure 5. For a degree of neutralization 0% the curve is typical of the formation of a compact complex. For α values higher than the limit one, $\alpha = 15\%$ and 20%, there is no indication of complex formation. But for α between 0 and α_{lim} we observe a very important increase in viscosity, especially for $\alpha = 6\%$ and 10%.

This increase in viscosity is all the more pronounced when the molecular weight of polymers is high. In Figure 6, η_{sp} is plotted against the concentration ratio, r, for the couple PAA-800 000/PEO-750 000. In this system, when $\alpha < 3\%$, phase separation occurs, bulk solid particles appear and precipitate. So, no viscosity measurement is possible. For $\alpha \geqslant 4\%$ the specific viscosity of the mixture is very higher than the sum of viscosities of the two individual polymer solutions. The comparison may be easier if we define another parameter : the gain in viscosity, g, which is given by the relation :

$$ g = \frac{(\eta_{sp})_{mixture}}{(\eta_{sp})_{PAA} + (\eta_{sp})_{polybase}} $$

for instance, when $r = 2$ and $\alpha = 5\%$, the gain in viscosity is $g = 65$. As expected g decreases as α approaches the α_{lim} value but a residual gain in viscosity is observed even for $\alpha = 15\% > \alpha_{lim}$ (in figure 6 : $g = 10$ when $r = 2$). In our opinion this increase is mainly due to the chain entanglement promoted by the high concentration and molecular weight of polymers.

The gain in viscosity also depends on the nature of polymers. Mixtures of particularly high viscosity are obtained with the system PAA-800 000/PVP-900 000. For a PAA degree of neutralization of 10% a gain in viscosity of six hundred is reached (Figure 7). The value of α at the maximum of g is 10% for the PAA/PVP system whereas it is 5% for the PAA/PEO couple.

Another interesting feature of such systems is the reversibility observed by dilution/concentration or neutralization/acidification of a mixture. For instance a mixture of PAA-670 000 and PEO-100 000, at $\alpha = 0\%$ and [PAA] = [PEO] = 0.1 unit mol/l, having a very low viscosity, $\eta_{sp} = 0.2$, (see figure 5, curve $\alpha = 0\%$) can give a mixture of higher viscosity, $\eta_{sp} = 14.1$, by suitable neutralization of the PAA $\alpha = 6\%$ (figure 5, curve $\alpha = 6\%$). The latter mixture after a 5 times dilution leads to the system of figure 4, $\eta_{sp} = 2.6$ (curve $\alpha = 6\%$).

Structure of the Complex. To explain these viscometric results we must distinguish three cases (Figure 8) :

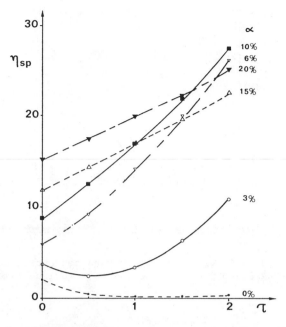

Figure 5. Specific viscosity versus concentration ratio. [PAA] = 0.1 unit mol/l. System as in figure 4.

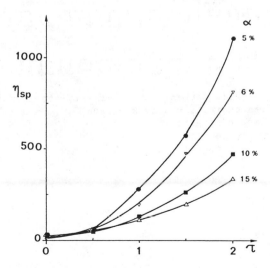

Figure 6. Specific viscosity of the PAA-800 000/PEO-750 000 sys—tem versus concentration ratio. [PAA] = 0.1 unit mol/l.

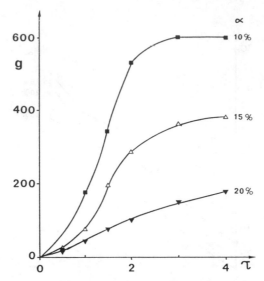

Figure 7.   Gain in viscosity, g, versus concentration ratio.
System : PAA-800 000/PVP-900 000. [PAA] = 0.1 unit mol/l.

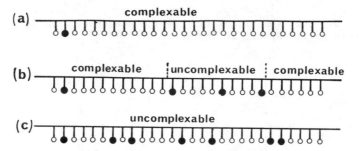

Figure 8.   Schematic representation of acrylate groups distribution on the PAA chain. $\top$ = acrylate group ; $\overline{\delta}$ = acid group.
(a) $\alpha \simeq 0$, compact complex ;
(b) $0 < \alpha < \alpha_{lim}$, gel-like complex ;
(c) $\alpha > \alpha_{lim}$, no complexation.

a) If the degree of neutralization of PAA is close to zero, the chain of PAA contains only a few acrylate groups due to the dissociation of the acid groups. Thus the sequences of acid groups are very long and higher than the minimum chain length. In practice all the PAA chain is complexable, the formed complex is compact and the mixture viscosity is very low (Figures 8(a) and 9(a)).

b) If the degree of neutralization is higher than the limit value, there are a lot of acrylate groups on the PAA chain, so the sequences of acid groups are very short, shorter than the minimum chain length and consequently the PAA chain is uncomplexable (Figure 8(c)).

c) Finally, if the degree of neutralization is between zero and the limit value, there are both complexable and uncomplexable sequences on the PAA chain. Hence each chain of PAA can interact with several chains of polybase and vice-versa. Such a complex has a highly branched structure, very similar to a gel and the mixture viscosity becomes very large. The junction zones are the complexed sequences (Figures 8(b) and 9(b)).

The proposed structure of the complex does not assume a static distribution of the sequences. The system is of course a dynamic one, but we study it at equilibrium. A given COOH group, involved in a complex at the moment t, may be free or in the carboxylate from at t + dt. However the average number of complexed sequences remains invariant with time for a fixed composition of the system. The situation can be compared with the behaviour of macromolecules adsorbed at a solid-liquid interface : their mean conformation is stable even if locally an adsorption/desorption equilibrium occurs.

Polarized Luminescence. The polarized luminescence technique gives information about local mobility of polymer sequences, and so about microscopic structure of the system (18-21).

We estimate the mobility of polymer sequences from the variation of the emission anisotropy r :

$$r = \frac{I_{||} - I_{\perp}}{I_{||} + 2I_{\perp}}$$

where $I_{||}$ and $I_{\perp}$ are respectively the polarized components of fluorescence whose optical vectors are parallel and perpendicular to the optical vector of the incident polarized light (18). The mobility of the marker is proportional to the reciprocal of emission anisotropy (mobility $\approx 1/r$).

In practice, the emission anisotropy of luminescent molecules in solution is considered to be proportional to the viscosity of the medium, except in the case where structural reasons arise, for instance helix-coil transition, cross-linking in polymer systems etc... (18-21). Therefore, if there is only the effect in viscosity, the mobility of the marker must be higher in the case of the compact complex system which have a very low viscosity.

In Figure 10 the reciprocal of emission anisotropy (1/r) is plotted versus concentration ratio (r), three kinds of curves are obtained :
   - when the degree of neutralization is higher than the limit

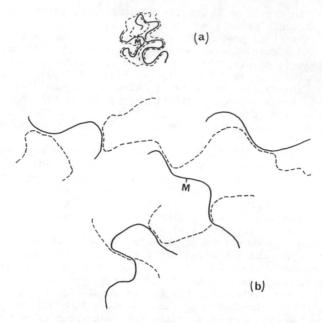

Figure 9. The two kinds of polymer complex structure. (a) compact complex ; (b) gel-like complex. (——) PAA ; (---) PEO ;
(═══) complex ; (M) marker.

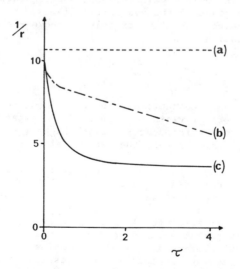

Figure 10. Variation of marker mobility (1/r) as a function of
concentration ratio, τ.
(a) $\alpha > \alpha_{lim}$;
(b) $\alpha = 4\%$, [PAA-M] = 0.1 unit mol/l, $500 < \eta_{sp} < 6\,000$;
(c) $\alpha = 0\%$, [PAA-M] = 0.02 unit mol/l, $\eta_{sp} < 2$.

value no complex formation occurs and the mobility of the marker   is not affected ;

- in the case of the compact complex formation (α = 0%, [PAA-M] = 0.02 unit mol/l, polybase = PEO-100 000), the mobility drastically falls to a minimum level   ; moreover, the apparent viscosity   of the solution is very low (η_{sp} < 2) ;

- in the case of a highly branched structure(α = 4%, [PAA-M]   = 0.1 unit mol/l,   polybase = PEO-750   000) and in   spite of the   very high viscosity of the system (500   < η_{sp} < 6 000) the   mobility only smoothly decreases.

These results are simply explained in the patterns of Figure 9: in the   compact complex,   the marker   (M) is   wedged in   between the polymer sequences and its mobility is low. In the gel-like structure the mobility of   the marker is   not affected, because   the marker is mainly   surrounded   by   solvent   molecules   since   the cross-linking between macromolecules is   very low. Polarized   luminescence results lead to confirmation of   the complex structure proposed   from visco-metry studies.

<u>Modelization of the System</u>. Theoretical treatment of   polyfunctional monomers condensation   polymerization has   been firstly   proposed by Flory and Stockmayer (<u>22,23</u>)   and later by Gordon,   Bruneau, Macosko and   others   (<u>24-26</u>).   These   theories   lay   out   the basic relation between   extent   of   reaction   and   average   molecular weight of the resulting non linear polymers.

The complexation between   two complementary macromolecules   can be seen as a polycondensation reaction between two distinct   coreac-tive   polyfunctional species   -   polyacid and polybase chains. The functionality of each species is given by the number of   complexable sequences per chain, which is a function of the acrylate ratio p. In practice, the   acrylate groups   subdivide the   PAA chain   in various length, acid group sequences.   The average functionality of   a chain can be   readily calculated   under the   following assumptions   (<u>27</u>) : acrylates and therefore acid   sequences are randomly distributed   on PAA chain ;   only acid sequences   which lengths are   higher than the minimum chain length can be complexed ;   PAA chain is   a succession of complexable sequences (average length L) and uncomplexable sequences (average length M) ;   see figure   8. Furthermore,   in this model we take into   account the   possible formation   of more   bonds than   one between two complementary chains, corresponding to small ring forma-tion (intramolecular reaction). Consequently the condensation   reac-tion between PAA and polybase can be illustrated by the figure 11   : if one PAA complexable sequence   is actually complexed the next   one may lead to intra or inter polybase chain association.

This theoretical model allows to predict the variation of   com-plexation degree θ and the molecular   weight of the   complex versus PAA concentration,   molecular   weight of   the primary chains (PAA, polybase), concentration ratio τ = [polybase]/[PAA], acrylate   ratio p, and the minimum chain length l_c (<u>27</u>). The theoretical predictions about   the   evolution of   the   system are confirmed by experimental results. For instance, in figure 12 $(\overline{DP}_w)_{complex}$ - which is the num-ber of   primary   chains per   macromolecular aggregate - is plotted against the acrylate ratio   p for various polymerization   degrees of the primary chains N.   In a first approximation $(\overline{DP}_w)_{complex}$ varies as the viscosity of the mixture ;   it increases with N and presents a

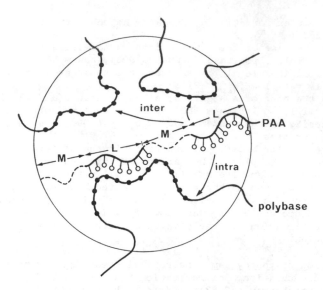

Figure 11.   Schematic representation of inter and intrachain complexation.

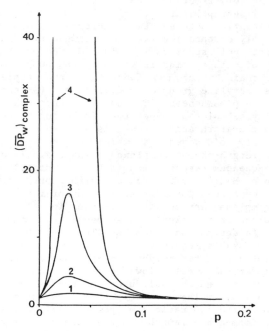

Figure 12.   Theoretical curves : effect of polymerization degree
of primary chains on $(\overline{DP}_w)_{complex}$.
$DP_{PAA} = DP_{polybase} = 1\ 000$ (1), $2\ 000$ (2), $2\ 500$ (3), $3\ 000$ (4).
$[PAA] = [polybase] = 0.1$ unit mol/l. $1_c = 40$.

maximum for a given value of p in agreement with the experimental results (see viscometry section).

Conclusions

In this work we studied a model system which forms reversible poly-mer complexes stabilized through hydrogen bonds. Complexation results from cooperative interaction between long sequences of functional units (acid-base). Each complexable sequence must be longer than a critical chain length depending on the nature of polymers. Consequently the presence of non-active groups in the polymer chain strongly influences the formation and the structure of complex. It was pointed out an exponential relation between degree of complexation, θ, and acrylate ratio, p : $\theta = \exp(-A.p)$, with $A > 0$.

The complexation power of the three polybases towards PAA was easily estimated from potentiometric results : PVP > PVME > PEO. The mean stoichiometry of the polymer complex depends on the degree of neutralization of the polyacid, α.

For α higher than a limit value, α_{lim}, no specific complexation is observed. When complexation occurs, two kinds of structure are distinguished :

- if α is close to zero and concentration and molecular weight of polymers are low, the structure of complex is compact and the viscosity of the system is low ;

- if α is about $\alpha_{lim}/2$ and concentration and molecular weight of polymers are high enough, the complex gets a highly branched structure, close to a gel. Thus, the mixture viscosity may be very high, for instance several hundred times higher than those of the original polymer solutions.

Acknowledgments

The authors would like to thank Dr J.L. Halary for valuable discussions and help in the field of polarized luminescence experiments. Scholarship support to I. Iliopoulos from the Greek State Scholarship Foundation is also gratefully acknowledged.

Literature Cited

1. Krause, S. J. Macromol. Sci., Revs. Macromol. Chem. 1972, C7, 251.
2. Djadoun, S. ; Goldberg, R. ; Morawetz, H. Macromolecules 1977, 10, 1015.
3. Lecourtier, J. ; Lafuma, F. ; Quivoron, C. Eur. Polym. J. 1982, 18, 241.
4. Hefford, R.J. Polymer 1984, 25, 979.
5. Becturov, E. ; Bimendina, L. Adv. Polym. Sci. 1981, 41, 99.
6. Tsuchida, E. ; Abe, K. Adv. Polym. Sci. 1982, 45, 2.
7. Kabanov, V. ; Papisov, I. Vysokomol. Soyed. 1979, A21, 243.
8. Antipina, A. ; Baranovskii, V. ; Papisov, I. ; Kabanov, V. Vysokomol. Soyed. 1972, A14, 941.
9. Ikawa, T. ; Abe, K. ; Honda, K. ; Tsuchida, E. J. Polym. Sci., Polym. Chem. Ed. 1975, 13, 1505.
10. Osada, S. J. Polym. Sci., Polym. Chem. Ed. 1979, 17, 3485.

11. Valuyeva, S. ; Zezin, A. ; Savin, V. Vysokomol. Soyed. 1974, A16, 212.
12. Bimendina, L. ; Tleubayeva, G. ; Bekturov, E. Vysokomol. Soyed. 1977, A19, 71.
13. Bekturov, E. ; Bimendina, L. ; Saltybaeva, S. Makromol. Chem. 1979, 180, 1813.
14. Bimendina, L. ; Kurmanbaeva, A. Polym. Bull. 1984, 11, 557.
15. Valeur, B. ; Noel, C. ; Monjol, P. ; Monnerie, L. J. Chim. Phys. 1971, 68, 97.
16. Chen, H.L. ; Morawetz, H. Eur. Polym. J. 1983, 19, 923.
17. Iliopoulos, I. ; Audebert, R. Polym. Bull. 1985, 13, 171.
18. Anufrieva, E. ; Gotlib, Y. Adv. Polym. Sci. 1981, 40, 1.
19. Papisov, I. ; Sergieva, E. ; Pautov, V. ; Kabanov, V. Dolk. Akad. Nauk. SSSR 1973, 208, 397.
20. Papisov, I. ; Nekrasova, N. ; Pautov, V. ; Kabanov, V. Dolk. Akad. Nauk. SSSR 1974, 214, 861.
21. Ghiggino, K. ; Tan, K. In Polymer Photophysics ; Phillips, P., Ed. ; Chapman-Hall : London, 1985 ; p 341-375.
22. Flory, P. Principles of Polymer Chemistry ; Cornell University Press : Ithaca-New York, 1953 ; p 347.
23. Stockmayer, W.H. J. Chem. Phys. 1943, 11, 45.
24. Gordon, M. Proc. R. Soc. London, Ser. A 1962, 268, 240.
25. Durand, D. ; Bruneau, C.M. Br. Polym. J. 1979, 11, 194.
26. Macosko, C.W. ; Miller, D.R. Macromolecules 1976, 9, 199.
27. a) Iliopoulos, I. Thesis, P. et M. Curie University, Paris, 26-11-1985.
    b) Iliopoulos, I. ; Audebert, R. ; to be published.

RECEIVED January 24, 1987

Chapter 7

Association and Gelation of Polystyrenes via Terminal Sulfonate Groups

Martin Möller, Jürgen Omeis, and Elke Mühleisen

Institut für Makromolekulare Chemie der Universität Freiburg,
Hermann-Staudinger-Haus, Stefan-Meier-Strasse 31, D-7800 Freiburg,
Federal Republic of Germany

A series of polystyrenes with sulfonate groups either at one or at both chain ends was synthesized by anionic polymerization techniques. In bulk or in nonpolar solvents the terminal salt groups interact strongly. Soluble micelles were formed by the molecules which were functionalized at one end. In the case of molecules with the ionic groups at both chain ends the association leads to a gel. Light scattering, osmosis, sedimentation and viscosity experiments in cyclohexane on the monosulfonated polymers revealed star-like micellar aggregates which consist of twelve unimers. The association behavior can be described by a "closed association" model. These results are discussed with regard to the dissolution and swelling behavior of the telechelic polystyrene sulfonates.

Substances of totally different structure, composition, and properties have been described as reversible gels. In a general survey Flory distinguished three types of reversible gels (1). The first group includes polymer networks in which chains of finite length are crosslinked by crystalline domains, by segments of multistranded helices, or by nonbonding specific interactions. The second group of reversible gels is formed when anisotropic submicroscopic particles or molecules become interlocked in disarray. Examples are voluminous precipitates of stiff rod molecules or branched particles. The third group includes lyotropic · mesophase gels of amphiphilic molecules such as tensides or lipids.

Only the first group resembles a covalently crosslinked polymer network. A disordered three dimensional reticular topology is built up by particular crosslinks between long chain molecules of finite length. While the covalently linked polymer networks are typically homogeneous, effectively crosslinked reversible gels of the first group are often heterogeneous. The crosslinks are formed by three dimensional domains or aggregates. The reason is obvious if one considers the following points. Covalent crosslinks can be regarded as permanent. In reversible gels the crosslinking interactions can be described in terms of an equilibrium between the bonded and the nonbonded state with a finite equilibrium constant. The reversibility of the gelation results from the fact that the equilibrium can be shifted from the bonded to the non-bonded state by a change in temperature, solvent, pH, ionic strength, etc. In all cases this equilibrium between the bonded and nonbonded state is dynamic. This results in permanent reformation of the crosslinks. For the gel, this leads to a transitory character. Under a finite stress it is a question of the time scale of observation as to whether the gel will exhibit plastic flow or be able to recover from deformation. Typically, rather high exchange rates are observed between the bonded and the nonbonded state of non-covalent interactions. However, if the crosslinks include multiples of the underlying interactions within three dimensional domains or extended sequences of the binding sites the rate of reformation will be reduced drastically. For example, a gel that is crosslinked by crystalline domains may alter its structure with time as the initial crystallites are dissolved and others are formed. The larger the crystallites or helices are, the less rapid the process of reorganization of such a network is. Correspondingly, crosslinking by means of specific interactions like hydrogen bonds, strong dipole-dipole interactions, or charge-transfer-complexation, will not be a simple function of the number of interacting groups per chain. It will also depend strongly on whether, and to what extent the interacting sites organize themselves into multimers.

Taking these points into account, it is not surprising that the only important example of a synthetic system effectively crosslinked by specific nonbonding interactions is represented by the so-called "ionomers". Typically, ionomers are nonpolar macromolecules to which small amounts (less than 10%) of ionic groups are attached. Several extensive reviews describe the synthesis and characterization of these materials (2-7). Small angle X-ray scattering results give clear evidence for the formation of aggregates. Most studies have dealt with samples in which the ionic groups were distributed randomly along the chain. In the bulk or dissolved in a nonpolar solvent, the ions do not dissociate and the ionpairs can be regarded as strong electric dipoles. The dipole-dipole interactions result in the formation of multiplets (8). The multiplets are believed to form clusters that include both ionic and nonionic material. The detail remain unclear. All models consider the multiplet as the basic scattering unit. However, a characteristic broad maximum is explained either by an interference between aggregates or by the internal structure of the domains.

In contrast to polymers with ionic moieties distributed along the chain, ionic groups can also be introduced solely at the chain ends (9-20). In this case, the number of interacting groups per chain is two and the distance between two interacting groups is related to the molecular weight. If the structure is fairly monodisperse, well-defined multimers can be formed. Consequently, SAXS experiments can give rather clear evidence of the existence of ordered spatial organization of the multiplets (16). Such systems offer a unique opportunity for the investigation of the correlations between the strength of the ion pair interactions, the domain size, the dynamics, and the gelation process. In addition, the expected highly ordered structure which can be varied greatly by changing the molecular weight, the nature of the ions, and the dielectric properties of the medium offers the intriguing possibility for the synthesis of systems with very specific properties. However, important questions concerning the size and the size distribution of the multiplets, and the thermodynamics of the multiplet formation remain open.

When the ionic groups are attached to only one end of the chain, association in nonpolar solvents yields soluble multimers. These systems can be investigated in dilute solution. Comparison with corresponding samples which lack the ionic substituent can give information about the association behavior. The results should be helpful for the interpretation of the gelation process and for understanding the physical properties of gels formed from the corresponding telechelic samples in solution and in the bulk.

The present study is directed towards that problem through the preparation of two series of end-group functionalized polystyrene samples. In the first series, a sulfonate group is attached to one end of the chain. The second series represents samples of the same molecular weight but with sulfonate residues attached to both ends of the chain. Narrow molecular weight distributions were achieved by "living" anionic polymerization with organolithium compounds as initiators. Terminal salt groups were introduced by reaction of the polystyryllithium with propanesultone. Special care was taken to carefully characterize the unimers, i. e. molecular weight, molecular weight distribution, and the exact proportion of the chain ends which remain unfunctionalized due to incompletion of the termination reaction.

SYNTHESIS AND CHARACTERIZATION OF THE NONASSOCIATED POLYMERS

All polymers were prepared by high vacuum line techniques. For the monofunctional samples, n-butyllithium was used as the initiator. The bifunctional samples were polymerized with naphthyllithium at -78°C with THF. A fivefold excess of 1,3-propanesultone in a 5% THF solution of THF was added under rapid stirring to the cooled solution to terminate the polymerization. Extreme care was taken since 1,3-propanesultone is known to be highly carcinogenic. Control samples were prepared in some cases by withdrawing a small sample from the reaction solution before the addition of the sultone, followed by termination with methanol. In this way, the corresponding non-functionalized polymer samples were obtained (21).

Table I shows the molecular weight and the degree of end group substitution of the monofunctional polystyrene samples obtained. In Table II the corresponding data for the bifunctional samples are given. The samples were characterized by GPC in THF. $\bar{M}_n$ and $\bar{M}_w$ were calculated. Comparison with the corresponding nonfunctionalized control samples show good agreement. The results of the light scattering and osmotic pressure experiments with the acid form of the sulfonated polystyrenes were in agreement. No association was observed for THF solutions.

Table I. Characterization of α-Polystyrenesulfonates

Sample	$\bar{M}_n$(calc) $\times 10^{-3}$	$\bar{M}_n$(Osm) $\times 10^{-3}$	$\bar{M}_n$(GPC) $\times 10^{-3}$	$\bar{M}_w$(LS) $\times 10^{-3}$	$\bar{M}_w$(GPC) $\times 10^{-3}$	M_w/M_n	f
PS-SO$_3$Li-40	40.0	42.0	45.9	49.8	48.8	1.06	0.65
PS-SO$_3$Li-40^P	--	--	--	--	--	--	1.00
PS-SO$_3$Li-80	80.0	86.0	79.9	--	85.0	1.06	0.70
PS-SO$_3$Li-80^P	--	--	--	--	--	--	1.00

^{P} denotes samples purified from nonfunctionalized polystyrene, molecular weight data are identical to the samples as polymerized according to the calibration using polystyrene standards.

Table II. Characterization of the α , ω -Polystyrenedisulfonates

Sample	$\bar{M}_n$(calc) $\times 10^{-3}$	$\bar{M}_n$(GPC) $\times 10^{-3}$	$\bar{M}_w$(GPC) $\times 10^{-3}$	$\bar{M}_w/\bar{M}_n$	f
PS-(SO$_3$Li)$_2$-20	20.0	17.5	18.5	1.06	1.20
PS-(SO$_3$Li)$_2$-40	40.0	47.0	65.8	1.39	1.30
PS-(SO$_3$Li)$_2$-40^P	40.0	--	--	--	1.95
PS-(SO$_3$Li)$_2$-80	80.0	86.0	100.0	1.20	1.25

^{P} denotes sample purified from nonfunctionalized and monofunctional
polystyrene, molecular weight data are identical to the samples as
polymerized.

    The actual functionalizations were checked by a colorimetric
method based on the complexation of a dye molecule with the sulfonate group (22). The acidic form of fuchsin does not easily dissolve
in chloroform. However, it forms a complex with the long chain sulfonates which is highly soluble in chloroform. After a water solution
of fuchsin had been mixed with chloroform, the organic phase remains
practically colorless. If end group-sulfonated polystyrene molecules are present, the chloroform phase becomes colored to a degree
which corresponds to the molar concentration of the sulfonate end
groups. Figure 1 shows the extinction of chloroform/fuchsine/PS-
SO$_3$Li solutions at 548 nm against the absolute concentration of
sulfonate groups. For calibration, sodiumdodecylsulfonate as well
as PS-SO$_3$Li samples with a molecular weight of 1000 and 10000 were
used (21).
    As can be seen from Tables I and II, the actual functionaliza-
tions are rather low, about 70% of the theoretical value. However
functionalizations close to one and two are crucial for the characterization of the association behavior and the gelation process. Hence,

chromatographic methods for the separation of the nonfunctionalized chains, the monofunctional chains, and the bifunctional chains had to be developed. For this purpose preparative chromatography using a macroreticular ion exchange resin was employed. A cation exchange column of polystyrene with sulfonate sites (research and development product, courtesy of Bayer AG) was used. With THF as the solvent, the column could be loaded with different cations and used for the exchange of the SO_3^--counterion, e. g. Li^+ to H^+ or Li^+ to Cs^+. For the separation of the fractions with different functionalities a step gradient of toluene/cyclohexanol with the cyclohexanol varying from 0 to 5% was used. Due to the different tendencies of nonfunctionalized, monofunctionalized and bifunctionalized material to associate with the $SO_3^-Li^+$-groups of the resin and the ability of cyclohexanol to destroy these associates, a good separation could be achieved (21).

ASSOCIATION OF MOLECULES WITH A SULFONATE GROUP AT ONE CHAIN END

Figure 2 shows a plot of the reduced osmotic pressure for the PS-SO_3Li-40^P sample in THF at 25°C and in cyclohexane at 30°C. In THF, the molecular weight does not differ significantly from that obtained for the nonassociated polymers as given in Table I. However, in cyclohexane the formation of multimers is evident. A strong increase in molecular weight could be observed. Figure 3 shows the light scattering intensity of two cyclohexane solutions of the PS-SO_3Li-40 sample plotted against the amount of cyclohexanol added to the solution. Cyclohexanol is isorefractive with cyclohexane. The decrease in intensity of scattered light reflects a decrease in molecular weight. Hence, the addition of small amounts of a protic cosolvent like cyclohexanol leads to complete dissolution of the multimers (23).

Cyclohexane is not only a nonpolar solvent which favors the association of ionic sites, but it is also a theta solvent for polystyrene at 35°C. At 30°C the reduced osmotic pressure of the sulfonated polymer in cyclohexane is nearly independent of the concentration. Clearly, the degree of association does not change within the concentration range investigated. An increase of the association with increasing polymer concentration should result in a corresponding decrease of π/c. In addition, the concentration independence at 30°C indicates a supression of the theta temperature compared to linear polystyrene, as has been reported for star-type polymers. Figure 4 shows a plot of the apparent A_2 values obtained from light scattering measurements of the PS-SO_3Li-40 sample in cyclohexane at different temperatures. Theta conditions are reached at 27.5°C. For comparison, the theta temperatures of linear polystyrene, of a six arm star-polystyrene and of a twelve arm star-polystyrene sample are given in figure 4 (24,25). Figure 5 shows a plot of $\log[\eta]$ against $\log \bar{M}_w$ for linear polystyrene, six arm star-polystyrene, (24), and end group sulfonated polystyrene samples of different molecular weight in cyclohexane. For comparison, the intrinsic viscosity of a twelve arm star-polystyrene, (26), is also given in the figure (□). The ratio of the intrinsic viscosities of the ionic multimers with respect to the linear polystyrenes can be explained according to the Stockmayer-Fixman theory (27) for the conformation of star-type polymers. Table III gives the results for the g' ratios

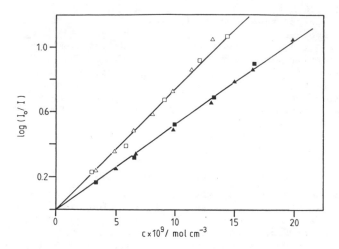

Figure 1: Plot of the extinction versus concentration for fuchs-in-sulfonate complexes in chloroform at 25°C, = 548 nm. (■) Sodiumdodecylsulfonate, (▲) PS-SO$_3$Li-01^P, (□) PS-SO$_3$Li-10^P, (△) PS-SO$_3$Li-40^P.

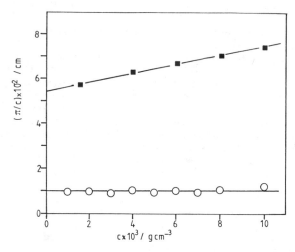

Figure 2: Plot of the reduced osmotic pressure versus concentration for PS-SO$_3$Li-40, (O) in cyclohexane at T = 30°C, (■) in THF at T = 25°C.

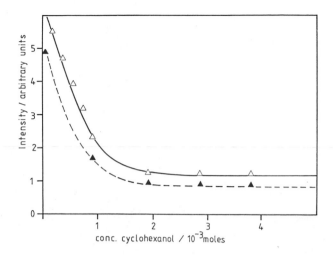

Figure 3: Influence of the addition of cyclohexanol on the θ = 90° light scattering intensity for PS-SO$_3$Li-40 in cyclohexane (12 ml), (▲) c = 4.293 g/l, (△) c = 12.879 g/l.

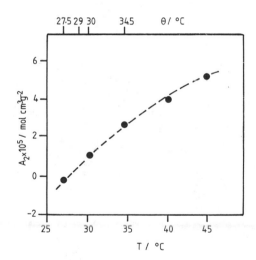

Figure 4: Temperature dependence of A$_2$ for PS-SO$_3$Li 40 in cyclohexane. The temperatures for A$_2$ = 0 of a six arm (24), T = 30°C, and a twelve arm (25), T = 29°C, star-polystyrene as well as of linear polystyrene, T = 34.5°C are given for comparison.

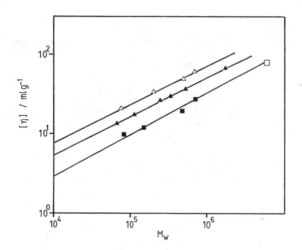

Figure 5: Log[η]/log M_W plot for PS-SO$_3$Li samples (■) in cyclohexane in comparison to linear polystyrene (Δ) and six arm star-polystyrene (▲).

determined from the viscosity experiments and compares these with the g' ratios calculated for twelve arm star polystyrenes.

Table III. [η] and g'Values of the α-Polystyrenesulfonates

Sample	f	$\overline{M}_w$(LS) $\times 10^{-3}$	[η][a] mlg^{-1}	[η][b] mlg^{-1}	g'(exp)	g'(calc)
PS-SO$_3$Li-20	0.70	200	40.0	12.2	0.359	0.382
PS-SO$_3$Li-40	0.65	380	46.8	18.7	0.400	0.410
PS-SO$_3$Li-40[P]	1.00	600	58.3	18.5	0.317	0.242
PS-SO$_3$Li-80[P]	1.00	1000	80.1	29.3	0.365	0.242

[a] unmodified polystyrene with identical molecular weight, [b] monosulfonated samples in cyclohexane.

Figure 6 shows the results of a sedimentation analysis. Comparison with a sample of a functionality of f = 0.7 allows an unambiguous assignment of the remarkably sharp peak in the upper trace as resulting from the multimers. The narrow width of the signal and the fast sedimentation is typical of compact sphere-like molecules having a narrow molecular weight distribution.

So far, all of the data indicate the applicability of the closed association model (28):

$$N \; M_1 \rightleftharpoons M_N \qquad\qquad [1]$$

N unimers   multimer

This model implies a critical micelle concentration (CMC) below which the molecules do not associate and above which the molecules in excess to the CMC form multimers of N unimers.

$$K_{1,N} = \frac{[M_N]}{[M_1]^N} \qquad\qquad [2]$$

Even in the case where the unimers as well as the multimers are of uniform molecular weight distribution, the mixture of unimers and multimers has a bimodal molecular weight distribution which changes with concentration according to equation [2]. Hence, independent of the different nonspecific interactions between solute and solvent molecules, osmosis and light scattering experiments give different concentration dependences of the apparent molecular weights $K^*c/R = (M_{w,app})^{-1}$, $\pi/(c \, \mathcal{R} \, T) = (M_{n,app})^{-1}$. Consequently, the concentration dependence of the apparent molecular weight can be split up into a virial term and a association term (29), e. g.

$$1/(\overline{M}_w)_{app} = 1/(\overline{M}_{w,\Theta})_{app} + 2 \, A_2 c \qquad\qquad [3]$$

Under ideal conditions, the nonspecific interactions cancel each

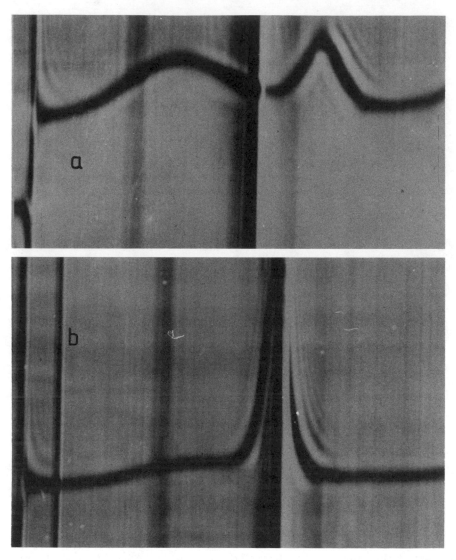

Figure 6: Sedimentation of PS-SO$_3$Li-40 (a) and PS-SO$_3$Li-40^P (b), 1 % solution in toluene at 25°C.

other ($A_2 = 0$) and the concentration dependence will reflect the equilibrium between unimers and multimers directly,

$$(\overline{M}_n)_{app} = \frac{c_1 + c_N}{c_1/M_1 + c_N/M_N} \qquad [4]$$

$$(\overline{M}_w)_{app} = \frac{c_1 M_1 + c_N M_N}{c_1 + c_N} \qquad [5]$$

where c_1 is the concentration by weight. For uniform molecular weights of the unimers and the multimers one can write:

$$M_1 = (\overline{M}_1)_n = (\overline{M}_1)_w, \quad (\overline{M}_N)_n = (\overline{M}_N)_w = N\, M_1 \qquad [6]$$

$$\text{for } c \longrightarrow 0, \quad (\overline{M}_n)_{app} = (\overline{M}_w)_{app} = M_1 \qquad [7]$$

$$\text{for } c \gg CMC, \quad (\overline{M}_n)_{app} = (\overline{M}_w)_{app} = M_N \qquad [8]$$

The concentration dependence of the apparent molecular weights can be calculated (29) with $c_1 = M_1 \cdot [M_1]$, $M_N = N \cdot M_1$, and $[M_N] = K_{1,N} \cdot [M_1]^N$:

$$\frac{1}{\overline{M}_n} = \frac{(1 + K_{1,N}\, [M_1]^{N-1})}{M_1\, (1 + N\, K_{1,N}\, [M_1]^{N-1})} \qquad [9]$$

$$\frac{1}{\overline{M}_w} = \frac{(1/N + K_{1,N} \cdot [M_1]^{N-1})}{(1/N + N\, K_{1,N} \cdot [M_1]^{N-1})} \qquad [10]$$

$$c = c_1 + c_N = [M_1] \cdot M_1 + K_{1,N} \cdot [M_1]^N \cdot N \cdot M_1 \qquad [11]$$

Three parameters must be considered: the equilibrium constant $K_{1,N}$, with $K_{1,N} = (K_1)^{N-1}$; the degree of association, N; and the second virial coefficient A_2. For a very small CMC (large $K_{1,N}$) the virial coefficient can be determined directly from the slope of $1/\overline{M}_{app}$ intensity in the region above the CMC. Under ideal conditions, osmotic pressure and light scattering experiments can give apparent molecular weights which are constant at rather low concentrations. In this case, the degree of association is obtained from the apparent molecular weights at high concentrations. hence, the equilibrium constant for the association is, in principle, the only parameter which must be fitted to the experimental data. However, a reasonable evaluation of the equilibrium constant requires experimental data which reflect the onset of the dissolution of the multimers towards lower concentration. This is shown in figure 7 for the PS-SO$_3$Li-40^P sample at 27.5°C. At low concentrations, the K^*c/R_θ-values approach the result for the unimers. At higher concentrations $1/(\overline{M}_w)_{app}$ becomes independent of the concentration ($A_2 = 0$). The molecular weight of the multimers is found to be $\overline{M}_w = 6 \cdot 10^5$ which corresponds to $N = 12$. With this values and an equilibrium constant of $K_{1,N} = 3 \cdot 10^{56}$ $(1/mol)^{11}$ the solid line in figure 7 has been calculated according to equation [6]. This corresponds to a CMC of $(K_{1,N})^{1/N-1}$ = 0.25 g/l. For the PS-SO$_3$Li-80^P sample, the equilibrium constant and the degree of association was determined to be $K_{1,N}$ = 1 · 10^{59} (1/mol)^{11} and N = 12 respectively, which also results in a CMC of 0.24 g/l.

So far nothing has been said about the molecular weight distribution of the multimers. While the unimers have uniform molecular weights due to the synthesis, the degree of association might vary for the single multimers. In this case, the evaluation of light scattering experiments yield a weight average degree of association, $\bar{N}_w$, and osmotic pressure experiments give the corresponding number average, $\bar{N}_n$. In addition, the equilibrium constant will depend on the method used. Figure 8 shows the data for the osmotic pressure of the PS-SO$_3$Li-80^P sample. It was not possible to collect experimental data in the concentration range of the CMC. As a result, the equilibrium constant and the degree of association could not be determined directly by fitting the model for closed association. However, the light scattering experiments set limits for the variations of the parameters for the osmotic pressure data. The resulting molecular weight of the multimers must be such that $\bar{M}_w > \bar{M}_n$, and the equilibrium constant must be smaller than the equilibrium constant determined for weight average data. For the calculation represented by the full line in Fig. 8, the equilibrium constant and the degree of association determined from the light scattering experiments was used. Variations of the equilibrium constant will most strongly affect the reduced osmotic pressure at low concentrations, while different degrees of association will have a significant effect at higher concentrations. To fit the experimental data, the number average degree of association, N_n, must be chosen between 10 and 12 for $K_{1,N}$ = 10^{59}(1/mol)$^{N-1}$; and the equilibrium constant $K_{1,N}$ may be varied between 10^{57} and 10^{59} (1/mol)^{11} for N_n = 12. Hence, $\bar{M}_w/\bar{M}_n$ appears to be smaller than 1.2. Thus in agreement with the data from the other experiments, the molecular weight distribution of the multimers is remarkably narrow. This can be checked independently. For monodisperse molecular weights of unimers and multimers, the following relation should hold (30):

$$N = \frac{[(\bar{N}_w)_{app} - 1]\ (\bar{N}_n)_{app}}{[(\bar{N}_n)_{app} - 1]} \qquad [13]$$

From the apparent number and weight averages at c = 2 x 10^{-2} g/ml the value N = 12 was obtained for the PS-SO$_3$Li-40^P sample and N = 11-12 for the PS-SO$_3$Li-80^P sample.

It can therefore be concluded that the aggregation of the monofunctional molecules in dilute solution of a nonpolar solvent leads to the formation of star-type inverse micelles of narrow molecular weight distribution. In addition, the extremely small CMC shows that the relative amount of material dissolved as unimers can be neglected at concentrations above 1%.

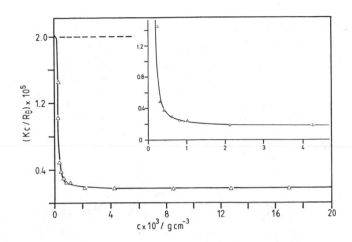

Figure 7: Concentration dependence of the reduced light scattering intensity extrapolated to zero angle for PS-SO$_3$Li-40^P in cyclohexane at 27.5°C. The solid line represents the model calculation with $K_{1,N} = 3 \cdot 10^{56}$ (1/mol)^{11} and N = 12. The dashed line indicates M_1 = 49,000.

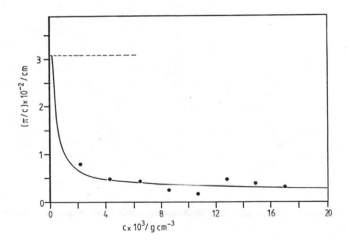

Figure 8: Concentration dependence of the reduced osmotic pressure of PS-SO$_3$Li 80^P under   conditions. The full line represents the model calculations with $K_{1,N} = 10^{59}$ (mol/1)^{11} and N = 11, the dashed line indicates M_1 = 86,000.

GELATION OF MOLECULES WITH SULFONATE GROUPS AT BOTH CHAIN ENDS

For comparison, a telechelic sulfonated polystyrene with a functionality f = 1.95 was prepared. In cyclohexane the material forms a gel independent of the concentration. At high concentrations the sample swells. When lower concentrations were prepared, separation to a gel and sol phase was observed. Thus, dilution in cyclohexane does not result in dissolution of the gel even at elevated temperatures. Given the high equilibrium constant determined for the association of the monofunctional sample, the amount of polymer in the sol phase can be neglected. Hence, the volume fraction of polymer in the gel phase can be calculated from the volume ratio of the sol and gel phases and the total polymer concentration. The plot in Figure 9 shows that the polymer volume fraction in the gel is constant over a wide range of concentrations.

In principle, the two models shown in Figure 10 for the gelation of the telechelic polymers result from the picture of the twelve arm inverse micelle. In the first model, micelles are formed from the telechelic molecules similarly to those described above. These micelles interact with each other via the ionic groups at the outer end of the chains. For topological reasons, the number of the interacting groups which form these interconnections must to be small. Thus, two kinds of chain junctions should result: (1) those with twelve chains coming together and (2) those with two or three chains coming together. In the second model, all chain junctions are the same. This might be achieved by a reduced degree of association, a high number of loops and by double connections between the same "crosslinks". While in the second model the system can be in thermodynamic equilibrium, this is not the case for the first model, which is only reasonable if long times are required for reformation of the interconnections and if structures formed in dilute solution can be preserved. A drastic reduction of the number of sulfonate groups that can associate seems unlikely because of the high equilibrium constant determined for the monofunctional polystyrene sulfonates. Thus the two types of networks should differ with respect to their density. When the structure of the micelles formed in dilute solution is preserved, the polymer volume fraction in the gel should be similar to the overlap concentration of the micelles formed by the monofunctional samples. In the case where all interconnections are of the same type, the polymer volume fraction in the gel should be significantly larger. From light scattering experiments, the overlap concentration of the PS-SO$_3$Li micelles was determined to be 5.4% (31). The polymer volume fraction in the gel of the telechelic polystyrene sulfonates was determined to be 15%. This difference strongly indicates a gel structure similar to the second model, implying that reformation of the ionic aggregates occurs within minutes.

A similar marked tendency to form gels was observed for solutions of telechelic sulfonated polystyrenes in toluene. Again, it was not possible to dissolve the gel by dilution. In principle this could be achieved using a solvent in which the equilibrium of the association of the ionic groups is shifted towards the side of the unimers. Alternatively, the efficiency of the crosslinks can be diminished by addition of monofunctional material. The chains sulfonated only at one end would be incorporated into the micellar

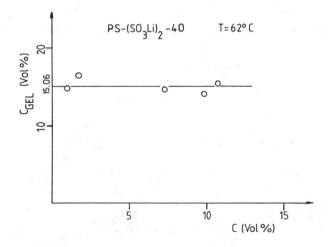

Figure 9: Polymer volume fraction of the PS-$(SO_3Li)_2$-40^P gel at different concentrations in cyclohexane.

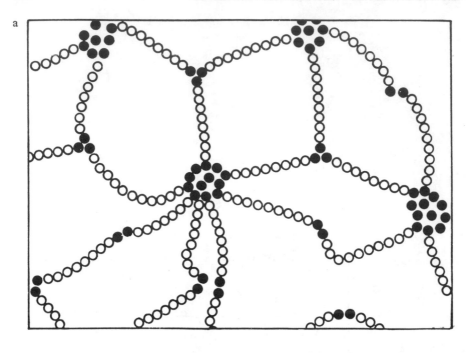

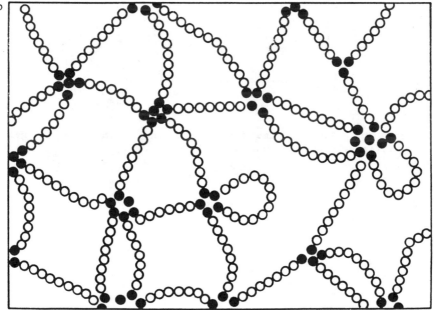

Figure 10: Models for the gelation of α, ω -polystyrenedisulfo-
nates. (a) with two types of interchain links, based on the
twelve arm inverse micelle and (b) homogeneous strucuturé with
loops.

type structures. The number of chains which interconnect different ionic multiplets would decrease. At the same time, the probability for the formation of associates (possibily including several ionic multiplets) which are not interconnected with each other would increase drastically. For a mixture of $PS(SO_3Li)_2$ with a solvent like cyclohexane or toluene, this probability depends on the concentration. This would result in a gel that can be dissolved by the addition of solvent. The average number of sulfonate groups per chain was determined to be about 1.3 for the telechelic samples as polymerized. Assuming Bernoulli-type statistics for the termination reaction, this results in a composition of 42% bifunctional, 46% monofunctional, and 12% non-functionalized polymer molecules. For these samples, reversible gelation could indeed be observed as a function of concentration.

Zero shear viscosities have been determined in solution over a wide range of concentrations with a cone-plate Rheometrics Stress Rheometer. For linear macromolecules, the viscosity is proportional to c below the so called "entanglement concentration", c'; above c', is proportional to $c^{3.4}$. However, the viscosity will rise steeply at some concentration below c' in the case where particular interconnections are formed at the concentration at which the molecules come into contact with one another. Ideally this will be the overlap threshold c^*. Below c^*, the molecules may associate partially but cannot form a network continuous over the entire sample space. Above c^*, plastic flow will require separation and reorganization of the interacting sites. If the interchain connections are strong and the rate for the reformation is slow compared to the time scale of observation, the viscosity will go to infinity under a finite yield stress. Figure 11 shows the zero shear viscosities of dilithiumsulfonated polystyrenes as a function of the concentration in cumene. Cumene is a good solvent for polystyrene; comparable to toluene but less volatile. For comparison, the zero shear viscosities of the corresponding non-modified polystyrene samples are also given. The sulfonated material clearly shows a steep increase in viscosity at concentrations significantly below the onset of entanglements, as indicated by the unmodified polystyrene samples. Three points are worth mentioning. (1) With increasing molecular weight, the concentration c'' at which the gelation effect occurs, is shifted towards higher concentrations. (2) Above c'' the slope of the $\log \eta$ -log c dependence is steeper the lower the molecular weight is. (3) At high concentrations, the viscosity appears to reach a plateau. The first point can be explained by a decrease in the concentration for the overlap threshold when the molecular weight is increased. The steeper increase in the viscosity for the smaller molecular weight polymers can be explained by the higher absolute ion pair concentration which corresponds to a higher number of network junctions per volume. The bend in the viscosity curves at higher concentrations is in agreement with first creep experiments which show that the strain relaxes rapidly under an applied stress. The viscosity levels off to a value up to 6 orders of magnitude higher than the viscosity of the corresponding unmodified polystyrene samples. This is in agreement with the considerations concerning the transitory character of such a gel mentioned above. Within the limit of long observation times,

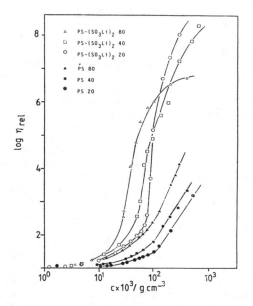

Figure 11: Logarithmic plot of the zero shear viscosities of PS-(SO₃Li)₂ against the concentration in cumene, samples as given in Table II.

the ionic linkages can dissociate and reorganize. The number of network junction points may even remain constant although the structure changes continuously. Of great importance with regard to this point is the poor functionality of the investigated samples. Reformation of the interconnected chains will be much more difficult in the case of perfect difunctionality.

The data discussed above are still too incomplete to draw quantitative conclusions, but they may be helpful in designing new experiments. We especially hope to gain additional insight from temperature dependent light scattering experiments on monofunctional samples, and from the equilibrium polymer volume fractions of the telechelic polymers in the gel in different solvents.

ACKNOWLEDGMENT

The authors cordially thank Prof. Dr. W. Burchard for many helpful discussions and support. Financial support was provided by the Deutsche Forschungsgemeinschaft within the SFB 60.

LITERATURE

1. Flory, P. J., Discuss. Faraday Soc. 1974, 57, 7
2. Eisenberg, A. and King, M., "Ion Containing Polymers", Academic Press, New York 1978
3. MacKnight, W. J. and Earnest, T. R., Polym. Sci. Macromol Rev. 1981, 16, 41
4. Holiday, C., Ed., "Ionic Polymers", Applied Sci. Publ. London 1975
5. Eisenberg, A., "Ions in Polymers", Adv. in Chem. Series 187, Am. Chem. Soc., Washington, D. C. 1980
6. Wilson, A. D. and Prosser, H. J., Eds., "Developments in Ion Containing Polymers", Applied Sci. Publ., London 1983
7. Eisenberg, A. and Bailey F. E., Eds., "Coulombic Interactions in Macromolecular Systems", ACS Symposium Series 302, Am. Chem. Soc., Washington, D. C. 1986
8. Dreyfuss, B., Macromolecules 1985, 18, 284
9. Broze, G.; Jerome, R. and Teyssie, P., Macromolecules 1982, 15, 927
10. Broze, G.; Jerome, R. and Teyssie, P., Macromolecules 1981, 14, 224
11. Broze, G.; Jerome, R. and Teyssie, P., Macromolecules 1982, 15, 920, 1300
12. Broze, C.; Jerome, R.; Teyssie, P. and Marco, C., Macromolecules 1983, 16, 996, 1771
13. Broze, G.; Jerome, R., Teyssie, P. and Marco, C., J. Polym. Sci.: Phys. Ed. 1983, 21, 2265
14. Jerome, R.; Horrion, J.; Fayt, R. and Teyssie, P., Macromolecules 1984, 17, 2447
15. Galland, D.; Belakhavsky, M.; Medrignac, F.; Pineri, M.; Vlaic, G. and Jerome, R., Polymer 1986, 27, 883
16. Williams, C. E.; Russel, T. P.; Jerome, R. and Horion, J. in ref. 7, pg 22
17. Kennedy, J. P.; Ross, L. R.; Lackey, J. E., and Nuyken, O., Polym. Bull. 1981, 4, 67
18. Mohajer, Y.; Tyagi, D.; Wilkes, G. L.; Storey, R. S. and Kennedy, J. P., Polym. Bull. 1982, 8, 47

19. Bagrodia, S.; Mohajer, Y.; Wilkes, G. L.; Storey, R. F. and Kennedy, J. P., Polym. Bull. 1983, 9, 174
20. Tant, M. R.; Wilkes, G. L.; Storey, R. and Kennedy, J. P., Polym. Bull. 1985, 13, 541
21. Omeis, J.; Mühleisen, E. and Möller, M., in preparation
22. Waite, J. H.; Wang, C. Y., Anal. Biochem. 1976, 70, 279
23. Omeis, J.; Möller, M., Polym. Bull., submitted
24. Roovers, J.; Bywater, S.; Macromolecules 1974, 7, 443
25. Huber, K.; Burchard, W. and Fetters, L. J., Macromolecules 1984, 17, 541
26. Roovers, J.; Hadijchristidis, N. and Fetters, L. J., Macromolecules 1983, 16, 214
27. Stockmayer, W. H. and Fixmann, M., Ann. N. Y. Acad. Sci. 1953, 57, 334
28. Elias, H. G. in "Order in Polymer Solutions", K. Solc, Ed., Gordon and Breach Sci. Publ., New York 1976, p. 275
29. Elias, H. G. in "Light Scattering from Polymer Solutions"; Huglin, M. B., Ed.; Academic Press, London and New York 1972, pp 370-457
30. Elias, H.-G. and Bareiss, R., Chimia 1967, 21, 53
31. Omeis, J.; Möller, M. and Burchard W., in preparation

RECEIVED January 24, 1987

Chapter 8

Solvent Mobility in Atactic Polystyrene-Toluene Systems

Frank D. Blum and Byaporn naNagara

Department of Chemistry, University of Missouri—Rolla, Rolla, MO 65401-0249

The solvent mobility in atactic polystyrene-toluene solutions has been studied as a function of temperature using NMR. The local reorientation of the solvent was studied using deuterium NMR relaxation times on the deuterated solvent. Longer range motions were also probed using the pulsed-gradient spin-echo NMR method for the measurement of diffusion coefficients on the protonated solvent. The measurements were taken above and below the gel transition temperatures reported by Tan et al. (Macromolecules, 1983, 16, 28). It was found that both the relaxation time measurements and the diffusion coefficients of the solvent varied smoothly through the reported transition temperature. Consequently, it appears that in this system, the solvent dynamics are unaffected by gel formation. This result is similar to that found in other chemically crossed-linked systems.

The structure and dynamics in reversible polymer gels have been the subject of several studies (1-10). In these, a few researchers have focused on the properties of gels formed from atactic polystyrene (aPS)-solvent systems (1-8). The phase behavior of aPS gels with a variety of solvents has been studied by Tan et al. (1). These gels show gelation temperatures, T_{gel} that are solvent dependent and occur above the glass transition temperature, T_g (2). Since these gels do not contain covalent cross-links, they are necessarily different from gels formed due to chemical cross-links. For example, they appear to be thermoreversible and, in the gel state, may reform into a new shape after deformation.

Evidence for the formation of gels from aPS systems is obtained from simple mechanical, (1,4,5) viscoelastic, (7,8) thermodynamic (1,6) and spectroscopic (6) techniques. Simple tube tilting, falling ball methods and differential scanning calorimetry have been used to determine the phase diagrams for a number of systems. Viscoelastic measurements on the aPS-carbon disulfide system show that the low frequency response indicative of a

Gaussian network increases dramatically at a temperature around the gel-transition temperature (7). The macroscopic kinetic response of the gel to a temperature change is rapid (in a viscoelastic experiment). Enhanced low-angle light scattering is also observed from aPS gels (6). However, in spite of all of the physical evidence, there is controversy over the cause of the gelation with chain overlap, (1) crystallinity (4) and polymer-solvent complexes (6) being suggested as alternative mechanisms.

The purpose of the present study is to probe the role that the dynamics of the solvent molecules play (if any) in the reversible gels formed from aPS. Since the gels recover quickly, it is possible that the molecular dynamics of the reversible gels are significantly different from their cross-linked counterparts. Since the T_{gel} values are strongly dependent on the nature of the solvent, the role of the solvent mobility should be clarified, particularly in light of the recent suggestion from light scattering that a "polymer-solvent complex" (6) may be responsible for gel formation. We have chosen the aPS-toluene system for study because toluene is a good solvent for aPS, has a relatively high swell ratio for cross-linked PS, (2) and is readily available as a deuterated material. While viscoelastic measurements have not been made on this system, a recent study has shown that enhanced low-angle light scattering is observed from aPS gels with tetrahydrofuran, which in many respects is a similar solvent with a similar solubility parameter and T_{gel} temperatures. NMR measurements probing rather different distance scales of solvent mobility will be made both above and below the reported gel transition temperature. They are: i) the longer range, self-diffusion measurements and the ii) shorter range rotational behavior of the solvent. The NMR pulsed-gradient spin-echo (PGSE) method can be used to measure the solvent self-diffusion coefficients. Longitudinal (T_1) and transverse (T_2) deuteron relaxation times of the deuterated solvent are the probes of the local solvent mobility.

EXPERIMENTAL

The NMR measurements were performed on systems composed of ca. 25 wt. % samples of aPS (M_W= 6.6x 10^5 g/mol, PD = 1.1, Pressure Chemical Company) in either reagent grade toluene (Aldrich) or toluene-d_8 (Aldrich). The protonated solvent was used for the diffusion measurements and the deuterated solvent for the relaxation studies. At this concentration, the T_{gel} for the system was determined to be about -65 °C (1). The NMR spectra were run on a JEOL FX-90Q NMR spectrometer operating at 90 and 14 MHz for protons and deuterons, respectively. The T_1 and T_2 measurements were made with the standard inversion-recovery and spin-echo (CPMG) sequences, respectively.

The self-diffusion coefficient measurements were made using the pulsed-gradient spin-echo (PGSE) method which has recently been reviewed (11). For a nucleus in an isotropic solution, the PGSE-NMR normalized signal intensity, I/I_o is given by:

$$I/I_o = \exp(-\gamma^2 G^2 D\beta) \qquad (1)$$

where γ, G and D are the magnetogyric ratio, gradient strength and self-diffusion coefficient, respectively. Constants such as any J-modulation effects or T_2 relaxation effects are factored into I_o term (11). The value of ß is related to the time that the gradient pulse is on, ∂, and the separation time between the radiofrequency pulses, Δ, ie. ß = $\partial^2 (\Delta - \partial/3)$ (11). A plot of the log of the signal intensity versus ß will yield a line with a slope from which D can be determined provided the gradient strength is known (11). In the present case, the gradient was determined to be 0.047 T/m. For a dispersion or phase separated material the decay curve may be markedly nonexponential, such as that found for water in smectic liquid crystals (12) or toluene in a dispersion of cross-linked swollen polymer beads (13,14).

RESULTS

The results of the PGSE-NMR experiment on toluene in a 24.4 wt % aPS solution are shown in Figure 1 as a function of temperature. The measurements were made for the methyl resonance because it has a longer T_2 value than the aromatic resonances. As can be seen in the figure, all of the plots of log intensity versus ß are linear indicating that the diffusion of the toluene is not restricted. Since bi-exponential behavior was not encountered, no significant decrease in intensity was found, and the solutions look homogeneous below T_{gel}: we conclude that neither micro- nor macro-phase separation occurs to any great extent. As the temperature is decreased, the slopes in Figure 1 decrease indicative of slower self-diffusion coefficients. The self-diffusion coefficients, calculated from the PGSE experiment are shown in Figure 2 as a function of temperature. Also shown is an arrow indicating the T_{gel} temperature. No break in the data, within experimental error, is found at or near T_{gel}. The diffusion coefficient appears to obey a simple Arrhenius law with an energy of activation of about 17.5 kJ/mol.

The deuterium NMR spectra of toluene-d_8 in aPS solutions consists of two resonances which are resolved and assigned to the methyl and aromatic groups. In these solutions spin-spin or dipolar couplings are small and consequently are not observed. As the temperature is lowered, the aromatic resonance systematically broadens while the methyl resonance remains relatively constant in width. The linewidths of the aromatic resonances are the same as those which would be predicted from the T_2 measurements reported below. The separated resonances make it possible to determine the relaxation times of each type of resonance.

The deuteron T_1 and T_2 values of both the methyl and aromatic resonances for toluene-d_8 in a 25.6 wt % aPS solution are shown in Figure 3 as a function of temperature. As expected the T_1 and T_2 of the methyl groups are larger than those for the aromatic groups because of their fast internal rotation. The T_2 data seem to be Arrhenius-like and the apparent energies of activation for both resonances are about 35 and 29 kJ/mol for the aromatic and methyl resonances, respectively. The energy of activation is about twice that found in the diffusion case although the physical significance of the energy of activation of the relaxation times is not necessarily straightforward, particularly in polymer solutions.

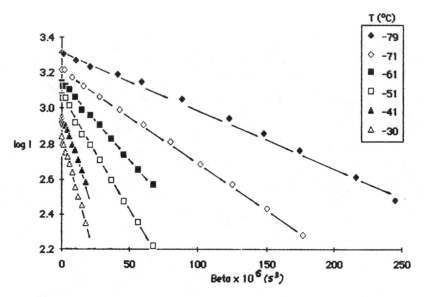

Figure 1.   The PGSE-NMR behavior of toluene in a 24.4
wt % aPS sample as a function of temperature.   The
diffusion coefficients are calculated from the slopes
using equation 1.   The intensity scale is arbitrary.

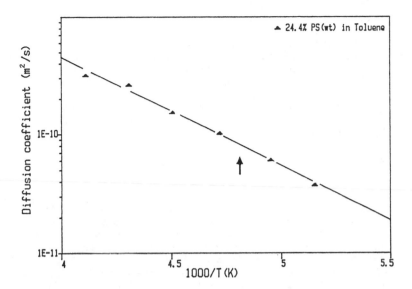

Figure 2. Plot of self-diffusion coefficient, D (in m^2/s, log scale) of toluene in a 24.4 wt% aPS sample as a function of temperature. The arrow indicates the reported gel transition temperature for this concentration (ref. 1).

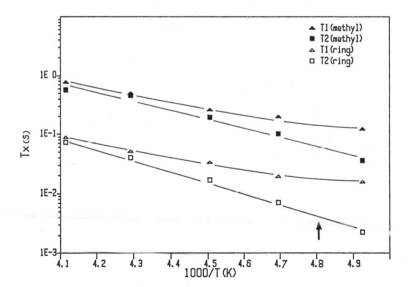

Figure 3. The T_1 and T_2 (in seconds, log scale) behavior of deuterated toluene in a 25 wt% aPS solution as a function of temperature. The arrow indicates the reported gel transition temperature for this concentration (ref. 1).

The T_1 curves are smooth with some curvature near the lower temperatures noted. In this case the system may be near a broad T_1 minimum suggesting that the correlation time of the C-D bond vector is approaching the larmor frequency. However, no abrupt break in the curves is found near the gel transition temperature. In Figure 3 it is seen that the T_2 values are somewhat smaller than the T_1 values at the same temperatures for the same resonance. This is indicative of slow and/or anisotropic rotation. The T_2 values appear to be approaching the T_1 values at the higher temperatures where approximately isotropic reorientation occurs.

DISCUSSION

In the present work, the timescale of the diffusion experiment is on the order of 100 ms. During this time, the solvent molecules will move approximately 2 microns which is greater than any structural effects expected in the gels. In addition, the lifetime of a solvent molecule in solution "bound" to a polymer segment is much shorter than the experimental timescale so that a fast exchange between "free" and "bound" solvent occurs. This yields a diffusion coefficient which is weighted over all solvent environments (15). The values of the diffusion coefficients found are similar to those from other polystyrene solutions well above the gel temperature provided the diffusion coefficient is "normalized" to the diffusion coefficient of the pure solvent at the same temperature (15). This is because the energies of activation for the solvent in bulk through semi-dilute solution are fairly similar in magnitude (16). The energy of activation for the diffusion of pure toluene is around 10 kcal/mol (17).

A variety of relaxation time studies have been performed on toluene. The choice of deuterated toluene avoids certain complicating factors which affect proton NMR studies, such as, dipolar or spin-spin couplings. The dominant relaxation mechanism is quadrupolar and the relaxation times are determined by the reorientation of the C-D bond vector. Relaxation times such as T_1, are sensitive to the motions of the solvent around the larmor frequency, which is on the order of 14 MHz in this study. T_2 measurements may probe slower motions if the molecule undergoes slow and/or anisotropic motion. The relaxation time results presented in Figure 3 are significantly shorter than those found in bulk toluene solutions (18,19). In bulk toluene, the T_1 and T_2 values are equal above the melting temperature (19). In this polymer system $T_2 < T_1$ indicative of slow and/or anisotropic reorientation.

This study is similar to those previously done by Derbyshire and Duff (20) and Nystrom et al. (21) who studied water swellable gels. However, in the first of these, the use of proton NMR complicated the relaxation data because of proton-proton coupling. Furthermore, their study focused on the freezing (or non-freezing) of water which also complicated matters. In the present study, we are always well above the freezing point of toluene so that one need not worry about the freezing of the solvent. The study by Nystrom et al. (21) used deuterium NMR of D_2O, but an unusual temperature dependence was observed, possibly due to the exchange of the protons or deuterons. Our present data are not complicated by these effects and show more expected behavior with monotonic T_2 variations. While a number of models could be quantitatively used to fit the data, (20,21) the qualitative results are perhaps the more important in this case. Most significant is that the smooth transition in solvent mobility across the gel transition suggests that very little of the solvent is involved in the gel formation. Formation of long-lived polymer-solvent complexes would result in two different types of solvent resonances. While the instrumentation used in this study could not be used to observe a solid-like solvent resonance, its presence would reduce the intensity of the liquid-like resonance. This was not observed at or near the gel-transition temperature. However, this type of situation has been observed for the polystyrene-toluene system, but only much closer to the glass transition temperature (22). Rossler et al. (22) have extrapolated their data to the first appearance of a static toluene component in a 28 wt% PS solution as -95 °C. One would expect this to be even lower for the 25 wt% solution studied here. Consequently, these two effects seem to be unrelated but the absence of a static component above their $T_{g\ SE}$ is consistent with the present results.

Conclusions

Based on the current work, we conclude that the solvent mobility, as probed by a variety of NMR techniques is not affected by the formation of a gel. The solvent self-diffusion in these gels is similar to those found in chemically cross-linked gels, (14) which are similar to polymer solutions. Thus, it appears that the role of the solvent in the formation of the gels is primarily thermodynamic, rather than kinetic. The solvent is responsible for the increased polymer-polymer contact resulting in a gel, but its motion is not significantly restricted by the gel. Therefore, the gel is not similar to a glass, where a significant portion of the solvent has greatly restricted rotational and translational motion relative to polymer solutions. Finally, it appears that a large amount of solvent is not involved in formation of whatever interaction is responsible for the gel.

Acknowledgments

The authors wish to thank the E.I. du Pont de Nemours Co., Marshall R&D Laboratory and the donors of the Petroleum Research Fund administered by the American Chemical Society for their financial support.

REFERENCES

1. H.M. Tan, A. Moet, A. Hiltner, E. Baer, *Macromolecules*, 1983, 16, 28.
2. R.F. Boyer, E. Baer, A. Hiltner, *Macromolecules*, 1985, 18, 427.
3. S. Wellinghoff, J. Shaw, E. Baer, *Macromolecules*, 1979, 12, 932.
4. R.C. Domszy, R. Alamo, C.O. Edwards, L. Mandelkern, *Macromolecules*, 1986, 19, 310.

5.   J.Y.S. Gan, J. Francois, J.M. Guenet, Makromol. Chem. Rapid
     Commun., 1985, 6, 225.
6.   J.Y.S. Gan, J. Francois, J.M. Guenet, Macromolecules, 1986, 19,
     173.
7.   J. Clark, S.T. Wellinghoff, W.G. Miller, Polym. Preprints,
     1983, 24(2), 86.
8.   B. Koltisko, A. Keller, M. Litt, E. Baer, A. Hiltner,
     Macromolecules, 1986, 19, 1207.
9.   J.M. Guenet, B. Lotz, J.C. Wittmann, Macromolecules, 1985, 18,
     420.
10. P. R. Sundararajan, N.J. Tyrer, T.L. Bluhm, Macromolecules,
     1982, 15, 286.
11. F.D. Blum, Spectroscopy, 1986, 1(5), 32.
12. F.D. Blum, A.S. Padmanabhan, R. Mohebbi, Langmuir, 1985, 1,
     127.
13. S. Pickup, F.D. Blum, Polym. Mater. Sci. Eng., 1985, 53, 108.
14. S. Pickup, F.D. Blum, W.T. Ford, M. Periyasamy, J. Am. Chem.
     Soc., 1986, 108, 3987.
15. F.D. Blum, S Pickup, K.R. Foster, J. Colloid Interface Sci.,
     1986, 113, 336.
16. A.I. Maklakov, Russ. J. Phys. Chem., 1983, 25, 1631.
17. G.J. Kruger, R. Weiss, Z. Naturforsch., 1970, 25a, 777.
18. R.G. Parker, J. Jonas, J. Magn. Reson., 1972, 6, 106.
19. E. Rossler, H. Sillescu, Chem. Phys. Lett., 1984, 112, 94.
20. W. Derbyshire, I.D. Duff, Faraday Disc., 1974, 57, 243.
21. B. Nystrom, M.E. Mosely, W. Brown, J. Roots, J. Appl. Polym.
     Sci., 1981, 26, 3385.
22. E. Rossler, H. Sillescu, H.W. Speiss, Polymer, 1985, 26, 203.

RECEIVED January 24, 1987

Chapter 9

Physical Gelation of a Steroid–Cyclohexane System: Kinetic Phenomenological Approach

P. Terech

Centre d'Etudes Nucléaires de Grenoble, Département de Recherche Fondamentale
Service de Physique, Groupe Physico Chimie Moléculaire, 85 X,
38041 Grenoble Cedex, France

Physical gelation of a steroid/cyclohexane system was studied. Structural informations are obtained both from Electron Spin Resonance and Small Angle Neutron Scattering experiments. Electron microscopy confirms the helical gel network geometry as determined by SANS. Kinetics of gelation are investigated by recording the evolution with time of typical features of the spectrum from the fluid phase to the gel phase both by SANS and ESR. Supersaturation of the initial solution is the kinetic driving force of the system. Kinetic behaviors are dependent upon the location within the phase diagram. A phenomenological modelisation is achieved according concepts of random or in-phase growth of microdomains and is in qualitative agreement with experiments.

Numerous low molecular weight molecules are known to form physical gels when put in solution (1); such as sodium deoxycholate in water (2) and 12-hydroxyoctadecanoic acid in CC14 (3). For these systems, such structural information has been obtained by infrared spectroscopy (4), diffraction experiments (5, 6) and electron microscopy (7), but very few kinetic data are available even for macromolecular systems such as DNA (8) and gelatin (9).

Here, we are concerned with the physical gelation of cyclohexane by low molecular weight molecules 1 and 2.

1 R = H
2 R = O·

(a, with ; b, without
$C_5 - C_6$ double bond)

Molecule 2b (MW = 390.6) is a spin labeled derivative of

cholesterol and its gels are obtained indifferently with the homologous diamagnetic amine derivative 1 or with 2a and 2b radicals in alkanes or cyclanes. The best stability of gel samples, regard to crystallization, is obtained with cyclohexane.

We have chosen this binary system to study the kinetics of aggregation of a low molecular weight amphiphile . During this aggregation process, gelation occurs.

Definition of the System

Gels are obtained for concentrations shown in the temperature-concentration phase diagram (Figure 1). Electron spin resonance (ESR) shows (10) that for a given temperature only a fraction (p) of the initial steroid concentration C_o is transferred from the solution to the gel network. The picture of this gel is thus of a supersaturation gel : there is a dynamic equilibrium between free molecules in solution and aggregated steroid molecules included in the long objects which constitute the gel network. The free steroid molecules concentration at a temperature where the gel state is stable is $C_o(1-p)$, while $C_o p$ is the steroid concentration within the solid-like gel aggregates.

The difference between this system and an usual supersaturated solution is that two dimensions of the crystallites which are deposited are in the colloidal range, ca 10-200 nm. Only part of the phase diagram has been represented and exploited. For higher concentrations ($> 10^{-1}$ M), gelation is complicated by some turbidity and existence of lyotropic mesophases (11).

In order to gain information about the actual geometry and composition of these long objects, a detailed small angle neutron scattering (SANS) study was made (12). For very low values of the momentum transfer modulus (Q), a characteristic Q^{-1} divergence is observed and demonstrates the scattering by infinitely long objects. Data are then analysed in terms of the radius of gyration R_g of the section and absolute intensities. Contrast variation measurements show that the long objects are essentially composed of steroid molecules. The number of steroids per unit length of objects is estimated (n_L = 70 ± 20 steroids per nm length). To deduce the geometrical parameters, these above data and the full scattering curves are compared with the simple models of a homogeneous cylinder, a hollow cylinder, helices and a homogeneous double helix. The best fit (Figure 2) is obtained with this last model and independent arguments as given by electron microscopy experiments (see below) support the chiral character of the objects.

Taking into account a distribution of radii coming from the peculiar geometry of the reticulation zones, it was found that a global geometrical diameter is R_o = 9.9 ±0.3 nm.

These results were confirmed by an electron microscopy study using a freeze-etching replication technique (13). The aim of this technique was to conserve the real gel structure by blocking any diffusion processes in the gel sample by the freezing action of liquid nitrogen. The three-dimensional network is then recovered

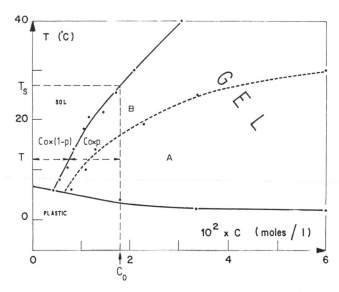

Figure 1. Phase diagram of the gelling steroid/cyclohexane system. The upper full line is the saturation curve $C_s(T)$ and T_s the saturation temperature for the initial concentration C_o. The dotted line indicates the separation between the two zones A and B. The lower full line indicates the transition to the cyclohexane plastic phase.(Reproduced with permission from Ref. 17. Copyright 1985 Academic Press.)

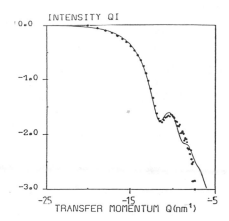

Figure 2. Comparison between experimental and theoretical scattering curves for double helices. The points are experimental (compound 1b, $C_o = 2 \times 10^{-2}$ M, T = 19°C) ; the full line is the best fit of equations in reference (12)).(Reproduced with permission from Ref. 17. Copyright 1985 Academic Press.)

by etching the solvent at a given temperature and pressure conditions. An example of the filamentary network is shown in Figure 3.
      Stereo images reveal clearly the three-dimensional gel
network which has a mesh size of about 300 nm (for $C_o \sim 3 \times 10^{-2} M$)
(13).
      A statistical analysis on a large number of diameter
measurements ($\sim$ 2500) shows that the most probable diameter is 9.1
$\pm$ 1 nm and is in agreement with previous SANS results. The 9.1 nm
filaments appear to be made from two or more twisted protofilaments
of 4.6 nm diameter. The helical structure is detected as striations
of about 5.0 nm pitch; this chirality is likewise seen in the dried
gels (xerogels) where some collapse of fibers has taken place,
however diameters and pitches are bigger (see Figure 4) (14).
      In both case (gel and dried gels) the advantage of a scheme
based on the protofilament is the high degree of resultant
structural flexibility. Interfilament contacts of the physical
reticulation can occur by filament juxtaposition, by a fusion of all
protofilaments of the two incoming filaments (say n protofilaments)
to form an n-start helical fusion zone of reticulation or by an
interfilament exchange of just one or more protofilaments.
      While investigations at the molecular stage are under progress
(wide angle X-ray scattering on oriented fibers of the solid-like
gel network), it is nevertheless reasonable to assume the following
picture of the cross section. One of the long filaments of the
network is in fact an helix composed of at least of two protofilaments.
The number and shape of cross section of protofilament and the
resulting pitch are directly correlated to the mass per unit length
as determined by SANS. For instance, the simplest case of double
helix is represented in Figure 5. The most probable configuration
for the amphiphile 2 in an apolar solvent as cyclohexane is a
reverse micelle geometry.

Kinetic Method

The purpose of this study is to follow the aggregation process from
the small amphiphile molecule to the infinite network of Figure 3.
For a critical density of fibers, viscosity diverges while an
elastic modulus appears (15,16).
      To do this, two complementary methods, ESR and SANS, are used
in a phenomenological description of the phenomenon. The starting
point of all kinetic experiments is the fluid phase. At the
experimental gelation temperature, the fluid phase is an unstable
supersaturated solution and evolves to give the gel phase, see phase
diagram (Figure 1). With ESR the decrease in steroid concentration
in the fluid phase is recorded while with neutrons it is the growth
of the rods . For each of the two spectroscopic methods used, the
spectrum is different in solution and in the stabilized gel. The
principle of the method is to record the variations with time of
some characteristic feature h of the spectrum.

1. SANS experiments
For the fluid phase, no Q-dependent small angle scattering signal

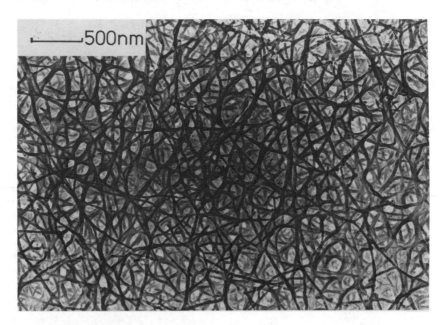

Figure 3. Solid-like gel network. Freeze-etching replication technique. (Reproduced with permission from Ref. 17. Copyright 1985 Academic Press.)

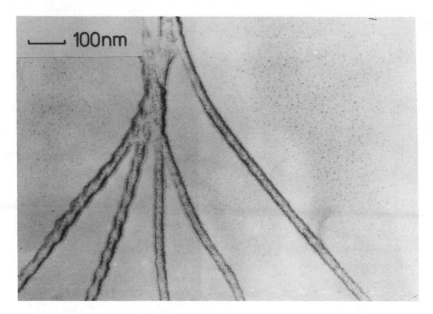

Figure 4. Helices in the dried gel network. Replication technique.

exists. By contrast, a strong scattered intensity is observed to grow during the gelation process. Equation of this scattering curve has been studied in the structural SANS analysis and is characteristic of an infinitely long double helix with some distribution of radii taking into account the particular mode of reticulation of these gels (12). For low Q-values, a sufficient approximation is given by the scattering law of isolated homogeneous infinite cylinders of radius R :

$$I(Q) = \frac{1}{Q} \times \left(\frac{2 \times J_1(QR)}{QR} \right)^2 \qquad (1)$$

where J_1 is the Bessel function of order 1.

Since we have checked that the shape of the scattering curves does not change with time, integrated intensity within a central window of Q is proportional to the total amount of scattering rods.

$$(QI)_0 = \Pi C\, M_L\, (\Delta b)^2 \qquad (2)$$

where $(QI)_0$ is an absolute cross section intensity (QI) for Q = 0, C is the mass concentration of the long objects ($C = pC_0$), M_L the mass per unit length of objects, and Δb the specific neutron scattering contrast (in $cm.g^{-1}$) for the volume of a steroid molecule. Figure 6 shows the scattering curves for different times during gelation .

Figure 7 is a typical variation of the intensity $h^{SANS}(t)$ integrated between 0.0008 and 0.02 nm^{-1}, versus time. ($h^{SANS}(t) - h^{SANS}_{min}$) values are then directly proportional to $C_0.p(t)$ and constitute the kinetic SANS raw data; h^{SANS}_{min} is a background level mainly due to incoherent scattering.

2. ESR experiments

The gel phase spectrum is assumed to be the superposition of two components : a three narrow Lorentzian-lines component, which is the spectrum of free radical 2 in the fluid part of the gel phase, and a broad Lorentzian component, which is the spectrum of radicals involved in the network (see Figure 8, in which the nitrogen hyperfine splitting is $a_N = 14.65$ G).

Decrease of the lowfield line amplitude during gelation is chosen as the spectrum feature $h^{ESR}(t)$ used for the kinetic analysis (Figure 9). This variation is related to the growth of the gel solid-like component . The big difference in linewidth between the sharp lines of the fluid component and the broad Lorentzian of the solid-like component allows a sufficient sensitivity for the method.

As it can be noticed, we obtain a positive kinetic variation (Figure 7) with SANS which is related to an increasing steroid concentration $C_0\, p(t)$ in the solid-like gel network as well as a negative kinetic variation (Figure 9) with ESR which is related to a decreasing steroid concentration $C_0\,(1-p(t))$ in the gel's fluid part. The two techniques are complementary : a negative picture of the kinetics by ESR and a positive picture by SANS . The main

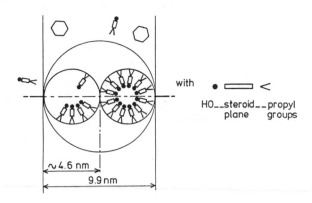

Figure 5. A simple reverse micelle model for the steroid/cyclohexane gelling system. Protofilament cross-section is represented as a circle but could be elliptic or rectangular at this stage of the modelisation.

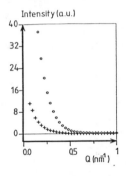

Figure 6. Scattering curves during the gelation at 19°C of a steroid solution ($C_o = 2.4 \times 10^{-2}$ M in C_6D_{12}). Intensity versus transfer momentum Q for $\tau = 7$ min (+++) and $t = 10$ min (ooo). (Reproduced with permission from Ref. 17. Copyright 1985 Academic Press.)

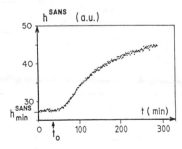

Figure 7. Typical integrated scattered intensity h^{SANS} during the gelation of a solution $C_o = 2.4 \times 10^{-2}$ M at 19°C. Minimum level h^{SANS}_{min} and induction time t_o are indicated.

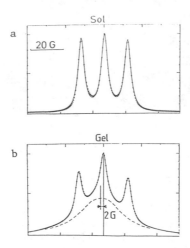

Figure 8. Integrated experimental spectra (---) and fitted spectra (+++) for two typical samples in the sol (a, $C = 1.8 \times 10^{-2}$ M), T = 19°C) and gel (b, $C = 2.28 \times 10^{-2}$ M, T = 10.3°C) phases. The broad line component is shown in b. It corresponds to p = 0.68.

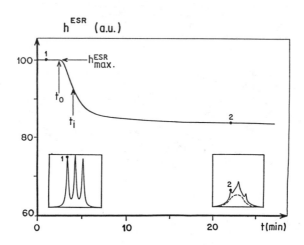

Figure 9. Amplitude variation of the derivative ESR lowfield line h^{ESR} during gelation of the solution $C_0 = 1.8 \times 10^{-2}$ M at 8°C. Induction time t_0 and characteristic gelation time t_i are shown. The insets show the integrated ESR spectra before and after gelation.

differences between the two methods are : (i) with ESR, continuous records are obtained and the kinetic information can only be extracted after a complete simulation of the spectroscopic problem (17, 18); (ii) with neutrons experiments, the records are discontinuous but the kinetic information is pure and needs no more treatment since the diffusion law is unchanged during the gelation phenomenon (at low Q-values).

Results

We can apply classical germination laws to this supersaturated system ; thus, the Avrami-Mempel laws confirm the unidimensional growth of the solid-like gel network. Induction times can also be studied in this framework (17). Here, we are interested first by the different kinetic behaviors which are dependent upon the location in the phase diagram of the initial solution defined by its supersaturation degree.

The gel region of the phase diagram in Figure 1 is divided in two zones :

. In zone A, induction times are short ($0 \leqslant t_0 \leqslant 20$ min). Curves are sigmoid with a single inflexion point (t_i) (Figure 9). An asymptotic value of the amplitude signal is reached after typical times of about 40 min. For two distinct experiments on the same couple (C_0, T), reproducibility is preserved since the same equilibrium p_{max} value and nearly identical kinetic curves are obtained.

. In zone B, asymptotic values are reached after much longer times and the curves are either very flat or frequently constituted by a series of small jumps (Figure 10).

Now, our purpose is to simulate these different kinetic behaviors. A phenomenological description was tried with some simple models noticing that the starts were autocatalytic in zone A. The best agreements were obtained with a model composed of two successive reactions, the first step being autocatalytic :

$$
\begin{array}{lccccc}
 & A & \longrightarrow & B & \longrightarrow & C \\
t = 0 & \Delta C & & o & & o \qquad (3) \\
\\
t & \Delta C - x & & y & & z
\end{array}
$$

where $\Delta C = C_0 - C_s(T)$ is the absolute supersaturation of the initial solution and $C_s(T)$ is the saturation concentration of 2 at temperature T. The fraction of steroids in supersaturation constitutes the species A and the aggregated molecules in the solid-like network the species C, while B is an intermediary aggregated state of steroids.

Agreement of model (3) with experimental data is shown on Figure 11 for ESR experiments in zone A and has been confirmed by SANS experiments(17).

In zone B, despite a reproductibility probably modified by heterogenous nucleation phenomena in these weakly supersaturated solutions, agreement of the model has been checked on the above

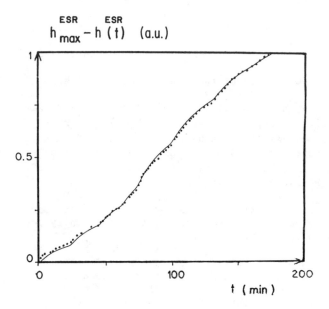

Figure 10. Typical kinetic behavior in the zone B of the phase diagram (•••). The full line is the best fit of model (3). Only some points of the continuous ESR kinetic record have been represented.

Ordinates are $(h_{max}^{ESR} - h^{ESR}(t))/(h_{max}^{ESR} - h^{ESR}(t_{max}))$ values.

mentioned flat curves (17), where the autocatalytic character is not preponderant, and on the curves with small jumps (Figure 10).

Discussion-Conclusion

All these results support our kinetic interpretations of these supersaturated gelling solutions. We assume that the network growth is described by the growth of individual domains, each one ruled by the autocatalytic model (3). This system behaves like an assembly of microdomains. Each steroid in a supersaturation state is a potential germ of microdomain. According to distribution curves of induction times for each microdomain, the typical kinetic curves for each part A and B of the phase diagram are obtained.

In part A, supersaturation is high and equivalent to a high "driving force" for the kinetics. The induction times distribution curve is very narrow and the resulting kinetic curve is of type (3) (Figure 12-1). It is a region of a **quite in-phase growth of the domains.**

In part B, supersaturation is low and the distribution curve is broad, since induction times are spread over the whole aggregation delay. Thus, the autocatalytic character is lost in the resultant kinetics. According to the width of the induction time distribution, flat or irregular curves can be obtained (Figure 10). It is a region of **random growth of the domains.**

   In conclusion, it is now possible to reproduce the kinetic behavior of this steroid/cyclohexane gelling system, including the shape (defined by model (3) and its kinetic rate constants k_o, k_1, k_2) and also the absolute values of $C_o p$ in zone A of the phase diagram. In Figure 13, we demonstrate the reversibility of the gelation process and the additivity of p_{max} values for different experimental temperatures. We can get the same gel at 15°C either by cooling down directly the solution to 15°C or cooling down first the solution to 35°C and then the obtained gel from 35 to 15°C.

   A logical development of this study will be to consider the microscopic point of view i.e the elementary reactions to build the infinite reverse micelles of the network. Detailed structural information is necessary to undertake a more microscopic approach of the kinetics. The aggregation mechanism involves hydrogen bonding as clearly demonstrated by an IR spectrocopy study (18) and has to be understood.

   Besides, comparisons with other non-macromolecular gelling systems are in progress. Specially, we can compare with a square planar copper complex, which aggregates in linear chains to gelify the cyclohexane (19). It is immediatly noticed that characteristic times of the aggregation kinetics are correlated to the complexity of the molecular aggregation mechanism involved.

   Another development underway is to try to locate on the above mentioned sigmoid curves the critical point (t_c), where gelation occurs. Rheological experiments and structural determinations will be used to calculate some critical quantities as a critical fiber density to gelify the system.

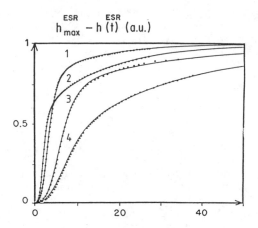

Figure 11. Best fits (———) of model (3) to ESR data (●●●). Only certain points of the continuous ESR kinetic records have been represented.
(1) C_o = 3.4 x 10^{-2} M, T = 20.4°C ; (2) C_o = 1.8 x 10^{-2} M, T = 3.8°C ;
(3) C_o = 2.28 x 10^{-2} M, T = 15.2°C ; (4) C_o = 1.3 x 10^{-2} M, T = 8°C. For all curves, induction times are not represented.
Ordinates are $(h_{max}^{ESR} - h^{ESR}(t))/(h_{max}^{ESR} - h^{ESR}(\infty))$ values.
(Reproduced with permission from Ref. 17. Copyright 1985 Academic Press.)

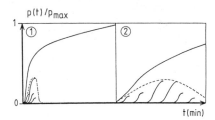

Figure 12. Gel network growth mechanism.Kinetic curves according to the width of the induction times distribution of the domains. 1 = narrow distribution: zone A, k_1 = 0 ; 2 = broad distribution: zone B, k_1 = 0.

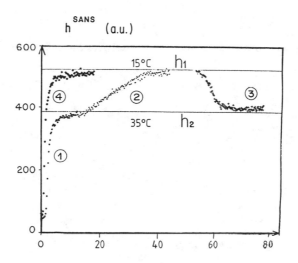

Figure 13. Kinetic SANS curves. Gelation transitions between 35
and 15°C showing additivity and reversibility of the system.
$C_o = 5.9 \times 10^{-2}$ M. $h_1 = 1 + 2$; $h_2 = 3 + 4$.

Acknowledgments

The author is grateful to Drs C. CHACHATY,J. GAILLARD,G. GEBEL,A.M. GIROUD, E. HEWAT, R. RAMASSEUL, F. VOLINO and R. WADE for their contribution to this work.

Literature Cited

1. HERMANS, P.H. in "Colloid Science" (H.R. Kruyt, Ed.) Elsevier, Amsterdam, 1969.
2. SOBOTKA, H. and CZECZONOWICZKA, J. Colloid Sci., 13, 188 (1958)
3. TACHIBANA T., MORI T. and HORI K., Bull. Chem. Soc. Japan, 53, 1714 (1979).
4. TACHIBANA T. YOSHIZUMI T. and HORI K., Bull. Chem. Soc. Japan, 52, 34, (1979)
5. RICH A. and BLOW D.M., Nature, 182, 423 (1958)
6. ITO N., YUDASAKA M. and FUJIYAMA T., Bull. Chem. Soc. Japan, 54, 1939 (1981)
7. TACHIBANA T. and KAMBARA H., J. Colloid Interface Sci., 28, 173 (1969)
8. HOYER H.W. and NEVIN S., Anal. Calorim., 3, 465 (1974)
9. GODARD P., BIEBUYCK J.J., BARRIAT P.A., NAVEAU H. and MERCIER J.P., Makromol. Chem., 181, 2009 (1980)
10. TERECH P., RAMASSEUL R., and VOLINO F., J. Colloid Interface Sci., 91, 280 (1983)
11. TERECH P. to be published
12. TERECH P., VOLINO F., and RAMASSEUL R., J. Phys., (Les Ulis, Fr.),46, 895 (1985)
13. WADE R.H., TERECH P., HEWAT E.A., RAMASSEUL R., and VOLINO F. J.Colloid Interface Sci. (1986)
14. TERECH P. and WADE R.H. to be published
15. DE GENNES P.G., in "Scaling Concepts in Polymer Physics", Cornell Univ. Press, Ithaca, 1980
16. CALLEC G., GAUTHIER MANUEL B., TERECH P., and RAMASSEUL R., C.R. Acad. Sci. Paris II, 293, 749 (1981)
17. TERECH P., J. Colloid Interface Sci., 107, 244 (1985)
18. TERECH P., Thesis, Grenoble, France, 1983
19. TERECH P., CHACHATY C., GAILLARD J. and GODQUIN-GIROUD A.M. J. Phys. (Les Ulis, Fr) (1987)

RECEIVED April 9, 1987

Chapter 10

Nematic Solutions of Rodlike Polymers

Light Scattering from Nematic Solutions with Complex Texture and Phase Separation in Poor Solvents

Kazunori Se[1] and G. C. Berry[2]

Department of Chemistry, Carnegie-Mellon University, Pittsburgh, PA 15213

Light scattering studies are reported for solutions of the rodlike poly(1,4-phenylene - 2,6-benzobisthiazole), PBT, in methane sulfonic acid, MSA. Static and dynamic scattering are reported on a nematic phase with a smooth texture, and the polarized and depolarized static scattering is given during a heating and cooling cycle over the nematic-isotropic-nematic transition. The annealing of a nematic mottled texture formed on cooling the isotropic phase is followed by static scattering. The effect of absorbed water on the nematic phase is reported, including the following features which appear in order of the amount of water absorbed: transformation to a yellow isotropic state with the rodlike chains in an aggregated supramolecular structure; formation of a yellow birefringent state, probably through a spinodal phase separation; and formation of a red coagulated phase through deprotonation of the dissolved polymer.

Solutions of poly(1,4-phenylene-2,6-benzobisthiazole), PBT, exhibit an isotropic to nematic phase transition in a variety of solvents including methane sulfonic acid, MSA, chlorosulfonic acid, CSA, and polyphosphoric acid, PPA (1-4). In the latter case the transition occurs over a range of water $-P_2O_5$ compositions. In these acids the polymer, with repeating unit

PBT

[1]Current address: Department of Material Science and Technology, Technological University, Kamitomioka-Cho, Niigata 949-54, Nagaoka, Japan
[2]Correspondence should be addressed to this author.

$$\left[\begin{array}{ccccc} & N & & S & \\ C & & O & & C & O \\ & S & & N & \end{array}\right]_N$$

is protonated to form rodlike macrocations (5,6). In solution in MSA and PPA, electrostatic interactions among the macrocations are suppressed by the anions and cations created by self-protonation of the solvent and related reactions (6,7). In solution in CSA, the concentration of such cations is low, and electrostatic interactions among the macrocations are observed at low polymer concentration (7). In all three solvents, the temperature for the phase transition increases with increasing polymer concentration, and the biphasic range, in which isotropic and nematic phases coexist, is narrow (3,4), see below.

In this study we report measurements of the light scattering from a nematogenic solution of PBT in MSA solution in the vicinity of the isotropic – nematic transition. In a later contribution we will report on the preparation of a fully oriented nematic phase of this solution, and light scattering measurements to determine the Frank elastic coefficients and the Leslie-Ericksen viscosity coefficients (8,9). Here, the scattering will be reported for the nonequilibrium state formed on entry to the nematic phase by reduction of the temperature, along with the scattering as this phase is annealed toward equilibrium.

The addition of water causes the formation of a coagulated phase of PBT solutions in any of the solvents named above (of course, the amount of water tolerated varies with the solvent, with the PPA solvent being the most tolerant toward water) (4). In very dilute solutions, the water causes enhanced depolarized scattering, interpreted to be the result of the formation of aggregates in which the rodlike chains are in parallel arrays (10). In more concentrated solutions, a gel phase is created (11,12). In either case, the electronic absorption spectra is altered from that characteristic of the protonated chain to that characteristic of the deprotonated, dry polymer (10). In the following we will report observations on this phase transition.

EXPERIMENTAL

Material. The PBT polymer was obtained as a dry sample from Dr. J. F. Wolfe, SRI International. The intrinsic viscosity $[\eta]$ in MSA solution was 1800 ml/g. From the relation $[\eta] = 1.25 \times 10^{-5} M_W^{1.8}$ reported for PBT solution in MSA (6), $M_W \sim 3.4 \times 10^4$.

The PBT polymer was dried for 2 weeks at 60°C at 10^{-3} torr, to constant weight. The MSA was distilled under reduced nitrogen pressure. A solution was prepared by addition of the appropriate quantities of dry PBT and distilled MSA to a 35 ml glass tube containing a teflon coated magnetic stirring bar. The operation was performed in a dry bag filled with nitrogen. The glass tube was sealed, suspended between the poles of a magnet, and immersed in oil held at 60°C in a copper vessel that also fitted between the poles of the magnet. Slow stirring action was achieved by rotating the sample tube with the stirring bar held fixed by the magnet, with occassional vertical repositioning of the magnet. After stirring for 24 hours, a homogeneous concentrated solution was obtained. Concentrations are expressed as the weight fraction w calculated from the component weights used in the preparation.

Light Scattering Cells.   The extinction coefficient μ of PBT solutions in an acidic solvent is 190 ml g^{-1}cm^{-1} at the wavelength 647nm of light used in the scattering studies. Thus, it is necessary to use relatively thin samples for light scattering studies. Three configurations meeting this requirement were used in this study:

1. Cell A--a thin-wall capillary of the sort used in melting temperature determinations;
2. Cell B -- a cell similar to that used elsewhere (13), formed by pressing two thick (8 mm) optical plates onto opposite sides of a teflon spacer, with the polymer solution placed in a hole in the center of the spacer; and
3. Cell C -- a cell fabricated from rectangular glass tubing (Vitro Dynamics, Inc., Rockaway, NJ) as described elsewhere (1).

Cell A was 1.3 mm inside diameter, and could be up to 5 cm long. Cells were flame dried under vacuum prior to use. Solution was placed in Cell A using a syringe fitted with a teflon needle so that the upper length of the cell was maintained dry; the cell was filled in a dry bag under nitrogen, and then sealed under vacuum by fusing the (dry) tube with a flame. Samples so sealed may be held indefinitely without deterioration (provided the MSA is pure).

The spacer in cell B was 0.5 mm thick; the cell diameter was 22 mm. The glass plates were fitted with a hinge and suspended by teflon strands in a glass vessel over P_2O_5, with the hinged plate held open by a hollow glass hook. The vessel was held under vacuum at 60°C for about one week. The sample was then introduced under vacuum onto the glass plate through the hollow hook. Any entrained gas bubbles were removed as the solution exuded under vacuum through a small diameter orifice at the tip of the hook. The assembly was tilted to free the plate from the hook, so that the upper plate closed on the lower plate. The (partially) assembled cell was removed from the vessel in a dry bag under nitrogen and its perimeter wrapped first with a strip of teflon tape and second by a strip of aluminum foil coated with (uncured) epoxy resin. The assembly was then placed in a clamp to maintain pressure on the glass-teflon spacer-glass seals as the epoxy cured. The resultant cell provided a satisfactory barrier against moisture, permitting the solution to be held indefinitely. Omission of any of the steps can lead to coagulation of the solution (see below).

The rectangular section of cell C was 0.4 mm thick, 0.8 cm wide and 1.5 cm long between its open ends. The ends were fused to glass tubes fitted with glass Luer tips. The cell was flame dried under vacuum prior to use. Solution was placed in the cell using a syringe and teflon tubing fitted to one of the Luer tips, with the transfer being made in a dry bag. After being filled, the Luer tips were closed with teflon caps. The latter were wrapped with teflon tape and the ends dipped in epoxy resin to a depth sufficient to cover part of the exposed glass tubing. Cells so prepared will maintain the solution without deterioration for an indefinite period. When used in light scattering measurements, surface scattering from the glass-air interface was reduced by adhering a thin microscope slide to the cell surface using the capillary attraction from tritolyl phosphate held between the glass surfaces.

Light Scattering Measurements.   A light scattering apparatus described elsewhere (6) was used in this study.   A Krypton-ion laser (Lexel Model 95) with wavelength 647.1 nm was used as a light source. Polarized and depolarized light scattering measurements by methods described elsewhere (6) were used to determine the Rayleigh ratios $R_{Vv}(q)$ and $R_{Hv}(q)$, respectively, for the vertical and horizontal components of the light scattered with vertically polarized incident light; $q = (4\pi n/\lambda_0)\sin\theta/2$, with θ the scattering angle, n the refractive index of the solution, and λ_0 the wavelength of the incident light in vacuum. Scattering measurements were restricted to $\theta = 20$ deg. ($q^{-1}=200$ nm). The scattering volume was made small enough that surface reflections were not admitted by the detector optics.

Cell A could be accommodated in the cell holder usually used with the apparatus (6), in which the cell is immersed in a liquid in a larger cylindrical cell equipped with flat entrance and exit windows for the incident beam. This assembly was not used with cells B or C. With these cells, the plane construction results in a difference between the actual scattering angle θ and the goniometer setting θ_a of course, with cylindrical geometry $\theta = \theta_a$). Thus,

$$\theta = \arcsin(n^{-1} \sin \theta_a) \qquad (1)$$

In addition, the scattered beam is displaced a distance Δ perpendicular to the incident beam:

$$\Delta/t = \tan [\arcsin (n_q^{-1} \sin \theta_a)] \qquad (2)$$

where n_g is the refractive index of the cell wall (glass) and t its thickness. In order to accommodate the latter effect, the cell was mounted on a stage that could be translated along the optic axis of the incident beam. The scattered intensity was monitored as the cell was translated to determine the range of positions for which the intensity was invariant. Finally, the cell was positioned in the center of this range.

The cell stage was thermostatted, and means provided for motion in the x-y directions perpendicular to the incident beam axis. One hour was allowed for thermal equilibrium before light scattering measurements subsequent to any temperature change.

Photon correlation light scattering was carried out by methods described elsewhere (6) to give the (unnormalized) correlation function $G^{(2)}(q,\tau)$. Data were obtained with vertically polarized incident light for $G_{Vv}^{(2)}(q,\tau)$ and $G_{Hv}^{(2)}(q,\tau)$ obtained, respectively, with the vertical and horizontal components of the scattered light.

As usual (6,14), $G^{(2)}(q,\tau)$ was calculated from the autocorrelation of the photon counts:

$$G^{(2)}(q,k\Delta\tau) = -\ \frac{1}{M} \sum_{j=1}^{M} \left\{ \frac{1}{T} \sum_{i=1}^{M} n_i n_{i+k} \right\}_j \tag{3}$$

where $\tau = k\Delta\tau$, T is the number of intervals of duration $\Delta\tau$ observed in one experiment ($T = 2^{12}$), and M is the number of such experiments averaged. In general, M was made large enough that the total number of counts accumulated in the T x M intervals was about 10^6.

Optical Microscopy and Transmittance Measurement.   A microscope equipped with polarizing optics and thermostatted stage was used in certain studies described below. Transmittance measurements were made by use of a power meter (Lexel model 504) positioned close to the cell, on the optic axis of the incident beam. The cell was mounted on the light scattering stage for these measurements, and the transmittance was determined for light with wavelength 647 nm.

RESULTS

Coagulation Studies.   As mentioned in the introduction, solutions of PBT in any of the several acids that dissolve the polymer will coagulate in the presence of water. Coagulation rates were measured using a drop of the solution sandwiched between a glass slide and a cover glass to form a disk about 1 cm in diameter and 0.2-0.3 mm thick. A reservoir of water was placed in contact with the solution periphery to create a coagulation front that advanced radially toward the center of the solution disk. The front was easily identified by the difference in color of the coagulated material (red) and the solution (yellow). The coagulation front advances linearly with the square root of time such that $t^{-1/2}y(t)$ is a constant, where $y(t)$ is the distance advanced in time t. Values of $y/t^{1/2}$ were found to be 60 $\mu m \cdot s^{-1/2}$ and 2.8 $\mu m \cdot s^{-1/2}$ for coagulation by water with solutions of PBT in MSA ($w = 0.048$) and PPA ($w = 0.046$), respectively. This difference is not as great as that between the ratio of the viscosities of PPA and MSA (of order 10^3), indicating that diffusion is not the rate limiting step in the coagulation process.

The observed constancy of $y/t^{1/2}$ is in accord with theoretical predictions for one dimensional diffusion with reaction of the diffusant (15). In that case $y(t)$ is given by

$$y(t) = 2Z(Dt)^{1/2} \tag{4}$$

where D is the diffusion constant for the diffusing species, and Z is given implicitly by:

$$\pi^{1/2}Z\ \exp(Z^2)\mathrm{erf}\ Z\ =\ c_0/m_0 \tag{5a}$$

$$2Z^2 \left[1 + \left(\frac{\exp Z^2 - 1}{2Z / \sqrt{\pi}} \right)^{3/2} \right]^{2/3} \approx c_0/m_0 \qquad (5b)$$

with erf ( ) the error function, c_0 the initial concentration of the diffusing coagulant at the boundary, and m_0 that of the trapping sites. Equation 5b provides a useful approximation for Equation 5a, being exact for very small or large Z. A sharp coagulation boundary is assumed in Equation 4, consistent with our observations.

The coagulation process of PBT in solution in MSA was also studied using an arrangement shown schematically on Figure 1 in which a series of solution droplets were suspended in separate zones (eight in Figure 1) in a capillary tube of the type used in cell A. The end of the tube was left open and the tube placed in ambient humid air so that water gradually diffused into the solution. In this case c_0 in Equations 4–6 is very much reduced in comparison with the coagulation rate studies described above. At the outset, the droplets in all eight zones were nematic solutions, being yellow in color, birefringent, and exhibiting a dense field of disclinations (see below for further discussion of disclinations). As shown in Figure 1, after 4 hr the droplets in zones 3 to 8 were unchanged, but an isotropic (I) and a nematic phase (N) coexisted in zone 2, and zone 1 had been transformed to a turbid, birefringent phase (A_1) (not to be confused with the original nematic phase). As shown in Figure 1, the isotropic–nematic phase boundary translated through the zones at a rate in accord with Equation 4, with $y/t^{1/2}$ about equal to 65 $\mu m \cdot s^{-1/2}$. After one day, two additional phases were observed, a very turbid, dark yellow phase (A_2) in zone 2, and very turbid red phase (R) in zone 1. The front between A_2 and R also translated at a rate about in accord with Equation 4, with $y/t^{1/2}$ about equal to 25 $\mu m \cdot s^{-1/2}$. The latter may be compared with $y/t^{1/2}$ of 60 $\mu m.s^{-1/2}$ for coagulation by water, in which the advancing position of the red phase was used to mark the coagulation boundary. Since the concentration c_0 differs by about 100–fold in these experiments, whereas the values of $y/t^{1/2}$ differ by only a factor 2.6, this result indicates that c_0/m_0 must be small in air (e.g., of order 0.01) and about unity for coagulation by water if the data are to be fitted by Equations 4–5. After one week, a clear liquid (S) was observed over some zones, probably being an acid solution separated by volume contraction of the precipitated phase.

Light scattering studies were carried out on nematic solutions of PBT in MSA undergoing slow coagulation in light scattering cells of type B. The coagulation was due to moisture intrusion through an incomplete seal on the cell, with the epoxy resin being omitted. Light scattering measurements on the isotropic phase (I) created during coagulation in this cell gave $R_{Hv}(q) \approx 0.007$ cm^{-1}, and $R_{Hv}(q)/R_{Vv}(q) = 0.1$ for the scattering at 20 deg., with transmittance (at 647 nm) of 0.70. Data in Figure 2 show $R_{Hv}(q)$ and $R_{Vv}(q)$ for the scattering from phase A_1 ($\theta = 20$ deg.) for the scattering from two solutions (w equal to 0.04 and 0.046). Both $R_{Vv}(q)$ and $R_{Hv}(q)$ decrease sharply as phase A_1 is transformed to an isotropic phase

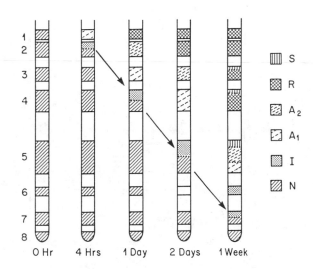

Figure 1.   Schematic diagram of phase separation in a
solution of PBT in MSA through the uptake of water from
humid air.   The solution was suspended as eight droplets
in a capillary (1.3 mm dia., 5 cm long); water diffused
into the solution from the open end.   Six distinct phases
were observed, with the following characteristics:

    N   –   Yellow, birefringent and transparent; disclinati
            ons present (the original nematic phase)
    I   –   Yellow, isotropic, transparent and homogeneous
    A_1 –   Dark yellow, birefringent and turbid; large scale
            structure
    A_2 –   Dark yellow, too turbid to transmit light
    R   –   Red, too turbid to transmit light
    S   –   Colorless, isotropic, transparent and homogeneous

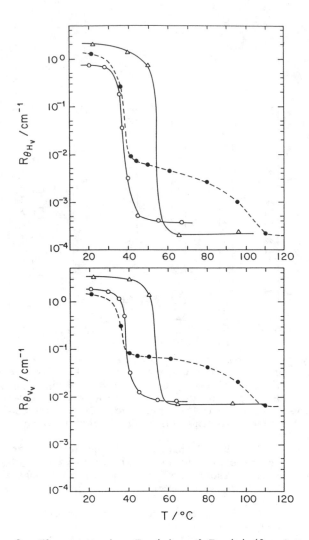

Figure 2. The scattering $R_{Hv}(q)$ and $R_{vv}(q)$ (for θ =
20 deg.) as a function of temperature T on heating samples
of phase A_1 for two compositions: weight fraction w equal
to 0.0406, 0, and 0.0459, ▵. For the dashed curve, the
sample (w = 0.046) was annealed at 40°C for 10 hr prior
to the scattering experiment.

with increasing temperature. In each case, the value of $R_{Hv}(q)$ levels off at the higher temperatures, at a level in excess of $R_{Hv}(0)$ expected for a true solution, but smaller than that reported above from phase I (see below). The light scattering data were reproducible on repeated thermal cycles. The two phases coexisted at 40°C for the solution with w = 0.041. The scattering was measured on a sample annealed at 40°C, with the results shown in Figure 2. In that case, both $R_{Hv}(q)$ and $R_{Vv}(q)$ tended to reach a plateau at values similar to those reported above for phase I. With increasing temperature, both $R_{Hv}(q)$ and $R_{Vv}(q)$ decreased to the values observed with the sample prior to the thermal annealing.

The Nematic – Isotropic Phase Transition. For nematic solutions kept free from moisture, the phase transformations described in the preceding were not observed, but the nematic phase could be reversibly transformed to the isotropic phase over a temperature interval $T_I - T_N \approx 10K$. For the sample with w = 0.041, this transition occurred over the range T_N = 92°C to T_I = 101°C. For temperatures between T_N and T_I, the sample was biphasic, with the isotropic and nematic phases coexisting. This behavior is similar to that observed in previous studies, in which $T_I - T_N$ is observed to be independent of w over a range of w for which T_I increases with increasing w (3,4).

When freshly installed in a cell, the nematic phase exhibits a mottled texture, with strong scattering and very low transmittance for light between either crossed or parallel polars. After being annealed for several hours in a cell (type A, B or C) the samples developed a smooth texture except near the glass–solution interfaces, where many disclinations could be observed, see Figure 3. When viewed between crossed polars in cells of type B or C the smooth texture exhibited a blotchy pattern of extinction (excepting the disclinations). The extinction pattern varied as the sample was rotated between crossed polars, but in many areas full extinction was not obtained. On being heated (10°C/hr), the disclinations became broad and diffuse for T = 32°C. The disclinations disappeared at about 50°C and were replaced by circular features as T approached 55°C, see Figure 3. As heating continued these features became more numerous in number and overlapped. At the same time, the transmittance between either crossed or parallel polars decreased markedly, see Figure 4. As the temperature approached 65°C, the ring features overlapped extensively, the texture became mottled and the transmittance very small. The mottled appearance (and low transmittance) was maintained until the sample developed two phases for $T_I < T_N$. The transmittance increased markedly in the interval T_N to T_I, finally returning to a normal value as the sample became fully isotropic for $T > T_I$. As shown in Figure 4, on cooling (-10°C/hr), the transmittance once again decreased as the texture took on a mottled appearance. After being annealed at 20°C for 50 hr, the sample exhibited a smooth

a

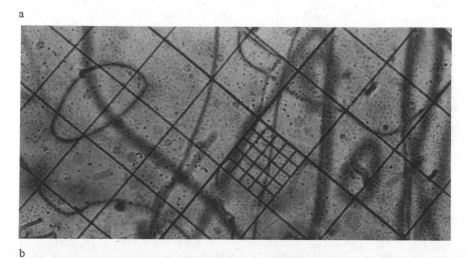

b

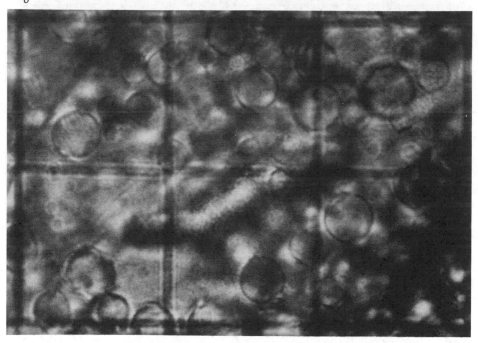

Figure 3. a) Disclinations in an otherwise smooth nematic
texture of PBT in MSA; b) Ring images observed on warming
a nematic PBT solution, see text. The large grid spacing
is 80μm.

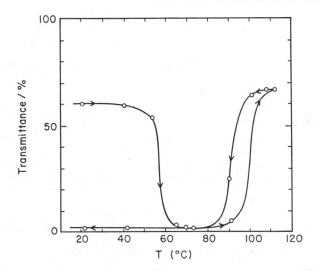

Figure 4. The transmission for light (647nm wavelength) obtained on a heating–cooling cycle of a PBT solution, initially nematic with a smooth texture (w = 0.0406). The arrows give the direction of temperature change. The sample is isotropic above 103°C.

texture, with diffuse disclinations. The latter appeared sharp after 100 hr; see below. Similar behavior was obtained with either cell B or C.

Data on $R_{Hv}(q)$ and $R_{Hv}(q)$ obtained on the same solution (θ = 20 deg) are shown in Figure 5. The sample had a smooth texture at the onset of the heating. Although these data differ markedly on heating and cooling, $R_{Hv}(q)$ and $R_{Vv}(q)$ are comparable and not too large for the scattering from the smooth texture. Both increase as the temperature nears that for which the circular images are observed by microscopy. The data shown in Figure 5 were obtained with a type B cell, but similar data were also obtained with type A or C cells.

As shown in Figure 5, after cooling to 20°C, both $R_{Hv}(q)$ and $R_{Vv}(q)$ were much larger than for the sample before the thermal cycle (corresponding to the decrease of the transmittance). As shown in Figure 6, both $R_{Hv}(q)$ and $R_{Vv}(q)$ decayed exponentially with time at 20°C, so that

$$[R_{xv}(q)]_t - [R_{xv}(q)]_{t=\infty} =$$

$$\{[R_{xv}(q)]_{t=0} - [R_{xv}(q)]_{t=\infty}\}\exp(-t/\tau) \qquad (6)$$

with τ = 105 hr, where x = H or V. For t $\gg$ τ, the sample recovered its smooth texture, and the scattering returned to that observed prior to the thermal cycle. The transformation from the mottled to smooth texture for a freshly filled cell followed Equation 6, with τ similar to that reported above. The scattering behavior described in the preceding was reproducible on repeated thermal cycles.

The smooth texture could be disrupted by causing flow in cells of type B by rotating a partially filled cell about its axis, with the latter in a horizontal plane. Flow resulted in the appearance of disclinations and increase in both $R_{Hv}(q)$ and $R_{Vv}(q)$ until these reached a maximum, and then decreased as the smooth texture was reestablished.

Measurements of $G_{Vv}^{(2)}(q,\tau)$ and $G_{Hv}^{(2)}(q,\tau)$ on the smooth texture nematic at 20°C and θ = 30 deg. gave about the same results. Only $G_{Vv}^{(2)}(q,\tau)$ was determined for the isotropic sample at 110°C. Results for $G_{Vv}^{(2)}(q,\tau)$ obtained for the solution at 20 and 110°C (using a type B cell) are shown in Figure 7. In Figure 7, $G^{(2)}(q,\infty)$ is taken to be $\langle n \rangle^2$. As shown in Figure 7, for the isotropic fluid at 110°C, the usual (16) exponential decay was observed, with

$$g_{Vv}^{(2)}(q,\tau) = \frac{G_{Vv}^{(2)}(q,\tau)}{G_{Vv}^{(2)}(q,\infty)} = 1 + f(A)\exp(-2\gamma\tau) \qquad (7)$$

with $\gamma^{-1} \approx 0.15$ s. The coherence factor f(A) depends on the optical arrangement (6).

For the nematic fluid, $g_{Vv}^{(2)}(q,\tau)$ is highly nonlinear, but can be represented by (e.g., see references 10 and 14)

$$g_{Vv}^{(2)}(q,\tau)-1 = f(A)[\Sigma\ r_\nu\ \exp(-\gamma_\nu\tau)]^2 \qquad (8)$$

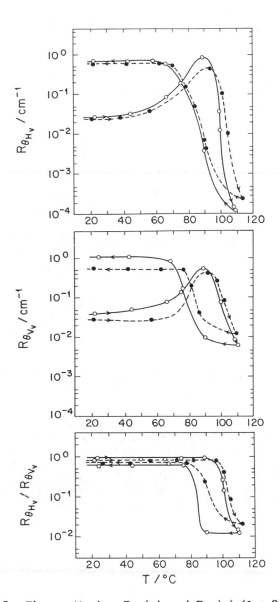

Figure 5.   The scattering $R_{Hv}(q)$ and $R_{Hv}(q)$ ($\theta = 20$ deg.) and their ratio as a function of temperature T on heating a PBT solution, initially nematic with a smooth texture (w = 0.046).   The arrows give the direction of temperature change.   The solid and dashed lines show results in cells of type B and C, respectively.

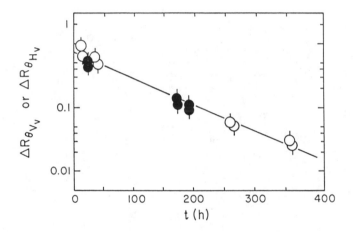

Figure 6.   The change in $R_{Vv}(q)$ (pip up) and $R_{Hv}(q)$ (pip down))θ = 20 deg.) for nematic solutions of PBT (w = 0.0406) during the transformation from the mottled to the smooth texture: open circles are a mottled state formed on cooling from 110 to 20°C and the filled circles are for a mottled state immediately after filling the cell. $\Delta R_{Vv}(q)$ is $[R_{Vv}(q)]_t - [R_{Vv}(q)]_{t=0}$, etc.

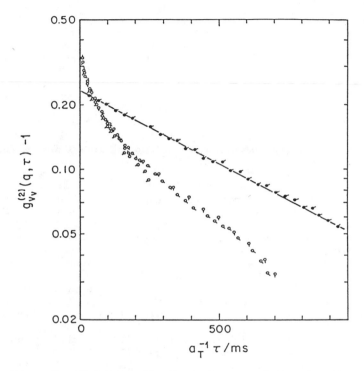

Figure 7. The (normalized) photon correlation function $g_{VV}^{(2)}(q,\tau)$ as a function of the reduced correlation time $a_T^{-1}\tau$ for a solution of PBT ($w = 0.0406$), where a_T is the ratio of the solvent viscosity at the measurement temperature to that at a reference temperature (20°C). The filled circles are for data at 110°C on an isotropic fluid ($a_T = 0.105$) and the open circles are for data at 20°C on a nematic with a smooth texture ($a_T = 1$).

where $\Sigma r_\nu = 1$. In Equation 8 the r_ν represent the fraction of the scattered light with time constant γ_ν^{-1}. The data in Figure 7 for the nematic solution at 20°C can be fitted by three terms, with γ_ν^{-1} equal to 0.13, 0.42 and 8.7 s.

DISCUSSION

Coagulation of PBT Solutions. A phase diagram calculated for a rodlike chain by Flory ([17]) is shown in Figure 8, along with a similar curve for a flexible chain according to the Flory-Huggins model ([18]) -- the chains have 100 segments in each case. In Figure 8, χ represents an excess free energy of mixing (which may depend on T), ϕ is the volume fraction of the solute and the lines represent (binodal) coexistence curves. A solution with interaction parameter χ and concentration ϕ interior to the coexistence curves is predicted to separate into two phase, with compositons ϕ_D and $\phi_C > \phi_D$ determined by the interaction of the coexistence curve with a horizontal line through the point (χ, ϕ). As is well-known, both compositions are predicted to be disordered fluids for a flexible chain, but for a rodlike chain, the phases with concentration ϕ_D and ϕ_C are predicted to be disordered and ordered fluids, respectively. For dilute solutions, the second virial coefficient A_2 is zero for $\chi = 1/2$ ([18]). As seen in Figure 8, phase separation is not expected for any ϕ with flexible chains unless $\chi > 1/2$, or equivalently, for conditions for which $A_2 < 0$ (phase separation is predicted for $\chi = 1/2$ for a particular ϕ for an infinitely long chain). By contrast, with the rodlike chain, phase separation is predicted if ϕ is large enough for any χ. For $\chi > 0.05$, a special phase separation is predicted, in which two phases coexist, with $\phi_C \gg \phi_D$ -- this behavior is predicted even though $\chi < \frac{1}{2}$. Although these phase diagrams are only qualitatively correct, the general features are in accord with experiment ([2,19,20]), and provide a convenient frame for discussing the results obtained here.

Addition of water to solutions of PBT in the strong acid solvents has the effect of increasing χ ([21]). Thus, A_2 is positive for such solutions in the absence of added water ([6]), but may be reduced to zero by the addition of salt ([10]) or water ([21]). In either case, with dilute solutions, as A_2 is reduced to zero, it is found that $R_{Hv}(q)$ increases markedly (up to one thousand-fold). Based on data on A_2, $R_{Vv}(q)$, $R_{Hv}(q)$, $G_{Vv}^{(2)}(q,\tau)$, the solution viscosity, and the electronic absorption spectra, it was concluded that ordered aggregates were produced in the dilute solution as χ was increased toward 0.5. In these metastable supramolecular structures, the rodlike chains are aggregated in arrays with their axes parallel. With the concentrated solutions studied here, the dry, ordered (nematic) solution has $\phi > \phi_C$ and, in terms of Figure 8, $\chi < 0.05$. To a first approximation, we may consider the effects added water in terms of a pseudo-binary phase diagram such as that in Figure 8, with χ a function of the water concentration. Thus, addition of water has the effect of increasing χ, and would be expected eventually to result (at equilibrium) in separation into a very concentrated, ordered, fluid phase with concentration $\phi_C \gg \phi$, and a dilute phase with concentration $\phi_D \ll \phi$. Apparently, however, a metastable state may intervene with increasing water

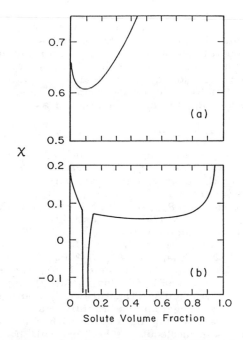

Figure 8.   The reduced excess free energy of mixing χ versus the volume fraction of solute for: a)   flexible chain polymers (18) a and b)   rodlike chains (17).   The chains have 100 segments in both cases.

uptake, producing an isotropic phase I with ordered aggregates, similar to those observed in dilute solution. Since the actual system is ternary, the phase behavior may be more complicated than that described in terms of a pseudo-binary phase diagram. Nevertheless, the appearance of an equilibrium phase with increasing water content would be unexpected, e.g., see ternary phase diagrams in reference 23.

For the solution free of aggregation, the volume fraction ϕ may be given as

$$\phi = \frac{\pi}{4} d^2 L \, \nu \qquad\qquad (9)$$

where ν is the number of chains per unit volume, d is the chain diameter and L its length (i.e., d is equal to $(4\bar{v}_2 M_L/\pi N_A)^{\frac{1}{2}}$, with M_L the mass per unit length and $\bar{v}_2$ the partial specific volume of the solute). The postulated supramolecular aggregates would act as thermodynamic components, their concentration ν_{AG} being less than ν. The value of $R_{Hv}(q)$ for phase I indicates that the supramolecular structures comprise many chains. Thus, for the aggregated solution, $R_{Hv}(0)$ can be expressed as

$$R_{Hv}(0) \approx (R_{Hv}(0)/c)^0 \; G_2 \; c \; \nu_{AG}/\nu \qquad\qquad (10)$$

where $(R_{Hv}(0)/c)^0$ is the limiting value of $R_{Hv}(0)/c$ at infinite dilution. With Equation (10), G_2 accounts for deviation from randomness among the orientations of the supramolecular structures. For dilute solutions of PBT in MSA, $\nu_{AG}/\nu = 1$ and G_2 is close to unity (6) The observed $R_{Hv}(q) = 0.0001 \text{ cm}^{-1}$ for the dry isotropic solutions (ie. $\nu_{AG}/\nu = 1$) provides the estimate $(R_{Hv}(0)/c)^0 G_2 = 0.0025 \text{ cm}^2/g$, use of the estimate for $(R_{Hv}(0)/c)^0$ of $0.0012 \text{ cm}^2/g$ based on data obtained in dilute solution for a PBT with a similar molecular weight gives $G_2 \approx 2$. Thus, with $R_{Hv}(0) \approx R_{Hv}(q) = 0.007 \text{ cm}^{-1}$, ν/ν_{AG} is calculated to be about 100 in phase I for the solution studied with w = 0.041, or c = 0.061 g/ml at 20°C. Owing to the efficient packing in the supramolecular structure, d^2L would not be expected to increase with aggregation as rapidly as ν_{AG}^{-1}. Thus, the effective volume fraction ϕ_{AG} calculated with Equation 9 using ν_{AG} and d^2L for the supramolecular structure will be smaller than ϕ. For the PBT used here, solutions with $\phi < 0.034$ are isotropic at 20°C. Owing to the steepness of the coexistence curves for small χ, the effect of this reduction in the effective ϕ can be to transform a nematic solution into an isotropic one in the initial stages of water uptake.

With further water uptake χ increases to a value large enough to cause reentry to the biphasic zone, this time in the wide gap for which ϕ_D is very small and ϕ_C is nearly unity, giving what is termed phase A_1 in the preceeding section. Although two physically separated phases were not observed, the strong scattering from phase A_1 could arise from the large fluctuations inherent in a microphase separation. The large $R_{Hv}(q)$ obtained for phase A_1 is associated with appreciable order for the microphase component with concentration ϕ_C, as expected (17). The microphase may separate spinodally, giving rise to a fibrillar-like texture for the concentrated phase, with the chain axis parallel to the fibrillar axis, giving rise to large $R_{Hv}(q)$ and $R_{Vv}(q)$. Such supramolecular sturctures have been reported for poly(γ-benzyl glutamate) (20) and a fibrillar texture has been observed in coagulated fibers of PBT (23).

As shown in Figure 2, phase A_1 may be converted to an isotropic phase with increasing T, indicating that in this system χ decreases with increasing T (the reverse behavior can obtain [12]). As seen in Figure 2, for large T, $R_{Hv}(q) \approx 0.0004$ cm^{-1}, which is smaller than $R_{Hv}(q)$ for phase I, but larger than $R_{Hv}(q)$ for the dry, isotropic fluid. With Equation (10), and $G_2 = 2$, the observed scattering gives $\nu/\nu_{AG} \approx 5.5$. Evidently, the aggregates in phase I may be partially dissociated by increased T.

As shown by the data in Figure 2, annealing the biphasic composition (i.e. phase A_1 coexisting with the isotropic fluid) at 40°C for 10 hr leads to enhanced values of $R_{Hv}(q)$ and $R_{Vv}(q)$ over the temperature range 40 to 80°C. In this range $R_{Hv}(q)$ is about equal to the value found for phase I. With increasing T above 80°C, $R_{Hv}(q)$ decreases to the value observed at high temperatures for the sample prior to annealing. The annealing apparently stabilized the supramolecular aggregates to some extent, presumably through the development of slightly enhanced packing.

Light scattering data were not obtained on either the dark yellow phase (A_2) or the red phase (R). The former appears to be similar to the yellow, birefringent phase (A_1), but more dense. The latter, representing the final stage of coagulation, is associated with deprotonation of the rodlike macroions (21), and occurs with sufficient intrusion of water with any of the acidic solutions of PBT. With solutions in PPA, this stage may be reversed by removal of water under vacuum (12). The red color results from essentially complete deprotonation of the polymer (21), leaving the polymer in an immobile state. Thus, the red phase exhibits gel-like mechanical integrity (12). Similar effects have been reported for solutions of other heterocyclic aromatic polymers in strong acids (2,15). The mechanical properties of the red phase may be expected to depend on the details of the coagulation process, e.g., the extent to which the ordered phase is allowed to perfect itself. The data obtained here do not address the question of the solvent content of the coagulated phase. Some work (23) has suggested that the phase may contain appreciable solvent.

The Nematic-Isotropic Phase Transition. As shown in Figure 5, the scattering data are not identical on heating and cooling, including over the biphasic range T_N to T_I. In the latter range, the sample is believed to be closer to equilibrium on heating, with the torpid chain diffusion leading to slow reestablishment of the ordered state on cooling. The scattered intensity is expected to increase rapidly for the isotropic fluid as T decreases toward a critical temperature T*, e.g., the scattered intensity is predicted to scale with $T(T-T*)^{-\gamma}$ with $\gamma \approx 1$ [8, 24], with the scattered intensity increasing toward infinity as T approaches T*. The intervention of the ordered phase appearing at $T_I < T*$ circumvents this unphysical behavior. Proportionality of $R_{Vv}^{-1}(q)$ and $R_{Hv}^{-1}(q)$ with T has been reported for low molecular weight nematogens (24). Insufficient data were

obtained here on the isotropic fluid to permit evaluation of the
temperature dependence of the scattering. The data do, however,
show that for the isotropic fluid, $R_{Hv}(q)/R_{Vv}(q)$ is smaller than the
limiting value 3/4 predicted for small θ from the relations ($\underline{24}$)

$$R_{Hv}(q) \propto T(T-T*)^{-1}\{1-[\xi_{\parallel}^2 + \xi_{\perp}^2(\cos^2(\theta/2))/2]q^2\} \qquad (11)$$

$$R_{Vv}(q) \propto (4/3)T(T-T*)^{-1}[1 - (\xi_{\parallel}^2 + \xi_{\perp}^2/6)q^2] \qquad (12)$$

where $\xi_{\parallel}$ and $\xi_{\perp}$ are coherence lengths for gradients in the order
parameter parallel and perpendicular to the director axis,
respectively. As mentioned above, for the isotropic fluid studied
here, at 110°C the $R_{Hv}(q)$ may be represented by Equation 10 (with
$\nu_{AG}/\nu = 1$) with the correlation function $G_2 \approx 2$, indicating that the
extent of intermolecular orientational correlation is small for the
isotropic fluid.

As shown in Figure 5, $R_{Vv}(q)/R_{Hv}(q)$ is about 4/3 for the data
on heating or cooling cycles for T < 80°C, despite substantial
differences in the individual scattered intensities on heating and
cooling. Similarly, the ratio is nearly constant during annealing at
20°C. The annealing of the mottled texture developed on cooling to
the smooth texture is apparently driven by the tendency to
suppress gradients in the director orientation in the nematic fluid
along with the effect of preferred orientations near the glass–fluid
interface. The latter may result from an adsorbed polymer layer on
the glass, in which the axes of the adsorbed chains are everywhere
parallel to the glass, but have orientation with coherence lengths $\xi_{\parallel}$
and $\xi_{\perp}$ in the plane that are small in comparison with the diameter
of the planar cell. In this situation, the equilibrium texture will
exhibit smooth variation in the director orientation throughout the
sample volume, as observed here. To a first approximation, the time
constant τ in Equation (6) for the decay of the scattered intensity
during annealing might be given by the expression $\tau = \eta\xi^2/K$, where
η and K are some orientational average of the anisotropic viscosity
coefficients and Frank elasticity constants, respectively, and ξ is an
averaged orientational coherence length. Typically ($\underline{2}$), K $\approx$ 1 pN,
and η will be of order of the shear viscosity, here about 100 Pa·s
(the order of these estimates is verified for the fluid studied here
in Part 2 of this series. Thus, with $\tau = 3.8 \times 10^3$ s, the relation
above given $\xi \approx 20$ μm, which appears resonable in view of the
strong   scattering observed for the mottled texture.

The values observed for $R_{Vv}(q)$ and $R_{Hv}(q)$ for the nematic
fluid with a mottled or smooth texture represents an average over
the director orientations present. For example, if the three Frank
elastic constants are equal, then [9]

$$R_{\underline{i},\underline{f},\underline{n}}(q) \propto (Kq^2)^{-1} \sum_{\alpha=1,2} (i_\alpha P_0 + A_0 f_\alpha)^2 \qquad (13)$$

where K is the Frank elastic constant, $\underline{i}$ and $\underline{f}$ are, respectively,
unit vectors along the polarization of the incident light and the
detected scattered light, and n is a unit vector for the director.
The coeffiecients $P_0 = \underline{n} \cdot \underline{f}$ and $A_0 = \underline{n} \cdot \underline{i}$ depend on the director
orientation, as do $i_\alpha = \underline{e}_\alpha \cdot \underline{i}$ and $f_\alpha = \underline{e}_\alpha \cdot \underline{f}$, where $\underline{e}_2 = (\underline{n} \times \underline{q})/|(\underline{n}$

x q)| and $\underset{\sim}{e}_1 = \underset{\sim}{e}_2$ x $\underset{\sim}{n}$. Consequently, even in the simple case (a single elastic constant) the orientational average is complex, and the appearance of the factor 4/3 in the averaged scattering is reasonable -- eg., the ratio $R_{Hv}(q)$ divided by the anisotropic part of $R_{Vv}(q)$ with full orientational averaging is just 3/4 for small q, suggesting that $R_{Vv}(q)$ is dominated by contributions from orientational fluctuations for the nematic fluid. For the isotropic phase, $R_{Vv}(q)/R_{Hv}(q) \approx 10$, showing that concentration fluctuations contribute significantly to $R_{Vv}(q)$ in that case.

The photon correlation scattering, represented by Equation 8 with three components, also suggests that the total scattering comprises contributions from an orientational average over the scattering volume. Thus, the dynamic scattering may be represented in terms of $\underset{\sim}{i}$, $\underset{\sim}{f}$ and $\underset{\sim}{n}$ along with the scattering angle and time constants τ_T, τ_S and τ_B for twist, splay and bend of the director field, respectively (8,9,24). As shown in part 2 (24) for the fluid studied here, $\tau_T \approx 9$ s, $\tau_S \approx 0.45$ s and $\tau_B \approx 0.15$ s, which are remarkably close to the three values of γ_ν^{-1} reported above.

The ring features that develop on heating the smooth texture nematic sample are not well-understood. The diameter of the rings is smaller than the spacing between the parallel plates. Their overlapping character indicates that they do not represent impenetrable spherical objects, but rather that they may be thin circular objects, or result from some more tenuous suprastructural effects producing refractive index gradients with radial symmetry. The rings may result as spherical nematic domains dispersed in an isotropic matrix grow and impinge on the surfaces.

CONCLUSIONS

The addition of water to solutions of PBT dissolved in a strong acid (MSA) causes phase separation in qualitative accord with that predicted by the lattice model of Flory (17). In particular, with the addition of a sufficient amount of water the phase separation produces a state that appears to be a mixture of a concentrated ordered phase and a dilute disordered phase. If the amount of water has not led to deprotonation (marked by a color change) then the birefringent ordered phase may be reversibly transformed to an isotropic disordered phase by increased temperature. This behavior is in accord with phase separation in the wide biphasic gap predicted theoretically (e.g., see Figure 8). The phase separation appears to occur spinodally, with the formation of an ordered, concentrated phase that would exist with a fibrillar morphology. This tendency may be related to the appearance of fibrillar morphology in fibers and films of such polymers prepared by solution processing.

The dry nematic solution exhibits a smooth texture after being annealed, with a field of disclinations at any glass-solution interface. A nematic phase produced by cooling the isotropic phase will exhibit a complex, mottled texture that slowly anneals to the smooth texture. The ratio $R_{Vv}(q)/R_{Hv}(q) \approx 4/3$ (for $\theta = 20$ deg.) for either morphology indicates appreciable orientational averaging of the orientation fluctuation. Photon correlation scattering on the smooth texture phase results in three contributions to the correlation function, with time constants close to those reported in Part 2 of this series for twist, splay and bend of the director field in the solution studied.

ACKNOWLEDGMENTS

This study was supported in part by a grant from the Air Force Office of Science and Technology.

LITERATURE CITED

1. Chu, S.-G.; Venkatraman, S.; Berry, G. C.; Einaga, Y. Macromolecules 1981, 14, 939.
2. Venkatraman, S.; Berry, G. C.; Einaga, Y. J. Polym. Sci., Polym. Phys. Eds., 1985, 23, 1275-1295.
3. Einaga, Y.; Berry, G. C.; Chu, S.-G., Polymer J. 1985, 17, 239.
4. Tsai, H.-H. Phase Equilibrium and Rheological Studies of Solutions of Rodlike, Articulated Polymers and Their Mixtures, Ph.D. Thesis, Carnegie-Mellon University, Pennsylvania, 1983
5. Wong, C.-P.; Ohuma, H.; Berry, G. C. J. Polymer Sci., Symp. 1978, 65, 173-92.
6. Lee, C.-C.; Chu, S.-G.; Berry, G. C. J. Polym. Sci., Polym. Phys. Eds., 1983, 21, 1573.
7. Cotts, D.; Metzger, P.; Berry, G. C. J. Polym. Sci., Ploym. Phys. Eds., 1983, 21, 1255.
8. de Gennes, P. G. The Physics of Liquid Crystals; Clarendon Press, Oxford, 1974.
9. Chandrasekhar, S. Liquid Crystals; Cambridge University Press, Cambridge, 1980.
10. Furukawa, R.; Berry, G. C. Pure and Appl. Chem. 1985, 57, 913-920.
11. Allen, S. R.; Filippov, A. G.; Farris, R. J.; Thomas, E. L.; Wong, C.-P.; Berry, G. C.; Chenevy, E. C. Macromolecules 1981, 14, 1135.
12. Charlet, A., Solution Processing of Rodlike Polymers into Ribbons, M.S. Thesis, Carnegie-Mellon University, Pennsylvania, 1981.
13. Goebel, K. D.; Berry, G. C. J. Polymer Sci., Phys. Eds., 1977, 15, 555.
14. Einaga, Y.; Berry, G. C. In Microdomains in Polymer Solutions; P. Dubin, Ed.; Plenum Publishing Co.; New York, 1985; Chapt. 11.
15. Wong, C.-P.; Berry, G. C. Polymer, 1979, 20, 229.
16. Berne, B. J.; Pecora, P. Dynamic Light Scattering; Wiley-Interscience, New York, 1976.
17. Flory, P. J. Proc. R. Soc., London Ser., A. 1956, 234, 73.
18. Flory, P. J. Principles of Polymer Chemistry; Cornell University Press, New York, 1953.
19. Flory, P. J. Adv. Polym. Sci. 1984, 59, 1.
20. Tohyama, K.; Miller, W.G. Nature (London) 1981, 289, 813.

21. Berry, G. C.; Wei, C. C.; Furukawa, R.   Polym. Preprints, Am.
     Chem. Soc. 1986, 27, (1), 228.
22. Russo, P. S.; Miller, W. G.   Macromolecules, 1984, 17, 1324.
23. Thomas, E. L.; Cohen, Y.; Frost, H. H.   Polym. Preprints, Am.
     Chem. Soc. 1986, 27, (1) 231.
24. March, N.; Tosi, M.   In Polymers, Liquid Crystals, and Low-
     Dimensional Solids, Chapter 8, Chandrasekhar, S., Ed.; Plenum
     Press, New York, 1984.

RECEIVED January 24, 1987

Chapter 11

Gelation of Poly(γ-benzyl-α,L-glutamate)

Paul S. Russo[1,3], Paul Magestro[1], and Wilmer G. Miller[2]

[1]Macromolecular Studies Group, Department of Chemistry, Louisiana State University, Baton Rouge, LA 70803-1804
[2]Department of Chemistry, University of Minnesota, Minneapolis, MN 55455

The reversible gelation of poly-γ-benzyl-α, L-glutamate in toluene and N,N-dimethylformamide is studied by light scattering and optical microscopy. The gels contain inhomogeneities with a characteristic size of about 1 μm. Under favorable circumstances, this structure can be visualized in the wet gel by epi-illumination microscopy. When it can be visualized, the structure has a "spongy" appearance, consistent with what one might expect of a system that has undergone spinodal decomposition. So far, however, there is no concrete evidence to support this mechanism of phase separation. The complex diffusion of the rodlike polymers during phase separation is also discussed.

Rodlike polymers are an increasingly important class of macromolecules prized for their utility in making high-strength fibers.(1,2) In general, rodlike polymers are not thermoplastic; hence, manipulation must occur in solution, and the solution behavior of this class of polymer is increasingly studied. Attention has been lavished on the lyotropic liquid crystal forming abilities of rodlike polymers, and isotropic-liquid crystalline phase boundaries have been determined for several rodlike polymers dissolved in good solvents.(3) In agreement with the Flory lattice theory(4), it has been found that the single phase isotropic region is separated by a narrow biphasic zone from the single phase liquid crystalline regime.

The behavior of rodlike polymers in poor solvents has received comparatively little attention. However, the phase boundaries of the rodlike polypeptide poly-γ-benzyl-α, L-glutamate in dimethylformamide (PBLG/DMF) have been determined over a temperature range spanning both poor and good solvent limits.(5,6) As expected from the Flory

[3]Correspondence should be addressed to this author.

0097–6156/87/0350–0152$08.25/0

theory, the biphasic region in the poor solvent limit was found to be very broad. However, the polymer enriched phase was not readily discernible from the fluid isotropic phase, as in the narrow biphasic regime in the good solvent limit where coexisting phases may often be seen either by the naked eye or by an optical microscope. Instead, the system became a gel. The nature of these thermoreversible gels depended on sample treatment. In the first place, a gel was not formed by simple addition of a poor solvent to the polymer in either powdered or fibrous form. The gel occurred only when the solvation power of the solvent in a ready-made polymer solution was suddenly reduced — for example, on lowering temperature. Freeze fracture electron microscopic visualization of the gel in the poor solvent, toluene, revealed a bicontinuous, phase separated "beam and girder" structure in which the polymer was located in thick (≈1000Å) interconnected fibrils.(7) By X-ray analysis, the actual alignment of the rodlike polymers within the fibrils was judged to be rather poor.(8) Together, these observations prompted the suggestion(7,9) that a dynamic mechanism of phase separation — namely, spinodal decomposition(10,11) — might dictate morphology in these systems.

In this paper, we present further studies of the gel structure and gelation process in PBLG/DMF and PBLG/toluene, using light scattering and optical microscopic techniques. Gelation of another rodlike polymer, poly-p-phenylene benzobisthiazole, in 97% H_2SO_4, was also discussed at the symposium. However, this work has been published elsewhere(12).

Theoretical

A short review of light scattering from biphasic systems will be helpful. We shall consider the scattering to arise from a two-phase medium with average polarizability α and local inhomogeneities $\eta(r) = \alpha(r) - \alpha$.

Random Systems. The scattering from random two-phase systems was considered by Debye(13,14) and other accounts are available.(15,16) These formulations have been applied to gels of a fairly stiff polymer by Goebel, Berry and Tanner.(17,18) If the system is spatially isotropic then:

$$I(q) \propto 4\pi \langle \eta^2 \rangle \int_0^\infty \gamma(r) \; \frac{\sin(qr)}{qr} \, r^2 dr \qquad (1)$$

$$\gamma(r) = \langle \eta(r')\eta(r'+r) \rangle / \langle \eta^2 \rangle \qquad (2)$$

$$q = \frac{4\pi n}{\lambda_0} \sin \frac{\Theta}{2} \qquad (3)$$

Here λ_0 is the in vacuo laser wavelength, n the refractive index in the scattering medium and Θ the scattering angle measured within the sample. The brackets indicate the average over all r in the scattering volume. Thus, the zero angle scattered intensity is

$$I(0) \propto \langle \eta^2 \rangle w_0 \qquad (4a)$$

where the "correlation volume", w_0, is given by

$$w_o = 4\pi \int \gamma(r)r^2 dr \tag{4b}$$

It is convenient to expand the sin (qr) term in eq. 1 which, when compared to the usual expressions for isolated particles, allows us to define a scattering radius of gyration:

$$\langle R_G^2 \rangle = \frac{1}{2}\int r^2 \gamma(r)r^2 dr / \int \gamma(r)r^2 dr \tag{5}$$

As for independent particles $\langle R_G^2 \rangle$ can be obtained from the slope of a Guinier plot: ln I vs. q^2. However, $\langle R_G^2 \rangle$ is emphatically not to be considered as a particle radius in the systems under consideration. Rather, it is a more generally defined parameter which characterizes the size of the optical inhomogeneities.

For a random two-phase system,

$$\gamma(r) = e^{-r/a} \tag{6}$$

The parameter a is another measure of the extent of inhomogeneities, and is simply related to $\langle R_G^2 \rangle$ (cf. eq. 5 and 6).

$$\langle R_G^2 \rangle = 6a^2 \tag{7}$$

Debye plots, $I^{-1/2}$ vs. q^2, also provide a convenient measurement of a = (slope/intercept)$^{1/2}$ Thus, the correlation volume for random two-phase systems is given by

$$w_o = 2a^3 \equiv \langle R_G^2 \rangle^{3/2}/(2\sqrt{6}) \qquad (\gamma(r)=e^{-r/a}) \tag{8}$$

Non-Random Systems. As pointed out by Cahn and Hilliard(10,11), phase separation in the thermodynamically unstable region may lead to a non-random morphology via spinodal decomposition. This model is especially convenient for discussing the development of phase separating systems. In the linearized Cahn-Hilliard approach, the free energy of an inhomogeneous binary mixture is taken as:

$$F = \int_V dv[f(c)+\kappa(\nabla c)^2] \tag{9}$$

Here f(c) is the free energy density of a hypothetical completely homogeneous system with volume fraction c. It is understood that c=c(r). For small fluctuations, one can expand f(c) about c_o, the bulk composition of the mixture. Keeping only terms to second order and invoking conservation of mass, one may obtain an expression for ΔF, the difference between the free energy of homogeneous and inhomogeneous mixtures:

$$\Delta F = \int [\ 1/2 \ (\partial^2 f/\partial_c^2)(c-c_o)^2 + \kappa(\nabla c)^2]dv \tag{10}$$

κ is positive, representing the "surface" free energy at the boundary between emergent phases. Thus, if $(\partial^2 f/\partial c^2) > 0$ the solution is stable to the small fluctuations applicable to eqn. 9 and phase separation by a random nucleation and growth mechanism can only be initiated by a finite, thermally driven fluctuation. The limit of this metastability (i.e., the spinodal) occurs at $(\partial^2 f/\partial c^2) = 0$ and the solution becomes unstable whenever $(\partial^2 f/\partial c^2)$ is negative. The dynamics of phase separation is developed by computing the relative flux of volume elements associated with the two components, $J=M\nabla(\mu_1-\mu_2)$, where M represents the relative mobility of the molecules in the presence of a chemical gradient in a binary system, and applying continuity to get the diffusion equation:

$$\partial c/\partial t = M(\partial^2 f/\partial c^2)_{c_o} \nabla^2 c - 2M\kappa\nabla^4 c \qquad (11)$$

Appropriate units for J and M are $(\frac{volume}{area - sec})$ and $(\frac{length - J\ units}{energy})$

respectively. Since the system is assumed to be at rest overall, $J_1=-J_2$. The coefficient of the $\nabla^2 c$ term is associated with the interdiffusion coefficient for the 2 components in the nonequilibrium system:

$$D = M(\partial^2 f/\partial c^2)_{c_o} \qquad (12)$$

Thus, this diffusion coefficient changes sign at the spinodal. The general solution to eq. 11 is given by:

$$c-c_o = \sum_q \{exp\ (R(q)t)\}\{A(\underline{q})cos(\underline{q}r)+B(\underline{q})sin(\underline{q}r)\} \qquad (13)$$

$$R(q) = -M\ (\partial^2 f/\partial c^2)_{c_o} q^2 -2M\kappa q^4 \qquad (14)$$

where $q = 2\pi/\Lambda$ is the wavenumber of the concentration fluctuation with wavelength Λ.

The growth rate R(q), not to be confused with the Rayleigh factor $\mathcal{R}(q)$, is always negative for metastable mixtures, as expected. For unstable mixtures, R(q) becomes positive for fluctuations of a sufficiently long wavelength that $q < q_c$, and exhibits a maximum at

$$q_m = \frac{1}{2}\ (-(\partial^2 f/\partial c^2)_{c_o}\kappa)^{1/2} = \frac{q_c}{2} \qquad (15)$$

where the growth rate is

$$R_m = M\ (\partial^2 f/\partial c^2)_{c_o}^2/8\kappa \qquad (16)$$

R(q) can be measured from light scattering. Using the first-order Bragg relation, $2\pi/\Lambda = 4\pi n(sin\ (\theta/2))/\lambda_o$ the light scattered from fluctuation $\underline{q}$ in the sample is detected at the scattering angle given by eq. 3. Since $n^2 \propto (c-c_o)^2$, the intensity growth rate is twice that of the concentration fluctuations:

$$I(q,t) = I(q,0)e^{2R(q)t} \qquad (17)$$

A system in the early stages of spinodal decomposition should pass three tests. 1) An intensity maximum should be observed at some scattering angle q_m. 2) The scattered intensity should vary exponentially with time with a rate constant 2R(q) where R(q) > 0 for $q < 2^{1/2}\ q_m$ and 3) $R(q)/q^2$ vs q^2 should be a linear plot with intercept equal to the negative of the effective diffusion

coefficient $D = +(\partial^2 f/\partial c^2)$ M. All of the above development assumes
isotropic diffusion.

Experimental

PBLG samples of various molecular weights were purchased from Miles
Yeda or Sigma. A sample with viscosity-average molecular weight([19])
138,000 was prepared by the method of Blout and Karlson([20]) from
benzyl-L-glutamate-N-carboxyanhydride in dioxane using triethylamine
as initiator. Samples will be referred to by their molecular weights
– e.g. PBLG-138000. DMF was dried over molecular sieves and
distilled prior to use. ACS reagent grade toluene was used without
further purification.

     For measurements at scattering angle $\Theta \geqslant 20°$, a FICA model 42000
light scattering goniometer was equipped with solid state
electronics, a 2 mW HeNe laser and cell holders to accept flame-
sealable 13 mm diameter cylindrical cells or 1-2 mm pathlength
rectangular spectroscopy cells. The gaussian incident beam could
optionally be parallel with $1/e^2$ diameter ≈ 1.5mm or focused at the
sample to ≈ 0.2 mm. With toluene or silicone oil as the isorefractive
vat material, reliable background subtraction was possible down to
$\Theta \approx 20°$ (cylindrical cells) or $\Theta \approx 5°$ (spectroscopy cells).

     Scattering measurements at low angles $0.5° < \Theta < 5°$ were made on a
photometer designed and built for these studies. This device is
optically similar to the commercially available Milton Roy
(Chromatix) KMX-6, and accepts the forward cone of scattering from
samples held in 1- or 2-mm spectroscopy cells through annular
rings. The rings are mounted on a rotating wheel affixed to the
shaft of a stepping motor, which is electronically driven by a
dedicated programmer. Scattering angle is determined by the distance
from sample to annulus, the radius of the annulus, and the refractive
index of the sample. Scattering envelopes are obtained by moving the
wheel sequentially from one annulus to the next, stopping for a short
period (typically 1-2 sec) to measure the intensity.

     In both light scattering devices, rapid quenching to induce
gelation is possible. The low angle device is equipped with a copper
cell connected by means of a single-throw switch either to a hot or
cold bath. Ninety percent of a temperature jump can be accomplished
within 1 minute in the range $-15°C$ to $100°C$. In the FICA photometer,
gelation was initiated by placing the melted sample into the
isorefractive vat preset to the desired temperature. For either
photometer, the signal was saved on a strip chart recorder for later
analysis. Neutral density filters and the range switch on the nano-
ammeter (Pacific Precision Instruments Model 126) were used to keep
the signal on scale.

     Samples were either prepared by direct addition of polymer to
solvent (Method I) or by a careful method to reduce dust (Method
II). In Method II, PBLG was added from a stock solution in distilled
DMF via a 0.2µm filter (Millipore type FG) into preweighed cells that
had been exhaustively rinsed with nearly dust-free water from a
Millipore 4 stage purifier and dried. Under vacuum, the samples were
either concentrated or evaporated to dryness, depending respectively
on whether a PBLG/DMF or PBLG/toluene sample was desired. For

PBLG/toluene samples, toluene was added by weight via a 0.05 μm filter (Millipore type VM). The samples were then flame-sealed and homogenized by slow tumbling at room temperature (DMF) or ~100°C (toluene).

The measured intensity is the sum of polymer and solvent scattering, stray light and scattering by dust. Experience with early samples prepared by Method I showed that dust was almost never detected (i.e., as a short burst of scattered intensity) in either device when spectroscopic cells and focussed beams were used because of the small scattered volume detected and partly because of the substantial signal from the gel itself. Nevertheless, Method II was usually employed and we believe all our results to be free of artifact from dust. In the FICA photometer, stray light and solvent corrections could be made by measuring a blank inserted into the isorefractive vat. In the small angle device, this was not possible because of cell-to-cell variations and the problems associated with stray light at very low angles. The background was thus taken as the scattering from the sample prior to gelation. Frequently, there was a delay time observed after the quench prior to gelation (See Figure 4). If this exceeded about 2 minutes, the background was taken as the sample scattering during the delay time. For more rapidly gelling systems, the measurement of the melt prior to quench was used. For strong scatterers, the background uncertainty was unimportant. Only in the case of rapidly formed, weak scatterers was background uncertainty problematic, since the stray light contribution sometimes drifted during the quench (even for an empty cell) due to refractive index inhomogomeities in the cell wall or slight mechanical misalignment due to thermal contraction. In a few cases, we could not analyze the results due to background uncertainty. Also, some gelation processes occurred so rapidly that we could only monitor one angle. Some even faster gelation processes could only be observed qualitatively because thermal equilibrium was not achieved prior to gelation. Unfortunately, these are in some ways the most interesting gels.

Photographic light scattering at low angles was performed by replacing the detector optics with a Polaroid camera. The scattering pattern was cast onto a white observation screen during gelation, and the photos represent the final state.

Optical microscopy measurements were made on three microscopes: a Leitz Ortholux polarizing microscope, a Leitz Ortholux II epi-fluorescence microscope (excitation band: 340–380 nm; observation band >400 nm) or an Olympus BH-2 epi-fluorescence microscope (excitation band: 380–490 nm; observation band: >510 nm). For fluorescence observation PBLG was end-labelled with fluorescein isothiocyanate (FITC) in tetrahydrofuran. Unreacted FITC was removed by repeatedly: dissolving the labelled PBLG in DMF; precipitating it into filtered, deionized water; recovery by ultracentrifuge; washing with copious amounts of acetone; and vacuum drying at less than 60°C. A control on unlabelled PBLG was performed. Dynamic light scattering confirmed identical solution properties for labelled and unlabelled PBLG in DMF.

Results

High Angle Light Scattering Photometry. A typical set of high angle
scattering envelopes collected during gelation (kinetic envelopes) is
shown in Figure 1. No scattering maximum is observed. The
intensification at various angles is shown in Figure 2, and
scattering does seem to increase approximately exponentially over a
limited time range. We estimated $R(q)$ from the "linear" region of
the semi-log plots and $R(q)/q^2$ vs. q^2 is plotted in Figure 3.
Figures 1–3 do not resemble classical spinodal decomposition.

   Various times after quench are defined according to the
precentange of total intensification achieved: at t_{90} the
intensification is 90% complete. Figure 4 shows that the delay time
prior to gelation, as well as the time required after the process
begins, depends strongly on quench temperature. Experience shows
that, at a given temperature, the rate of gelation increases with
concentration, but this observation awaits quantitation.

Low Angle Light Scattering Photometry: Static Envelopes. We shall
first consider the final scattering envelopes obtained after gelation
is complete. The next subsection will be devoted to the kinetic
evolution of the scattering envelopes.

PBLG/toluene: Typical Guinier (ln I vs. q^2) and Debye ($I^{-1/2}$ vs q^2)
plots are shown in Figure 5 for 0.91 wt % PBLG–138,000/toluene gels
made by quenching from 70°C to different temperatures. Although
intensities are in arbitrary units, variation in experimental
parameters has been taken into account so the plots may be compared
directly. The plots were frequently linear (Figure 5a) but sometimes
displayed nonlinear behavior (Figure 5b) or a maximum (Figure 5c).
Between runs, the sample was "renewed" by heating at 100°C (well
above the melting transition) with slow tumbling for at least 15
minutes. Samples that were not renewed but merely heated at 70°C and
re-gelled generally gave reduced scattering intensity, as may be seen
by comparing 5-a and 5-d. The adherence to linear Debye or Guinier
plots was capricious, to say the least. Nevertheless, in order to
examine the general trends, we performed least squares analysis on
the linear regions of the plots. The results are listed in Table I.

   We see that the inhomogeneities in the system have a size of a
few microns and that the extrapolated forward scattered intensity can
vary by a factor of $\sim$ 1000. It should be remarked that in 1-mm
pathlength cells none of these gels was visually opaque. The more
weakly scattering gels had a visual clarity indistinguishable from
pure toluene and the most strongly scattering samples were very
slightly turbid in appearance. The Guinier intercept is plotted
against temperature in Figure 6. The relationship $\langle R^2 \rangle/a^2 = 6$ (eq. 7)
is not well obeyed although this is probably due to experimental
uncertainty in estimating the intercept of the Debye plots. Studies
at other concentrations and temperatures have not yet indicated a
clear trend. Qualitatively, the results are similar: linear and
nonlinear plots are found; ill-defined peaks are occasionally seen;
and the characteristic size of the inhomogeneities is generally a few
microns. Some of these results are listed at the bottom of Table I.

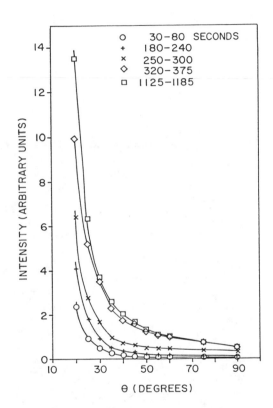

Fig. 1

Scattering at $\Theta \geqslant 20°$ for gelation of PBLG–138,000/toluene (c = 7.3×10^{-4} gm/ml). Initial temperature: 115°C; final temp: 10°C. Times after quench are indicated by symbol. Note the absence of a maximum. (115°C obtainable because sample is sealed).

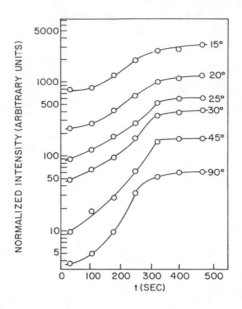

Fig. 2

    Semilogarithmic plot of intensification at various
angles. Same run as Fig. 1. Though not strictly exponential,
it is possible to estimate R(q) at each angle.

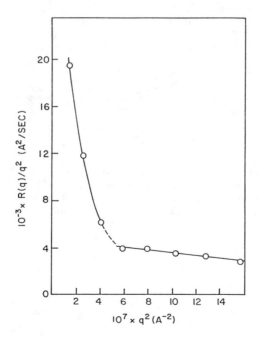

Fig. 3

Plot suggested by eq. 13 for same run as Figs. 1 and 2.

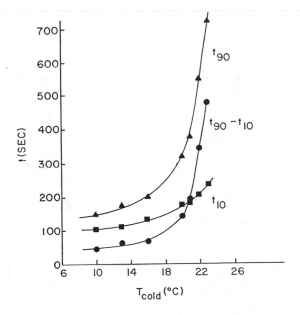

Fig. 4

Delay, completion and duration times for PBLG/toluene (c = 7.3 x 10^{-4} gm/ml) are strongly dependent on final quench temperature.

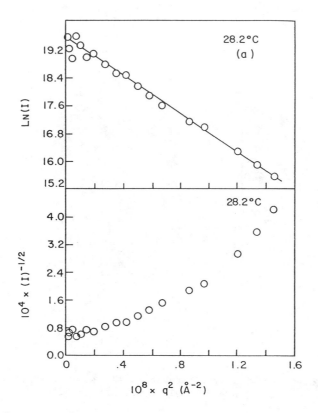

Figure 5. Typical Guinier and Debye plots observed for PBLG-
138,000/toluene prepared by quenching to various temperatures:
a) T = 28.2. Continued on next page.

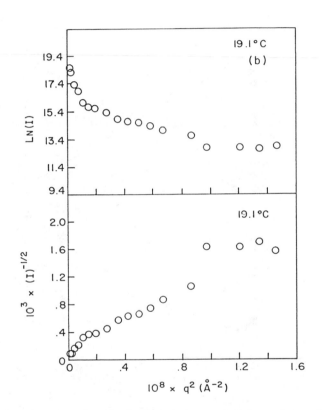

Figure 5.--<u>Continued</u>. Typical Guinier and Debye plots observed for PBLG-138,000/toulene prepared by quenching to various temperatures: b) T = 19.1. <u>Continued on next page</u>.

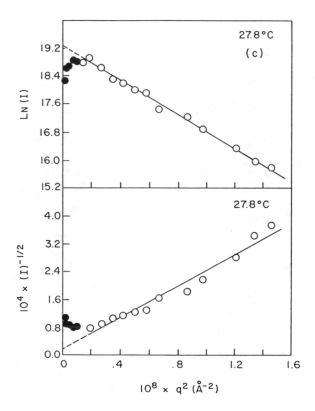

Figure 5.--Continued. Typical Guinier and Debye plots observed for PBLG-138,000/toulene prepared by quenching to various temperatures: c) T = 27.8. Continued on next page.

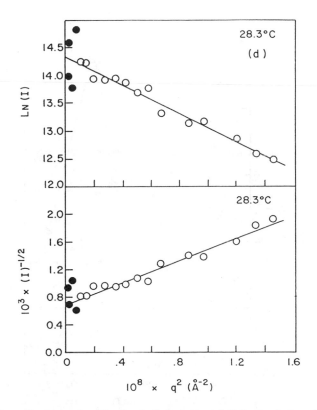

Figure 5.--<u>Continued</u>. Typical Guinier and Debye plots observed for PBLG-138,000/toulene prepared by quenching to various temperatures: d) T = 28.3, NOT RENEWED. Comparing a) and d) shows the effect of not renewing the sample by a long, high temperature melt between runs: the intensity of the unrenewed sample is much less, resulting in some imprecision at the lowest angles. Fully darkened points were not used in obtaining slopes.

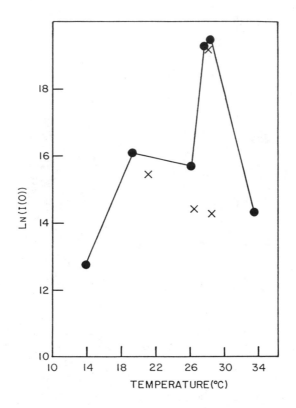

Fig. 6

    Extrapolated forward scattered intensity for PBLG-
138,000/toluene (0.91 wt %) depends on temperature of quench.
Temperature prior to quench: 70°C. ●: Sample first "renewed"
as described in text; X: Sample not "renewed". A similar trend
was observed for PBLG/DMF.

Table I.   Summary of PBLG-138,000/Toluene

Concentration	Figure	T(°C)	$\langle R_G^2 \rangle^{1/2}$ (μm)	a(μm)	Ln I(0)	Comment
0.91 wt %	–	13.7	3.2	2.2	12.8	
	5b	19.1	8.9 or 3.0*	2.7	16.1*	
	–	21	3.7	1.2	15.5	Not Renewed
	–	26.0	1.7	0.75	15.8	
	–	26.2	1.8	1.0	14.5	Not Renewed
	–	27.4	2.7	1.4	19.3	
	5c	27.8	2.7	1.7	19.2	Not Renewed
	5a	28.2	2.8	2.7	19.5	
	5d	28.3	1.9	1.0	14.3	Not Renewed
	–	33.3	–	–	12.6	
0.49 wt %	–	29.2	8.9	5.7	21.6	
2.9 wt %		40.0	–	2.1	~17	
		40.0	–	1.95	~15	Not Renewed

*taken from high angle region

PBLG/DMF: Gels prepared in PBLG/DMF displayed the same range of scattering envelopes seen in the PBLG/toluene samples. If the samples were renewed at 50°C for at least 15 minutes between runs the scattering power increased with temperature. Because DMF is a much better solvent than toluene, more concentrated samples could be studied. Unlike PBLG/toluene, concentrated PBLG/DMF gels can be extremely turbid — an optical density of ~5 was recorded for a 1mm sample of 10% polymer composition quenched to 1°C. While observing the melting of this gel between crossed polars in an optical microscope, birefringent regions appeared, only to disappear later. This is consistent with temporary conversion of the polymer rich phase into a liquid crystal followed by homogenization into the original liquid isotropic state. Some results for various compositions and temperatures are given in Table II.

Optical Microscopy and Low Angle Light Scattering Photography. Since light scattering suggests a size of 1-10 microns for the inhomogeneities, it should be possible to visualize the gels in an optical microscope, provided that sufficient contrast exists. At the same time, the scattering patterns are sometimes intense enough to enable low angle visual observation. In this section, we explore what may be learned merely by looking at the samples or their scattering patterns.

Table II. Summary of PBLG–138000/DMF

Concentration	Figure #	Temp. (°C)	R_G (µm)	a (µm)	Ln (I(0)) from Guinier plot
2.2 wt %	–	-7.5	1.8	0.9	18.4
	–	-6.7	1.3	0.6	16.9
	–	-6.4	1.2	0.5	16.0
	–	-2.8	1.9	1.0	19.6
	–	+1.0	5.6	3.3	21.5
4.7 wt %	–	-7.5	1.0	0.5	15.2
10.0 wt %	–	-8.0	1.1	0.5	16.0
	8a,b	+1.0	1.1	0.5	*

*Turbidity correction cannot be made accurately. No intensity can be computed; however, this sample was an extremely strong scatterer, nearly opaque.

PBLG/toluene: Figure 7a shows a spongy gel structure observed by epi–illumination fluorescence microscopy. Most PBLG/toluene structures seen by this method would <u>not</u> have such good contrast. Existence of high contrast structures in PBLG/toluene seems to rest upon a number of factors, including depth and rate of quench and concentration. A detailed study has not yet been made. However, two observations suggest that the structures are not artifact. First, structures with varying degrees of contrast have been observed under a number of conditions, in labelled samples having different molecular weights and concentrations. Secondly, the structures disappear upon melting, as shown by video tape during the symposium. (See also Figure 5 of ref. 21).
  Figure 7b shows a region of a very well–aged PBLG/toluene gel with a banded appearance similar to cholesteric liquid crystalline structure, as viewed through crossed polars. This region was highly colorful when viewed between crossed polars. It must be emphasized that structures such as this are rare and are found only in aged gels, and then only in some regions of the gel. Viewed between crossed polars, PBLG/toluene gels are almost always totally featureless and very dark. Occasionally, small spherulites were seen, more commonly in aged gels.
  The low angle scattering was generally featureless. However, on some occasions — more commonly at high concentrations — a very diffuse halo which intensified with time could be seen forming on the white observation surface.

PBLG/DMF: Isotropic solutions of PBLG in DMF resulted in gels qualitatively similar to the PBLG/toluene gels with scattering peaks only rarely visible. Since DMF is a good solvent for PBLG it becomes possible to prepare liquid crystalline solutions. Figure 8a shows the scattering pattern from a gel made by cooling a liquid crystalline solution of PBLG/DMF to which a small amount of nonsolvent (water) had been added. This whitish gel lies in the so-called "complex phase" and the water has the effect of enhancing the

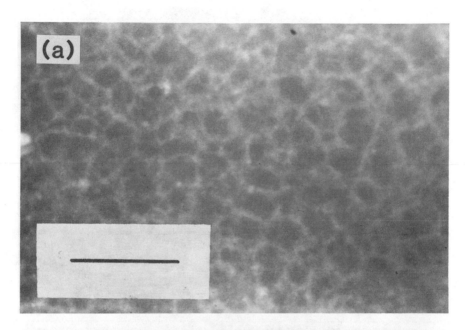

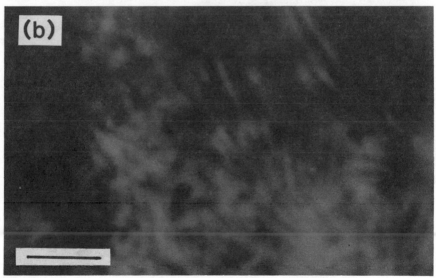

Fig. 7 a) Spongy structure seen in labelled PBLG-
50,000/toluene gel by epifluorescence. Bar marker = 50μm.
b) Well-aged PBLG/toluene gel, showing banded structure. Bar
marker = 20μm.; between crossed polars.

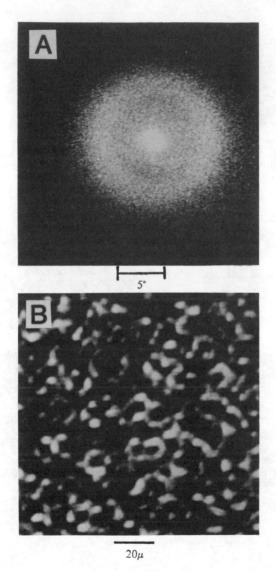

Fig. 8 20μ

A) A clear scattering maximum in 24% PBLG/DMF/H_2O (trace). The Bragg spacing is ~ 6µm. B). Photomicrograph of same sample as A between crossed polars. The correlation distance appears to be about 9µm.

scattering power.(22) The Bragg spacing in this figure is about
6μm. Figure 8b is a micrograph taken between crossed polars of the
same region illuminated by the laser to create the scattering pattern
8a. The structure appears to be bicontinuous and the correlation
distance (between bright regions, say) is about 9μm in reasonable
agreement with the diffraction peak. Qualitatively, this system
shows the greatest promise for observing classical spinodal
behavior. Unfortunately, our low angle spectrometer is not fast
enough to follow these processes at more than one angle, and indeed
it is hard to reach thermal equilibrium prior to gelation.

Kinetic Low Angle Scattering Envelopes. For gelation processes slow
compared to the 70-second acquisition time of the low angle
photometer, the kinetics may be followed. In Figure 9 an
intensification at six of the 18 angles is shown. These data are
from the run that ultimately produced the envelope shown in 5c. As
was the case at high angles, the intensification appears to be
approximately exponential at early times. We have estimated $R(q)$ in
this region and Figure 10 shows that $R(q)$ vs. q^2 is nonlinear, even
in this sample where there was an intensity maximum.

In those cases where there is an extended linear Guinier or
Debye region, one can plot the appropriate parameters against time,
as shown in Figures 11 and 12. In each case, the zero angle
intensity is seen to increase much more rapidly than the parameter
characterizing the size of the inhomogeneities.

Discussion

It is necessary to preface the discussion with some remarks about the
nature of the PBLG gels. The term gel is often used without a clear
definition. For example, it is now of great interest to study
transient network "gels" which may be regarded as entangled polymer
solutions having an elastic response to stimuli with characteristic
times less than T_{rep}, the reptation time of the chain. This,
however, is not what we mean by gel. In this paper, we adopt the
long standing definition of Ferry(23) that a gel is "a substantially
diluted system which exhibits no steady state flow". Thus, a gel is
to be regarded macroscopically as a weak solid. Transient network
pseudogels observed in semidilute or concentrated solution typically
do not fit this definition. The PBLG/toluene and PBLG/DMF gels do.
Samples may be inverted for many years with no detectable flow. This
does not, however, imply that entanglement is unimportant in these
phase separating systems which lie in (or above) the Doi-Edwards
semidilute range prior to gelation.(24) Indeed, we suspect that an
understanding of entanglement (perhaps enmeshment is a better word
for rodlike polymers) may be vital to an improved picture of the
phase separation/gelation process.

The most striking characteristic of these gels is the large
variation in scattering power obtainable, as measured by $I(0)$. It is
tempting to believe that the variation of contrast in optical
microscopy is related to the variations in scattering strength,
although this is not yet firmly established. Since $I(0)$ is a product
of $\langle n^2 \rangle$ and w_o one might seek to explain the variation in scattered
intensity by imagining $w_o \rightarrow \infty$ at the spinodal. In PBLG/DMF (Table II)

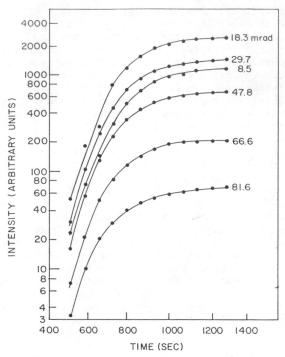

Fig. 9 Intensification during gelation of a 0.91 wt% PBLG-
138,000/toluene sample for several low scattering angles,
indicated. At early times, growth is approximately
exponential. Initial temp: 70°C; Quench Temp: 27.4°C.

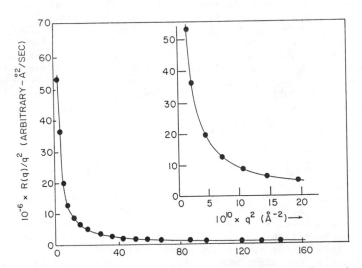

Fig. 10 Same run as fig. 9. R(q) has been estimated from the
initial slopes and plotted as suggested by equation 13. Inset
shows that no linear region exists, even at low angles.

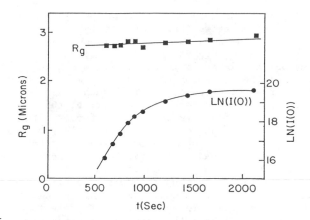

Fig. 11

Zero angle extrapolated intensities and R_G from Guinier analysis. Gelation of PBLG-138,000/toluene (0.91 wt%; initial temp: 70°C; Quench temp: 28.2°C) R_g (linear scale) is virtually unchanged during gelation, while I(0) (logarithimic scale) increases about 33 fold.

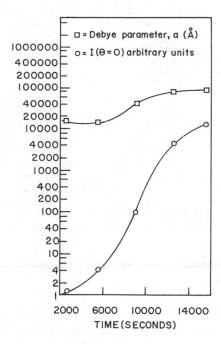

Fig. 12

Zero angle extrapolated intensities and size parameter a from Debye analysis. Gelation of PBLG-138,000/toluene (c = 0.49 wt%; Initial temp: 70°C; Quench Temp: 29.2°C) I(0) increases much more than a.

there does, in fact, seem to be a limited correlation between the
size of the inhomogeneities (related to w_o by equation 4) and $I(0)$.
On the other hand, there is no clear relationship between size and
$I(0)$ for PBLG/toluene, suggesting that variations in $\langle \eta^2 \rangle$ are
responsible for the variation in scattering strength, or turbidity.
However, this implies that for PBLG/toluene: a) the phase diagram
does not look at all like expected, with much wider separation (and
hence, higher $\langle \eta^2 \rangle$) at low temperatures; or, b) that equilibrium
phase separation is not always achieved uniformly within the
sample. X-ray measurements of PBLG/toluene gels prepared at room
temperature, aged and concentrated by ultracentrifugation suggested
that at least some portions of the samples do reach equilibrium or
pseudo-equilibrium phase separation in which the rods are poorly
organized.(8) However, the temperature-composition phase diagram in
PBLG/toluene remains undetermined. In the light scattering studies
described here, the gels were observed for no more than one day after
a given quench, so it is possible that all regions within the gels
did not reach their equilibrium composition and $\langle \eta^2 \rangle$ values.

Failure to reach equilibrium can be understood in terms of
entanglement and we begin with Figure 13. Gelation of isotropic
samples occurs along the pathway shown by the heavy line. During
phase separation the system generates regions with enhanced
concentration. The local viscosity within these regions should be as
large as that of uniphase, isotropic solutions of the same
composition. It is well established that the viscosity of such
systems increases rapidly near the concentration of the isotropic –
liquid crystalline phase transition, which implies that equilibrium
rod mobility, as, for example, expressed by the self diffusion
coefficient or rotational diffusion rate, is reduced due to
entanglements. Thus, there exists a mechanical barrier to formation
of the concentrated equilibrium phase. It is possible that polymer-
enriched regions in the system reach an intermediate concentration,
proceeding thence very slowly to the equilibrium concentration. In
connection with this hypothesis, which we emphasize is conjecture, it
is interesting to note that the most turbid gels are generally
produced at high temperatures where the driving force for phase
separation is less and both delay (t_{10}) and gelation ($t_{90}-t_{10}$) times
are long. Perhaps the creation of very tight entanglements can be
avoided under these conditions and the system can proceed to its
equilibrium concentration, and $\langle \eta^2 \rangle$, with less resistance. Likewise,
we have observed that a 10 wt % PBLG/DMF sample was much more turbid
when gelled at 1°C than at -8°C and that on melting the gel made at
1°C there was temporary birefringence, indicating that the polymer
enriched phase was sufficiently concentrated to be liquid
crystalline.

It is interesting to frame these very tentative considerations
in terms of rod diffusion, since this is the process by which the
polymer-rich phase must be formed. However, care must be taken to
isolate the effects of mutual diffusion of the collection of rods as
a (phenomenological) response to a concentration (chemical potential)
gradient and simple self diffusion of a single rod, which is the case
treated by Doi and Edwards.(24)

Let us begin by considering perfectly rigid rods. Neglecting at
first the effect of enmeshment, and using the spinodal decomposition

formalism, one sees that the diffusion associated with the phase
separation is an "inverse" mutual diffusion of the collection of rods
up a concentration gradient, with a rate proportional to the
curvature in the free energy surface (eq. 12), together with the flow
of solvent in the opposite direction. Now, the effect of the
entanglements is to constrain this type of collective diffusion;
unlike a random coil entangled network, there is no internal chain
flexibility to support collective diffusion for an enmeshed assembly
of perfectly rigid rods, even over relatively small distances. Thus,
thermodynamically driven, nonequilibrium inverse mutual diffusion in
an assembly of perfectly rigid rods will rapidly lead to a highly
enmeshed state that can only be relaxed by translational self
diffusion — i.e., thermal motion of individual rods with respect to
their neighbors and not in response to an overall concentration
inhomogeneity. These motions are the subject of much current
study,(25) and are clearly very complicated. For example,
translation may become highly anisotropic (faster along the long
axis) and coupled to rotational motion. To reiterate, the transient
network of perfectly rigid rods in the sol state will almost
instantly require translational self diffusion in order for an
inhomogeneity to grow or decay. However, the very initial response
of this transient network to the "command" to coalesce (i.e., to
temperature quenching) will be an uphill, mutual diffusion of the
collection of rods.

    Considering now imperfectly rigid polymers, it is likely that
the initial inverse mutual diffusion response to quenching could be
maintained if the rods could "escape" the ever more constricting
entanglements, for example, by simple flexural motions. There is a
growing body of evidence (25a-c) that PBLG molecules remain
remarkably free of entanglements even at $NL^3 \gg 1$, where N is the
number density of rods of length L and diameter d. Thus, there
exists a competition between the inverse mutual diffusion, given by
eq. 12, which tends to move the collection of rods together, thereby
creating or tightening entanglements, and entanglement-relaxing
motions such as flexural escapement and translational self diffusion
(probably coupled to flexural and rotational motions), which could
ultimately lead to increased order in the polymer-rich phase. The
balance struck between these competing factors may depend on the
initial concentration (with higher concentrations conferring more
importance on the self diffusive mode) and quench temperature (with
temperatures nearer the spinodal resulting in smaller inverse mutual
diffusion; see eq. 12). Near the spinodal boundary (corresponding to
the higher temperatures in this study) the slow gelation could be
governed by self diffusion of the rods. In this scenario, the rods
are not jammed together by the initial inverse mutual diffusion, and
thus can proceed to equilibrium, or near equilibrium,
concentrations. This is consistent with the high turbidities and
transient liquid crystalline structures seen on melting in the
samples gelled at high temperatures. Far under the spinodal, phase
separation may again begin by inverse mutual diffusion and this
behavior may be permitted to continue until the emergent polymer rich
phase is so concentrated that escapement is no longer possible, at
least in some regions of the sample which then exist as particularly
tight logjams. Portions of these systems may remain at an

intermediate concentration for many years, almost permanently trapped
in a strongly enmeshed, intermediate state with low scattering
power. Over a period of weeks or months, other regions may
concentrate sufficiently to display the type of liquid crystalline
behavior shown in Figure 9b.

There is a basis for the above hypothesis. Edwards and Evans
have studied the self diffusion of entangled rods and concluded that
$D_{self} = 0.5D^o(1-g(NdL^2)^{3/2})$ where g is predicted to be of order
unity(26) and D^o is the zero-concentration diffusivity. For PBLG-
138000 this equation predicts cessation of motion — a glass
transition — at a concentration of ~ 13 mg/ml. However, in much the
same way that rotational diffusion is less hindered than
expected,(25c) it appears that g will be smaller than 1. A
preliminary value of 0.02 has been determined for PBLG of
M=300000(25c). Thus, under equilibrium conditions, it is not likely
that an isotropic glass will occur. For example, if g ≃ 0.02 for
PBLG-138000 then the glass transition occurs at ≃ 640 mg/ml, which
would be a uniphase liquid crystal in a good solvent or under the
wide biphasic regime in a poor one. However, under conditions far
from equilibrium, such as during phase separation, concentrations
beyond the glass transition may be achieved locally (e.g., within
emergent fibrils) without true long-range liquid crystal formation.
Then these regions may become "frozen", resulting in the observed
gel. (Note: The above estimates of concentration would be
substantially lowered in case of end-to-end aggregation).

Whatever the microscopic details, it is interesting to note that
no system which we could thoroughly examine passed the three tests
for classical spinodal decomposition. Under some conditions,
especially at high concentrations, scattering maxima were seen, but
gelation was, unfortunately, too fast to follow. In cases where
gelation could be followed at more than one angle, the
intensification appeared to follow approximately an exponential
path. However, R(q) vs. q^2 plots were inevitably nonlinear. Higher
order terms in the free energy expansion are required to explain this
type of behavior, and the role of enmeshment (see above) is not yet
quantitatively defined.

The distinction between nucleation and growth (NG) and spinodal
decomposition (SD) in real systems need not be very sharp, and can be
very difficult to detect experimentally(27). In addition to
competition from NG processes which may begin while crossing the
metastability gap, there are the effects of thermal motion and, for
macromolecular systems, the uncertainty in the location of the
spinodal due to polydispersity. Nevertheless, spinodal-like behavior
has been seen in several studies of polymer blends(See, for
example,28,29) and compared(30) to non-polymer systems. Feke and
Prins found that gelation of agarose obeyed the linearized Cahn-
Hilliard theory(31) and Van Aartsen and Smolders(32,33) have
considered liquid-liquid phase separation in a polymer-solvent system
to proceed by a spinodal mechanism with a characteristic spacing Λ≈1
micron. The Van Aartsen & Smolders theoretical development relies on
the Flory-Huggins expression for the free energy of a random coil
polymer solution and an estimate for the "interaction distance".
However, it is easy to demonstrate that the Flory expression for
rigid rods(4) leads to the same result for solutions in the isotropic

portion of the phase diagram. If reasonable interaction distances
are selected, we compute that the inhomogeneities should be on the
order of one micron for the concentrations and temperatures studied
here. This is in agreement with the size parameters measured; still,
the case for classical spinodal decomposition remains incomplete.
Although the spinodal decomposition model provides a convenient
framework for conjecture regarding the role of diffusion (above), so
far as our studies are concerned, and in the absence of a spinodal
decomposition theory which takes anisotropic diffusion explicitly
into account, it is perhaps more appropriate to deal with the simpler
question of whether the growth of the emergent phase
(inhomogeneities) occurs by magnitude ($\langle \eta^2 \rangle$) or extent ($\langle R_G^2 \rangle$).
Figures 13 and 14 show that the growth in zero angle intensity
greatly outstrips that in the size parameter. Considering equations
4-8 we can obtain expressions proportional to $\langle \eta^2 \rangle$.

$$\langle \eta^2 \rangle \propto \ln(I(0))/\langle R_G^2 \rangle^{3/2} \quad \text{(Guinier Plot)}$$

$$\text{or} \qquad \langle \eta^2 \rangle \propto I(0)/a^3 \qquad \text{(Debye Plot)}$$

(18)

As shown in Figure 14 the growth in $\langle \eta^2 \rangle$ is approximately
exponential. These considerations are based on an exponential
correlation function $\gamma(r)$, and should be approximately applicable
even for scattering envelopes showing moderate degrees of nonrandom
structure if the size parameters are determined on the high angle
side of the scattering peak where the inter-"particle" structure
factor approaches unity. Unfortunately, our low angle instrument
does not possess sufficient angular range to allow a kinetic
determination of $\langle \eta^2 \rangle$ by the method of invariants(34) in these
systems. Within the approximation just stated, it appears that the
emergent phase grows primarily by concentration and retains its
initial size. This behavior is spinodal-like. However, growth could
be initiated by spontaneous decomposition as in the classical
spinodal mechanism or by appearance of incompletely formed nuclei
possessing a depletion zone.

Conclusions

An enormous variation in physical appearance, scattering power, and
contrast in the optical microscope of PBLG gels has been
documented. The gels contain inhomogeneities with a characteristic
size on the order of 1 μm. The very complex diffusion which occurs
in these evolving gels was discussed, and it was proposed that a
combination of a rapid inverse mutual diffusion, made possible by
escapement of the imperfectly rigid rods from entanglements, and a
slow self diffusive mode might govern the structural evolution. This
preliminary hypothesis is consistent with the limited observations.
However, its principle value may be to suggest that more detailed
information regarding the dynamics of rodlike polymers under
entanglement constraints is required. No conclusive evidence for a
classical spinodal decomposition was found. However, it appears that
the concentration inhomogeneities grow in magnitude (that is,
concentration), rather than in size. Concentrated solutions did
sometimes show perceptible scattering maxima during rapid gelation.

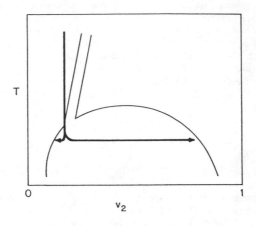

<u>Fig. 13</u>

     Schematic Flory binary rodlike phase diagram. Heavy
arrows show pathway of phase separation on cooling.

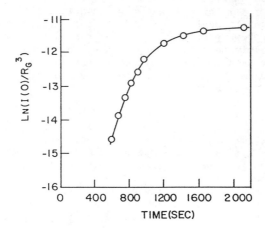

<u>Fig. 14</u>

     Initial growth in parameters proportional to $\langle \eta^2 \rangle$, (see
eq. 18) is approximately exponential.

It might be possible to study such systems in greater detail using a more rapid photometer. The large physical size of the emergent inhomogeneities suggested that, given enough contrast, direct visualization by optical microscopy might be possible, which appears to be the case when contrast is provided by fluorescent labelling, or for naturally fluorescent polymers (12).

Acknowledgments

PSR acknowledges the research support of the donors of the Petroleum Research Fund, administered by the ACS, and also the NSF (#DMR-8520027) for support during preparation of this manuscript. WGM wishes to thank the NIH.

Literature Cited

1. Allen, S. R.; Filippov, A. G.; Farris, R. J.; Thomas, E. L., in "The Strength and Stiffness of Polymers", Zachariades, A. E. and Porter, R. S., Eds.; Marcel Dekker: New York, 1983; Chapter 7.
2. Magat, E. E. Phil. Trans. Roy. Soc. Lond. 1980, A294, 463.
3. Miller, W., Ann. Rev. Phys. Chem., 29, 519 (1978).
4. Flory, P. J. Proc. Roy. Soc. Lond. 1956, A234, 73.
5. Miller, W. G.; Rai, J. H.; Wee, E. L.; in "Liquid Crystals and Ordered Fluids", Johnson, J. F. and Porter, R. S., Eds.; Plenum: New York, 1974; Vol. 2.
6. Russo, P. S.; Miller, W. G. Macromolecules, 1983, 16, 1690.
7. Tohyama, K.; Miller, W. G. Nature 1981, 289, 813.
8. Russo, P. S.; Miller, W. G. unpublished results.
9. Miller, W. G.; Kou, L.; Tohyama, K.; Voltaggio, V. J. Polym. Sci. Polym. Symp. 1978, 65, 91.
10. Cahn, J. W. J. Chem. Phys. 1965, 42, 93.
11. Cahn, J. W.; Hilliard, J. E. J. Chem. Phys. 1959, 31, 668.
12. Russo, P. S.; Siripanyo, S.; Saunders, M. J.; Karasz, F. E. Macromolecules 1986, 19, 2856.
13. Debye, P.; Bueche, A. M. J. Appl. Phys. 1949, 20, 518.
14. Debye, P.; Anderson, H. R.; Brumberger, H. J. Appl. Phys. 1957, 28, 679.
15. Alexander, L. E., "X-ray Methods in Polymer Science"; Wiley: New York, 1969.
16. Kerker, M., "The Scattering of Light and Other Electromagnetic Radiation"; Academic Press: New York, 1972.
17. Goebel, K. D.; Berry, G. C. J. Polym. Sci.-Polym. Phys. Ed. 1977, 15, 555.
18. Goebel, K. D.; Berry, G. C.; Tanner, D. W. J. Polym. Sci.-Polym. Phys. Ed. 1979, 17, 917.
19. Fujita, H.; Teramoto, A.; Yamashita, T.; Okita, K. and Ikeda, S. Biopolymers 1966, 4, 781.
20. Blout, E. R.; Karlson, R. H. J. Am. Chem. Soc. 1956, 78, 941.
21. Russo, P. S.; Magestro, P.; Mustafa, M.; Saunders, M. J. and Miller, W. G. ACS Polymer Preprints 1986, 27, 229.
22. Russo, P. S. and Miller, W. G., Macromolecules 1984, 17, 1324.
23. Ferry, J. D. "Viscoelastic Properties of Polymers", 3rd. Ed., Wiley: New York, 1980; Ch.3.

24. a. Doi, M.; Edwards, S. F. J. Chem. Soc. Faraday Trans.II 1978
    74, 560.
    b. Doi, M. and Edwards, S. F. J. Chem. Soc. Faraday Trans.II
    1978, 74, 918.
25. a. Zero, K.; Pecora, R. Macromolecules 1982, 15, 87.
    b. Kubota, K. and Chu, B. Biopolymers 1983, 22, 1461.
    c. Russo, P. S. Macromolecules 1985, 18, 2733.
    d. Odijk, T. Macromolecules 1986, 19, 2073.
    e. Keep, G. T.; Pecora, R. Macromolecules 1985, 18, 1167.
    f. Odell, J. A.; Keller, A.; Atkins, E.D.T. Macromolecules 1985,
    18, 1443.
    g. Fixman, M. Phys. Rev. Lett. 1985, 55, 2429.
26. Edwards, S. F.; Evans J. Chem. Soc. Faraday Trans. II 1982, 78,
    113.
27. Koenhen, D. M. and Smolders, C. A. J. Polym. Sci.-Polym. Phys.
    Ed. 1977, 15, 155.
28. Hashimoto, T.; Kumaki, J.; Kawai, H. Macromolecules 1983, 16, 641.
    Note that eq. II-8 of this article should read

    $$R(q_m) = D_c (\partial^2 f / \partial c^2)^2 / 8\kappa$$

29. Snyder, H. L.; Meakin, P.; Reich, S. Macromolecules 1983, 16, 757.
30. Snyder, H. L.; Meakin, P. J. Chem. Phys. 1983, 79, 5588.
31. Feke, G. T.; Prins, W. Macomolecules 1974, 7, 527.
32. Van Aartsen, J. J. Eur. Polym. J. 1970, 6, 919.
33. Van Aartsen, J. J.; Smolders, C. A. Eur. Polym. J. 1970, 6, 1105.
34. Koberstein, J.; Russell, T. P.; Stein, R. S. J. Polym. Sci.-
    Polym. Phys. Ed. 1979, 17, 1719.

RECEIVED January 24, 1987

Chapter 12

Structure Formation and Phase Transformations in Solutions of a Rigid Polymer

Yachin Cohen, Herbert H. Frost[1], and Edwin L. Thomas

Polymer Science and Engineering Department, University of Massachusetts, Amherst, MA 01003

An important stage in the processing of rigid polymers from their solutions is coagulation, in which a phase transition from a solution to a solid is affected by a nonsolvent. The microstructures obtained by coagulating solutions of poly(p-phenylene benzobisthiazole) are studied, and their formation is considered in terms of the phase equilibria in solutions of rigid polymers. Two different cases are investigated: coagulation which occurs during the spinning of fibers and films by immersion in a nonsolvent, and slow coagulation by absorption of atmospheric moisture. The morphology formed in the coagulation stage of the spinning process is an interconnected network of oriented microfibrils, with a typical diameter of about 100 Å. Slow coagulation results in formation of spherulites composed of lamellae of crystal solvates (co-crystals of polymer and solvent having a lower melting point than the crystalline polymer). In both cases the proposed mechanism of structure formation is nucleation and growth. The formation of Lamellae is related to a transformation of the solution to a crystal solvate phase, whereas a microfibrillar structure is related to a direct transition to the solid crystalline polymer. The controlling parameter is conjectured to be the nucleation density as determined by the degree of undercooling during the transition.

Fibers and films obtained from lyotropic solutions of rigid polymers exhibit high tensile modulus and strength and are therefore of interest for structural applications. Poly(p-phenylene benzobisthiazole) (PBT) is a rigid polymer from which high performance fibers have been obtained by a dry-jet wet spinning

[1]Current address: W. R. Grace and Company, 55 Hayden Avenue, Lexington, MA 02173

0097-6156/87/0350-0181$06.00/0

process (1). This process involves a succession of operations by which the solution is transformed to the solid material having the desired properties. The solution is extruded through a die into an air gap where a high degree of chain orientation is achieved by extensional flow, and is then immersed in a coagulation bath where a phase transition is induced by a nonsolvent. The solid fiber is subsequently dried and heat-treated under tension.

It is in the coagulation stage that the phase transition from a solution of oriented polymer chains to a solid fiber occurs by diffusion of a nonsolvent into the solution stream, and of solvent away from it. It has been observed that the diameter of the solution stream does not change appreciably during the coagulation process, whereas it decreases during drying to about 30% of its value in the wet-coagulated state (2). Despite the fact that the wet-coagulated fiber may contain more than 90% coagulant (usually water), its ability to sustain a tensile force is similar to that of the dry fiber (2). This indicates that the basic structural features responsible for the mechanical properties are set by the coagulation process. In preliminary investigations of the morphology in the wet-coagulated state, an interconnected network of oriented microfibrils, the diameter of which is about 80 - 100 Å, has been identified as the basic microstructure formed during coagulation (3).

The formation of a microfibrillar network during coagulation is reminiscent of thermoreversible gelation observed in solutions of rigid polymers either in the isotropic or liquid crystalline state (4-7). For example, a solution of poly(γ-benzyl-L-glutamate) in dimethylformamide has been observed to gel at room temperature under the influence of water (7). In the present case, the solution stream undergoing coagulation is in a monodomain nematic state, all chains being previously aligned along the fiber axis. The ability to redissolve the coagulated fiber indicates the reversibilty of the network formation.

The phase transition during the coagulation process occurs at conditions far from equilibrium. The kinetic pathway of the transformation may have a controlling effect on the morphology developed in the coagulation stage and hence on the properties of the fiber formed by this process. The kinetic mechanism by which a network is formed during gelation of solutions of rigid polymers is not fully understood. A spinodal decomposition mechanism has been proposed (4). Alternatively, nucleation and growth of one dimensional fibrils cannot be precluded as a possible mechanism (6). It is therefore of interest to compare the microfibrillar network formed in the coagulation stage of the spinning process with the microstructure obtained by a process closer to equilibrium, i.e. slow coagulation due to gradual absorption of atmospheric moisture.

Our objective is thus to characterize the structure of the polymer network formed during coagulation in the spinning process, as well as the structure obtained by slow coagulation, and to consider the formation of such structures in terms of the phase transformations in rigid polymer solutions.

Experimental Methods

PBT was synthesized by J. wolfe of SRI ($\underline{8}$). It has the following chemical structure:

Fibers and films were spun from a 5.6% (w/w) solution of PBT in polyphosphoric acid (PPA), its polymerization medium. The intrinsic viscosity of the polymer in methanesulfonic acid (MSA) was 18 dl/gr, from which a molecular weight of about 35,000 is estimated ($\underline{9}$). Fibers were spun through a die 0.18 mm in diameter, and films through a 1 mm wide rectangular die. Both were extended 2-3 times in an air gap, coagulated in water at room temperature and subsequently kept under water. In order to preserve as much as possible the structure in the wet-coagulated state, circumventing the collapse that occurs during drying, a procedure for impregnating the wet fibers and films with an epoxy resin ($\underline{3,10}$) was used. Gradual replacement of water with ethanol was followed by infiltration with increasing concentrations of the Spurr epoxy resin ($\underline{3,10}$). The specimen was mounted in polyethylene capsules and the resin cured. Longitudional section, in which the direction of cutting was either parallel or perpendicular to the fiber axis, were obtained with a Reichert ultramicrotome using a diamond knife. The sections were observed in a JEOL transmission electron microscope (TEM) operated at 100 KV. Images were recorded about 3.4 μm underfocus to enhance phase contrast. The small angle X-ray scattering (SAXS) from PBT films impregnated with epoxy-resin was measured using a Kratky camera (slit-collimation) and a Braun position sensitive detector. The film was placed with the extrusion direction parallel to the direction of the collimation slit, perpendicular to the detector.

For the slow coagulation experiment, PBT having an intrinsic viscosity of 2 dl/gr in MSA was used (approximate molecular weight 10,000). A drop of a 3% (w/w) isotropic solution of PBT in MSA was placed between a microscope slide and a cover glass, and allowed to coagulate in air for three days. Coagulation was indicated by a color change from green to yellow to bright orange. The phase transition behavior of the coagulated material was visually observed in an optical microscope equipped with a hot stage. The coagulated material was also scraped from the slide into gold pans for differential scanning calorimetry (DSC) measurements (Perkin-Elmer DSC-2). The microstructure was assessed by floating the coagulated material onto water and picking up thin fragments for TEM. For measurements of wide-angle X-ray scattering (WAXS), the PBT/MSA solution was placed in a thin walled glass capillary and exposed to atmospheric moisture for several days. WAXS patterns were recorded on flat film using a Statton camera. In all X-ray measurements Ni filtered Cu K_{α} radiation was used.

Results and Discussion

The Microfibrillar Network in Coagulated Fibers and Films.
The microstructure revealed in longitudional sections of coagulated
PBT fibers and films is demonstrated in Figures 1 and 2. The electron
micrograph shown in Figure 1 was obtained by sectioning an epoxy
impregnated film parallel to the extrusion direction, whereas that
shown in Figure 2 was obtained by sectioning an epoxy impregnated
fiber in a direction perpendicular to the fiber axis. In both
micrographs, dark longitudional striations appear parallel to the
extrusion direction, with a typical width on the order of 100 Å. We
have previously identififed these as PBT microfibrils embedded in an
epoxy matrix (3). The microfibrils appear darker due to a combination
of mass, diffraction and phase contrast between the microfibrils,
which are crystalline and more dense, and the epoxy matrix. Closer
inspection of the micrographs reveals "Y"-shaped junctions between
microfibrils as indicated by an arrow in Figure 1 and in the inset in
Figure 2. Such elements, the microfibrils and their junctions, which
are formed in the coagulation process, constitute the fundamental
structure of oriented PBT fibers and films, namely an interconnected
network of oriented microfibrils. The network formation is reversible
in the sense that replacement of the coagulant with a solvent (i.e. a
strong acid) results in dissolution of the microfibrillar network, so
that the system reverts to its original state. That this network is
formed during coagulation explains the tensile properties of wet-
coagulated fibers (2), and indicates that the microfibrillar network
is the basis for the structure and properties of the final material.
        A more quantitative measure of the microfibrillar morphology
can be obtained by SAXS measurements. A detailed analysis of the
small-angle scattering from PBT films and derivation of the relevant
equations will be given elsewhere. The main features of the analysis
are given below.
        In the experimental geometry used in this study, the
distribution of scattered intensity measured by the detector is the
two dimensional Fourier transform of the cross section of the
electron density correlation function with a plane perpendicular to
the extrusion direction (11).

$$\tilde{I}(s) = L\lambda \langle n^2 \rangle \int_0^\infty \gamma(r) J_0(2\pi sr) 2\pi r dr \qquad (1)$$

$\tilde{I}(s)$ is the absolute smeared intensity per unit volume [electron^2-
cm/cm^3], $s = 2\sin\theta/\lambda$ is the scattering vector, where 2θ is the
scattering angle and λ is the wavelength of radiation. L is the
sample to detector distance and J_0 is the zero order Bessel function.

$n(\vec{r})$ is the density fluctuation at position $\vec{r}$ in a cross section
plane perpendicular to the extrusion direction, where $r=|\vec{r}|$. $\gamma(r)$,
the density correlation function in the cross section plane, is
defined as (12):

$$\gamma(r) = \langle n(r) n(r+r') \rangle_{r'} / \langle n^2(r') \rangle_{r'} \qquad (2)$$

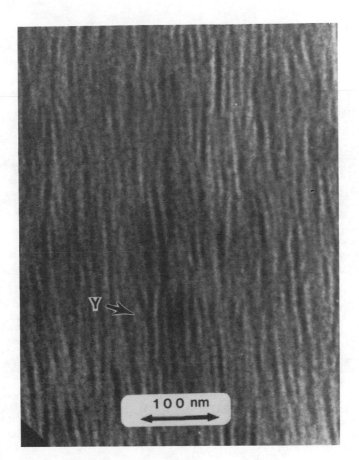

<u>Figure 1:</u>   Electron micrograph of a longitudinal section
of an epoxy impregnated PBT film.
Extrusion direction: vertical; cutting direction: vertical.
Y - "Y" shaped junction between microfibrils.

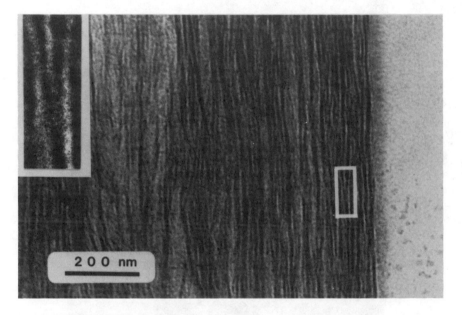

<u>Figure 2:</u>   Electron micrograph of a longitudional section
of an epoxy impregnated PBT fiber.
Fiber axis: vertical; cutting direction: horizontal.
Inset: 4X magnification of the framed area showing a junction
between microfibrils.

where the brackets denote spatial averaging. If we assume that the microfibrils are all parallel to the extrusion direction then $\gamma(r)$ reflects the shape and packing of the microfibrillar cross sections.

The SAXS pattern from an epoxy impregnated PBT film is given in Figure 3a. Figure 3b demonstrates that $s^3\tilde{I}(s)$ is a linear function of s^3 for large values of s. This is in accord with Porod's law for a two dimensional system (13), which states that for a two phase structure with sharp interfaces, the scattered intensity in the limit of large s is given by:

$$\tilde{I}(s) = K_p/s^3 + F_1 \tag{3}$$

K_p is Porod's constant, which is proportional to the length of the interfacial curve per unit area (13), and F_1 is the scattering from short range density fluctuations within the two phases. The scattering invariant Q for a two phase system with uniform (constant) electron densities and with sharp interfaces is given by (14):

$$Q = \int_0^\infty \tilde{I}(s) 2\pi s ds = L\lambda(\rho_f - \rho_m)^2 v_f v_m \tag{4}$$

where ρ_i and v_i are the electron density and volume fraction of fibrils (f) and matrix (m) respectively. From the length of the interface between the microfibrillar cross sections and the matrix, per unit area, as measured by Porod's constant, the average microfibril diameter $\bar{D}$ can be calculated as (15):

$$\bar{D} = \langle D^2\rangle/\langle D\rangle = Q / \pi^3(1-v_f)K_p \tag{5}$$

Using Equations 3-5, with the densities of the impregnated film and the epoxy matrix measured independently, the following characteristics of the microfibrillar network can be calculated from the SAXS measurements (Y. Cohen and E. L. Thomas to be published): a) the density of a microfibril: 1.46 gr/cm^3; b) average diameter of a microfibril: 71 Å; c) volume fraction of microfibrils: 0.18. The average diameter is in good agreement with the observations by electron microscopy shown in Figures 1 and 2. Comparison of the calculated volume fraction with the initial PBT concentration indicates that some shrinkage has occured during the coagulation or the infiltration processes. The density of the microfibril is smaller than that estimated for the PBT crystal, 1.69 gr/cm^3 (16). This indicates the presence of a significant number of defects within the microfibril.

A different analysis of the scattering pattern uses the Debye correlation function (14), derived for a random two-phase structure with sharp interfaces:

$$\gamma(r) = \exp(-r/l_c) \tag{6}$$

where l_c is the correlation length, from which the average cord length passing through a microfibrillar cross section , l_f, can be calculated:

$$l_f = l_c/(1 - v_f) \tag{7}$$

Substitution of Equation 6 in Equation 1 yields:

$$\tilde{I}(s) = 2\pi l_c^2 L\lambda\langle\eta^2\rangle / (1 + 4\pi^2 l_c^2 s^2)^{3/2} \tag{8}$$

In Figure 3c, $\tilde{I}(s)^{-2/3}$ is plotted as a function of s^2. The linearity of the plot in most of the experimentally accessible range implies that the microfibrillar cross sections have arbitrary (i.e. random) shapes. The average cord length is estimated as 45 Å, although it is difficult to measure due to the small value of the intercept in Figure 3c.

These results, together with previous studies of PBT fibers (16-18), allow us to suggest a structural model for the microfibrils. The PBT molecules, being rigid chains with a persistence length on the order of the chain length (9), pack parallel to each other in crystallites having a monoclinic unit cell with translational disorder along the chain axis (16,17). The width of regions of coherently packed chains formed by coagulation, as estimated from the breadth of the equatorial WAXS peaks (2), is smaller than the width of the microfibril. Drying increases the orientation of the crystallites along the fiber direction by removal of water from the spaces between the microfibrils, which causes their compaction, but the width of coherently scattering regions measured by dark field electron microscopy is still limited to about 20 Å (18). The width of such regions can be increased by heat treatment to about 100 Å (18), which is comparable to the full width of a microfibril. We thus conclude that the microfibrils formed by coagulation have irregularly shaped cross sections and are composed of smaller regions in which the PBT molecules are coherently packed. Whether these regions are independent crystallites, or are merely a manifestation of the many defects within a single crystallite which spans the width of the microfibril, can not be determined at this stage. The nature of the junction between the microfibrils is also not clear. Based on the mechanical strength of the wet-coagulated fiber we assume that the junctions are also a regions of coherently packed PBT chains.

Slow Coagulation.
An ordered solid phase is formed, at equilibrium with a very dilute isotropic solution, when the isotropic solution of PBT is slowly coagulated by gradual absorption of atmospheric moisture. The

spherulitic nature of this phase is clearly apparent in the optical micrograph shown in Figure 4, in which the typical "Maltese cross" extinction pattern appears when viewed between crossed polarizers. By use of a quarter wave plate and comparison with spherulites of poly(ethylene oxide), it was shown that the spherulites formed by slow coagulation are optically negative. As the main polarization axis of the PBT molecule is along the chain axis, the chains are thus oriented within the spherulite in the tangential direction.

The microstructure of these spherulites cannot be observed directly in an electron microscope due to the presence of the corrosive and volatile solvent. A lamellar morphology is revealed by electron microscopy of the slowly coagulated material, after removal of the solvent by washing with water and subsequent drying, as shown in Figure 5a. The electron diffraction pattern, shown with correct relative alignment as an inset in Figure 5a, demonstrates that the PBT chains are perpendicaular to the lamella. Similar morphologies have been observed to form in solutions of other rigid polymers such as poly(benzamide) (PBA) (19) and poly(p-phenylene terephthalamide) (PPTA) (19,20). The lamellar thickness, about 450 Å, is in line with the average molecular length determined by Crosby et al. (21) for this particular sample of PBT. Electron diffraction patterns from several regions within the spherulites exhibit all the characteristic reflections observed in PBT fibers, but in many instances, local regions of preferred $\underset{\sim}{a}$ or $\underset{\sim}{b}$ axis orientations, rather than fiber symmetry, are observed (22). We assume that the lamellar morphology observed by electron microscopy after removal of the solvent, is representative of the actual morphology in the slowly coagulated system as well. A very different morphology develops when the same solution is coagulated rapidly by immersion in water. A mat composed of randomly oriented lathe-like structures approximately 100 Å in width is obtained, as shown in Figure 5b. This demonstrates that formation of microfibrils is associated with rapid coagulation, in an isotropic system as well as in the spinning process described above. The formation of the lamellar morphology is thus a consequence of the slow coagulation

The nature of the phase formed in the slow coagulation experiment can be deduced on the basis of its thermal transitions, and from its X-ray diffraction pattern. In the DSC trace of the slowly coagulated PBT–MSA–water system shown in Figure 6, three endothermic transitions are observed between $90\,^{\circ}C$ and $240\,^{\circ}C$. Corresponding transitions were observed by optical microscopy using a hot stage. Solid PBT fibers or films do not exhibit thermal transitions below about $650^{\circ}C$ (1).

The X-ray diffraction pattern of the slowly coagulated material exhibits rings, characteristic of an unoriented material, the spacings of which are different than those of the PBT fiber diffraction pattern, as summarized in Table I. The observation of a 12.5 Å spacing, which is equivalent to the PBT chain axis repeat length, suggests a monoclinic unit cell. The observed spacings can be fitted to a monoclinic unit cell having the following dimensions:

$$a = 6.5 \text{ Å} \qquad b = 5.3 \text{ Å} \qquad c = 12.5 \text{ Å} \qquad \gamma = 101^{\circ}$$

These dimensions indicate a larger unit cell in the slowly coagulated PBT–MSA–water system as compared with solid PBT. On the basis of these results we conclude that the solid phase formed by slow

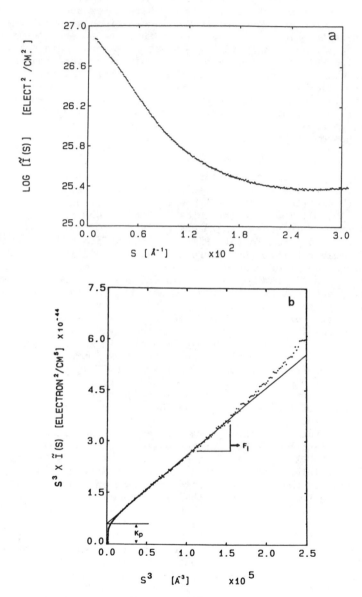

Figure 3.   Small angle X-ray scattering from an epoxy impregnated
PBT film. a) The measured scattering pattern; b) data plotted to
fit Equation 3. <u>Continued on next page</u>.

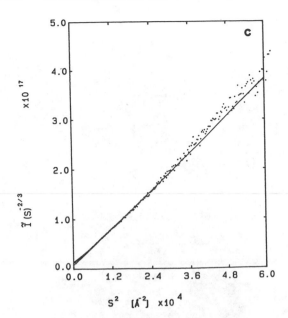

Figure 3. <u>Continued</u>. Small angle X-ray scattering from an epoxy impregnated PBT film. c) Data plotted to fit Equation 8.

Figure 4: Optical micrograph of spherulites formed by slow coagulation of an isotropic solution of PBT in MSA, viewed between crossed polarizers.

a

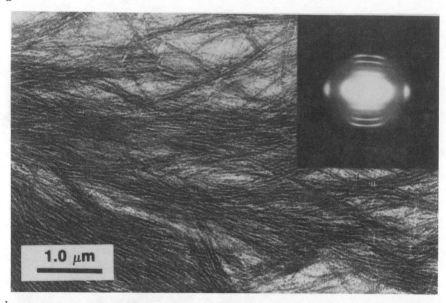

b

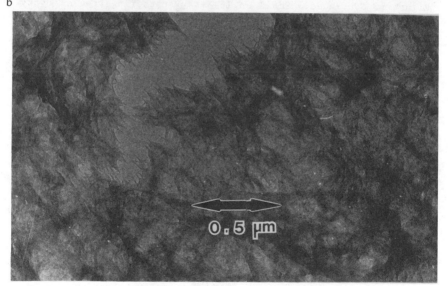

<u>Figure 5:</u>   Electron   micrographs   showing   the   morphology
which   develops   in   isotropic   PBT   solutions   under   different
coagulation conditions: a)   Slow coagulation by absorption of
atmospheric   moisture. Inset: electron diffraction pattern taken
from an area in the center of the image.
b)   Rapid coagulation by immersion in water.

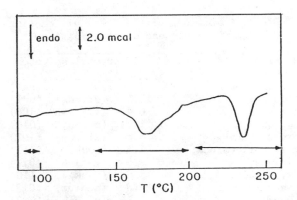

Figure 6:   DSC trace of the slowly coagulated PBT/MSA/water
system. Arrows indicate   the temperature ranges of transitions
observed by optical microscopy.

coagulation is a crystal–solvate phase, i.e. co–crystals of the protonated PBT and the acid anion. Crystal solvates have been previously observed in solutions of other rigid polymers such as PPTA (19,23) and PBA (19,24). Details of the structure and composition of the crystal–solvate, in terms of the three components present in the system, cannot be determined at this stage. Based on the proposed unit cell dimensions, a structure having one PBT repeat and one MSA molecule in a unit cell will have a density of about 1.4 gr/cm^3, whereas two MSA molecules per PBT repeat will result in a density of about 1.8 gr/cm^3, which is larger than the density of the solid PBT crystal. As the PBT monomer unit is likely to be doubly protonated, a model in which only one MSA molecule is associated with one PBT monomer unit suggests that in the crystal solvate observed, PBT is significantly deprotonated compared to the molecule in solution. This is in accord with spectroscopical evidence for deprotonation of PBT under similar cirumstances (25).

Table I. Comparison of the X–Ray Diffraction
from PBT Fiber and Crystal–Solvate

PBT Fiber		PBT crystal solvate		
layer line spacings:				(hkl)
12.5 Å	(medium)	12.5 Å	(strong)	(001)
6.3	(weak)	6.4	(v. weak)	(100)
4.2	(strong)	5.2	(strong)	(010)
+ high order spacings		4.5	(strong)	(102),($\bar{1}$10)
equatorial reflections:		4.2	(weak)	($\bar{1}$11),(003)
5.9	(strong)	3.9	(medium)	(012)
3.6	(v. strong)	3.6	(weak)	(110),($\bar{1}$12)
3.2	(medium)	3.3	(medium)	(013),(112)
2.9	(weak)	2.6	(v. weak)	(020)

The Relationship Between Phase Transformation and Morphology.

The difference between the microfibrillar morphology formed by immersion in a nonsolvent and the lamellar structure obtained by slow coagulation is striking. In order to relate these different structures to the phase transition by which they were formed we consider first the binary phase diagram of a rigid polymer/solvent system. A schematic phase diagram is shown in Figure 7. It features, at low polymer concentration and high temperature (or x < 0), the equilibrium between isotropic and ordered solutions, as described by Flory's theory (26). At higher polymer concentrations a biphasic region exists, in which the ordered solution is in equilibrium with the solid crystalline polymer (27), as well as a region in which the ordered solution is in equilibrium with the crystal solvate (19,23). At low temperature (large x), the isotropic solution is at equilibrium with the crystal solvate phase. For purpose of clarity, formation of a crystal solvate is considered only at one composition, although formation of several crystal solvates of different compositions is plausible.

The coagulation process can now be considered in perspective of a ternary polymer–solvent–nonsolvent system. A schematic ternary phase diagram, at constant temperature, is shown in Figure 8. The boundaries of the isotropic and narrow biphasic (isotropic-nematic) regions are based on an extension of Flory's theory ($\underline{27}$) to a polymer–solvent–nonsolvent system, due to Russo and Miller ($\underline{7}$). These boundaries are calculated for a polymer having an axial ratio of 100, and the following interactions parameters: $x_{P-S}=x_{S-NS}=0$, $x_{P-NS}=1$. Other boundaries of the biphasic regions are set schematically. Again, for purpose of clarity only one crystal solvate phase is considered. It is assumed to have a distinct polymer–solvent composition, with total exclusion of the nonsolvent, and thus appears as a single point on the polymer–solvent axis. In reality, these constraints may be somewhat relaxed.

In view of the ternary phase diagram in figure 8, addition of a nonsolvent is similar in its effect to a decrease in temperature (or increase in the x-parameter) in the binary system. The melting point of the crystal solvate was shown to be much lower than the melting temperature of the crystalline polymer. Therefore the degree of undercooling in the region of the phase diagram which is at equilibrium with formation of the crystal solvate is much smaller than in the region which is at equilibrium with formation of the solid polymer.

Formation of spherulites composed of crystal–solvate lamellae by slow coagulation suggests a nucleation and growth mechanism for this phase transition. Since the nucleation density is proportional to the exponent of the undercooling, the small undercooling relative to the melting of the crystal solvate results in a low density of nuclei, one per spherulite, which results in formation of lamellae. Formation of small aggregates in PBT solutions, at conditions equivalent to the onset of coagulation, has been observed ($\underline{25}$). Such aggregates may well be the nucleation centers for subsequent growth. If the microfibrillar network is formed by nucleation and growth of PBT crystallites, a much higher nucleation density is expected, due to the much larger undercooling relative to formation of PBT crystals. Long range chain alignment in the extrusion direction allows formation of long microfibrils. This is facilitated by the higher mobility in an oriented monodomain nematic solution parallel to the direction of alignment as compared to that in the perpendicular direction. We have previously suggested that in a solution with predominantly one dimensional mobility, a nucleation and growth mechanism is expected to result in a fibrillar morphology, whereas a spinodal decomposition mechanism may lead to a lamellar structure ($\underline{3}$).

We therefore conjecture that in the coagulation stage of the spinning process, a microfibrillar network is formed by a nucleation and growth process, in which the width of the microfibrils is controlled by the density of nuclei. It remains to be determined whether the nucleation rate is a sensitive function of the coagulation condition. The effect of the coagulation conditions on the microfibrillar morphology is currently being studied.

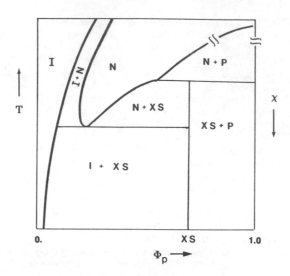

<u>Figure 7:</u>   A schematic phase diagram of a binary system
composed of a rigid polymer and a solvent: I – isotropic
solution; N – nematic solution; XS – crystal solvate; P –
crystalline polymer; φ – volume fraction.

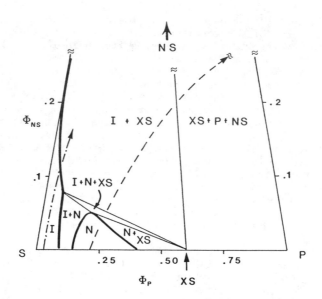

<u>Figure 8:</u>   A schematic phase diagram of a ternary system
composed of a rigid polymer, solvent and nonsolvent, at constant
temperature. S – solvent; NS - nonsolvent. Other symbols as in
Figure 7.   – – – – pathway of the coagulation process during
the spinning of fibers or films; ·– ·– ·– ·– pathway of the
coagulation process caused by gradual absorption of moisture.

Conclusions

1.   A network of oriented microfibrils is formed during coagulation in the spinning process of PBT fibers and films. The microfibrils have a typical diameter on the order of 100 Å, and have irregularly shaped cross sections. This network is the basis for the structure and the properties of the final material.
2.   Slow coagulation of an isotropic PBT solution by gradual absorption of moisture results in formation of crystal solvates, which are co-crystals of PBT and solvent. A lamellar morphology is developed in which the PBT chains are perpendicular to the lamellae. The lamellae are radially arranged to form optically negative spherulites. These crystal solvates exhibit several thermal transitions in the temperature range of 90° to 240°C, a range in which no transitions are observed in solid, crystalline PBT.
3.   We suggest that both the lamellar and the microfibrillar morphologies are formed by a nucleation and growth process. A low nucleation density of crystal solvates results in a lamellar morphology, whereas a high nucleation density of the crystalline PBT results in formation of microfibrils.

Acknowledgment

Financial support from the U.S. Air Force through grants F33615-82-K5068 and AFOSR-85-2075, is gratefully acknowledged.

Literature Cited

1.   Allen, S. R.; Filippov, A. V.; Farris, R. J.; Thomas, E. L.; Wong, C. P.; Berry, G. C.; Chenevey, E. C. Macromolecules 1981, 14, 1135.
2.   Pottick, L. A.; Farris, R. J. TAPPI Symposium 1985, p 65.
3.   Cohen, Y.; Thomas, E. L. Polym. Eng. Sci. 1985, 25, 1093.
4.   Miller, W. G.; Kou, L.; Tohyama K.; Voltaggio, V. J. Polym. Sci., Polym. Symp. 1978, 65, 91.
5.   Tohyama, K.; Miller, W. G. Nature 1981, 289, 813.
6.   Sasaki, S.; Hikata, M.; Shiraki, C.; Uematsu, I. Polym. J. 1982, 14, 204.
7.   Russo, P. S.; Miller, W. G. Macromolecules 1984, 17, 1324.
8.   Wolfe, J. F.; Loo, M.; Arnold, F. E. Macromolecules 1981, 14, 915.
9.   Lee, C.-C.; Chu, S.-G.; Berry, G. C. J. Polym. Sci., Polym. Phys. Ed. 1983, 21, 1573.
10.   Spurr, A. R. J. Ultrastruct. Res. 1969, 26, 31.
11.   Perret, A.; Ruland, W. J. Appl. Cryst. 1969, 2, 209.
12.   Debye, P.; Bueche, A. M. J. Appl. Phys. 1949, 20, 518.
13.   Kirste, R.; Porod, G. Kolloid Z. u Z. Polymere 1962, 184, 1.
14.   Debye, P.; Anderson, H. R.; Brumberger, H. J. Appl. Phys. 1957, 28, 679
15.   Paredes, E.; Fischer, E. W. Makromol. Chem. 1979, 180, 2702.
16.   Roche, E. J.; Takahashi, T.; Thomas, E. L. In Fiber Diffraction Methods; French, A. D.; Gardner, K. H., Eds.; ACS Symposium Series No. 141; American Chemical Society; Washington, DC, 1981; p 303.

17. Odell, J. A.; Keller, A.; Atkins, E. D. T.; Miles, M. J. J.
     Mater. Sci. 1981, 16, 3309.
18. Minter, J. R.; Shimamura, K.; Thomas, E. L. J. Mater. Sci. 1981,
     16, 3303.
19. Iovleva, M. M.; Papkov, S. P. Polym. Sci. USSR 1982, 24, 236.
20. Takahashi, T.; Iwamoto, H.; Inove, K.; Tsuji-oto, I. J. Polym.
     Sci., Polym. Phys. Ed. 1979, 17, 115.
21. Crosby, C. R.; Ford, N. C.; Karasz, F. E.; Langley, K. H. J.
     Chem. Phys. 1981, 75, 4298.
22. Frost, H. H. M.Sc. Thesis, University of Massachusetts, Amherst,
     1984.
23. Gardner, K. H.; Matheson, R. R.; Avakian P.; Chia, Y. T.;
     Gierke, T. D.; Abs. Pap. ACS 1983, 186(Aug), 37.
24. Takase, M.; Krigbaum, W. R.; Hacker, H. J. Polym. Sci., Polym.
     Phys. Ed. 1986, 24, 1115.
25. Berry, G. C.; Wei, C. C.; Furukawa, R. ACS Polymer Preprints
     1986, 27(1), 228.
26. Flory, P. J. Proc. Roy. Soc (London), Ser. A 1956, 234, 73.
27. Ciferri, A.; Krigbaum, W. R. Mol. Cryst. Liq. Cryst. 1981, 69,
     273.

RECEIVED January 24, 1987

Chapter 13

Ordering and Gelation in DNA Solutions

Victor A. Bloomfield

Department of Biochemistry, University of Minnesota, St. Paul, MN 55108

We present a review of the experimental findings
regarding the gelation and ordinary-extraordinary
(slow mode) diffusion transitions in solutions of
short DNA fragments, and propose some mechanistic
explanations. It is suggested that DNA rods may
associate end-to-end by stacking of terminal base
pairs, with gelation arising from the entanglement of
the linear multimers thus formed. The slow collective
diffusion in the extraordinary phase may result from
formation of an electrostatically stabilized colloidal
crystal. Numerical estimates support the plausibility
of these mechanisms of phase transition; but the lack
of sensitivity of light scattering to gelation, and
the failure of tracer diffusion experiments to reflect
slow mode diffusion, are puzzles that remain to be
explained.

Solutions of short, rodlike fragments of DNA can exist in at
least four different states or "phases": a normal, isotropic
fluid at low DNA concentration and moderate salt; a clear,
nonbirefringent, viscoelastic gel at moderate DNA concentrations
(1); a birefringent liquid crystal at higher concentrations (2);
and an extraordinary phase with a very low translational
diffusion coefficient in low salt (3). Higher molecular weight
DNA undergoes monomolecular and paucimolecular condensation into
toroids in the presence of multivalent cations (4-6). For
synthetic DNA with an alternating purine-pyrimide sequence, the
condensation is often accompanied by a transition from a normal
right-handed B-DNA helix to a left-handed Z-DNA helix or to some
other helical variant (7)
Transitions among these states depend strongly on ionic
strength as well as on other solution variables such as polymer
concentration and molecular weight, temperature, and specific ion
effects. In this paper, we shall review work from our laboratory
on the gelation and ordinary - extraordinary transitions observed
with rodlike DNA fragments, and discuss some ideas about the
mechanisms and intermolecular forces underlying these
transitions, particularly as they appear to relate to ionic
effects. Comparisons will be made with some other polyelectrolyte
systems that undergo the ordinary-extraordinary transition.

0097-6156/87/0350-0199$06.00/0
© 1987 American Chemical Society

Materials and Methods

The materials and methods used in this work have been described
in detail in the original publications (1,3). Briefly, the DNA
used in the gelation work was prepared by extensive sonication of
calf thymus DNA; it had a degree of polymerization of 200 ± 30
base pairs (bp). The DNA used in the ordinary-extraordinary
transition studies was prepared by nuclease digestion of
chromatin from chicken erythrocytes; it was an equimolar mixture
of two sizes, 140 bp and 160 bp, averaged to 150 bp.

A Rheometrics cone-and-plate rheometer was used to obtain
the storage (G') and loss (G") moduli and the complex viscosity
of the DNA gels. Quasielastic light scattering (QLS) was used to
monitor gel formation (by the magnitude of the dynamic scattering
at zero correlation time relative to the static scattering
background), to obtain diffusion coefficients and hydrodynamic
radii of diffusing molecules and aggregates. QLS also was used
to monitor the onset and extent of the ordinary to extraordinary
transition, through the appearance of distinctly
non-single-exponential decay of the autocorrelation function.
Total light scattering intensity, determined by photon counting
methods, was also used to characterize DNA gels and to follow the
appearance of the extraordinary phase.

Gelation

Under appropriate conditions of salt and temperature, short DNA
fragments, about 700 Å in length, form clear, non-birefringent,
thermally reversible gels at low concentrations, ca 1-2% by
weight (1). Such gels, though they have the optical properties
of normal solutions, will not pour out of the tubes in which they
are formed. The lowest gelation concentrations are in the range
$(L^2 d)^{-1}$, where L is the length and d the effective diameter of
the rod, at which inter-rod collisions become important (i.e., at
which the excluded volume per rod becomes comparable to the
solution volume per rod). Rheometric measurements show normal
viscous behavior for the ungelled solutions, but once the gel has
formed, G' dominates G" by about 8-fold over the entire range of
DNA concentrations. This is the behavior expected for an elastic
gel. Contrary to the expectations of Doi-Edwards theory (8), the
complex viscosity extrapolated to zero shear varies with DNA
concentration C rather than C^3. G' is also linear in C in the
gel region, rather than varying as the 1.6-1.7 power of $(C-C_{crit})$
as found for rodlike substituted polydiacetylene (9).

To monitor the gelation transition as a function of solution
conditions, we utilized the fact that in a QLS experiment the
ratio of the dynamic signal S due to mobile scatterers, to the
static scattering background B, is expected to vary as the square
of the concentration of mobile scatterers. Thus as sol turned to
gel, S/B decreased markedly; the midpoint of the curve was taken
as the gel transition temperature T_g. The total scattering
intensity from DNA solutions at a given C did not change during
the transition, and the translational diffusion coefficient of
the mobile scatterers in the gel phase was the same as that of
DNA molecules in solution, indicating that the gel structure
presents little impediment to the motion of ungelled molecules.

As C increases, the thermal transition range narrows, and T_g
increases in a roughly linear fashion. Assuming that the effect
of Na^+ ions on the transition could be expressed in the
mass-action form

$$DNA_{sol} + nNa^+ == DNA_{gel} \cdot Na^+_n \qquad (1)$$

we found that n was 1.7 (per DNA molecule of 200 bp), independent of T. For Mg^{++}, n was about 1.0. Mg^{++} was roughly 10 times more effective than Na^+ in provoking gelation. Analysis of the temperature dependence of gelation gave an apparent ΔH of -14.3 kcal/mol in NaCl, and -27.8 kcal/mol in $MgCl_2$, for the equilibrium implied by Equation 1. See below for an estimate of the thermodynamic parameters for the elementary association step in a particular model of the gelation.

The length dependence of gelation has not yet been carefully investigated, since it was studied with a single average size of DNA. Some preliminary gel electrophoresis observations on gelled DNA indicates that longer molecules were not preferentially trapped in the gel, but these require more detailed confirmation. The DNA concentration dependence of the gelation midpoint was approximately linear between 7.5 and 17 mg/mL (with a negative intercept, corresponding to the fact that a critical concentration is required to form a gel). This does not conform with the C^3 dependence predicted by Doi and Edwards ($\underline{8}$).

Mechanistic Ideas. Our observations show that DNA concentration and ion effects have dominant effects in gelation. General long-range Coulombic interactions certainly play a role, but the strong effectiveness of Mg^{++} compared to Na^+ in inducing gelation indicates that specific attractive ion effects are also important. The small number of ions that appear to be "bound" upon gelation suggests a small number of contacts between the rods; this is consistent with the percolation ideas of Sinclair et al ($\underline{9}$). The sizeable ΔH of the sol-gel transition indicates that some significant exothermal process helps to stabilize the gel. A mechanism that appears to be qualitatively consistent with all of these observations is association, either base pairing or base stacking, between residues at the ends of separate DNA molecules.

End-to-end association. The simplest model is one in which each association step has the same equilibrium constant K. This is equivalent to the familiar Flory most-probable polymerization scheme. Thus we write the recursion relations

$$c_i = Kc_1c_{i-1} = K^{i-1}c_1^i , \qquad i=2,3,\ldots \qquad (2)$$

Summation of the geometric series over all species for the total concentration C_t and rearrangement gives

$$c_i = K^{-1}(KC_t/(1+KC_t))^i$$
$$c_1 = C_t/(1+KC_t) \qquad (3)$$

Although the theory of gelation of an entangled solution of polydisperse rodlike molecules is poorly understood, it seems reasonable that entanglements would become important when the average center-to-center distance between molecules is significantly smaller than their length. This occurs for molecules of degree of polymerization i when

$$iL_1/ (N_AC_tf_i/1000)^{-1/3} > 1 \qquad (4)$$

where L_1 is the monomer length (680 Å for 200 bp B-form DNA). Since there is a wide range of degrees of polymerization, it should be an initially adequate approximation to replace Equation 4 with

$$\langle i \rangle'_w L_1 / (N_A C_t f'/1000)^{-1/3} > 1 \qquad (5)$$

where $\langle i \rangle'_w$ is the weight-average degree of polymerization, and f' the mole fraction, of molecules with $i \geq 2$. This implicitly assumes that the sol is monomeric DNA fragments, while molecules with $i \geq 2$ are incorporated in the gel. f' is simply $KP_t/(1+KP_t)$, and the sum for $\langle i \rangle'_w$ is easily evaluated. The value of the left-hand side of Equation 5 is plotted against KC_t in Figure 1 for $C_t = 10$ mg/mL $= 7.8 \times 10^{-5}$ M. It is obvious that the inequality is readily satisfied for $KC_t \geq 1$. To proceed further, we need a molecular mechanism that will enable us to estimate K.

Base Stacking at Ends. One possibility is that intact duplex molecules associate end-to-end by base stacking. In that case we can write

$$K_{app} = [DNA_{gel}]/[DNA_{sol}] = f'/f_1 = KC_t. \qquad (6)$$

At $T=Tgel$, $K_{app} = 1$, so

$$\ln K(T=T_g) = -\ln C_t = -\Delta H/RT_g + \Delta S/R. \qquad (7)$$

From data on T_g vs C_t in NaCl solutions, (Figure 4 in ref. (1)), it is possible to solve Equation 7 for the thermodynamic parameters: $\Delta H = -10.9$ kcal/mol and $\Delta S = -16.6$ cal/mol-deg. The fit to the gelation data is shown in Figure 2. These values compare reasonably well with values measured for stacking of bases in dinucleoside phosphates (10,11). They are in the same range, but differ somewhat from those given in Table II of ref. (1) for NaDNA ($\Delta H = -14.3$ kcal/mol and $\Delta S = -38.8$ cal/mol-deg). The discrepancy arises in part because the values in (1) were obtained from van't Hoff analysis of K vs T at a particular DNA concentration, while those given here are from analysis of T_g vs C_t; and in part because the fit here is to the parameters of a particular model in which all species beyond monomer are in the gel form.

Base Pairing at Ends. The process of breakage during sonication might well produce dangling single-strand ends, which could then pair with complementary sequences on other molecules, leading to extensive three-dimensional networks. However, we found that treatment of the sonicated DNA preparation with S1 nuclease, which removes single stranded regions, had no effect on the gelation process.

On the other hand, it might be conjectured that normally paired bases at the ends of DNA molecules might transiently unpair, and then form intermolecularly base-paired complexes. Since the DNA studied is short, melting in the middle of the duplex (loop formation) is extremely unlikely, and the single sequence approximation, with melting from the ends only, is well satisfied.

If a molecule is L base pairs long, with the two strands held in register by at least a single bond, and the equilibrium constant for converting a single base pair from unbonded to bonded is s, then the statistical weight of a configuration with m bases paired is proportional to $(L-m+1)s^m$, where the prefactor is the number of ways m consecutive bonded bases can be arranged among L possible locations. Thus the probability P_v that at least v base pairs are open is

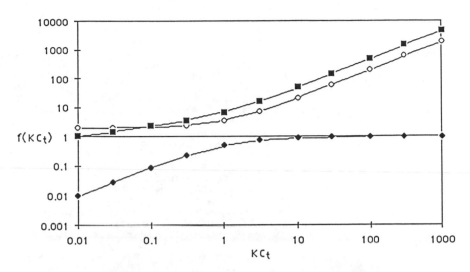

Figure 1.   Variation of (♦) mole fraction of dimeric and larger
molecules, (◊) weight-average degree of polymerization for dimers
and larger, and (■) ratio of weight-average length to average
center-to center distance of polymerized molecules, as function
of KC_t.

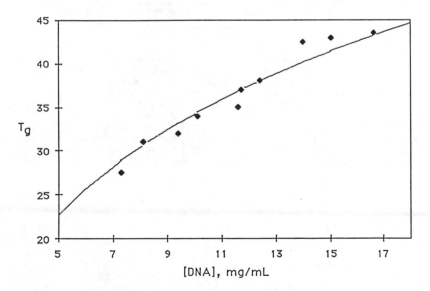

Figure 2.   Dependence of temperature of gelation midpoint on DNA
concentration in 50 mM DNA (points) , compared with predictions
of end-stacking model (line).   Data from (1).

$$P_v = \sum_{m=1}^{L-v} (L-m+1) \ s^m \ / \ \sum_{m=1}^{L} (L-m+1) \ s^m \qquad (8)$$

which may be summed to give

$$P_v = [s^{(L+1-v)} - (L+1-v)s + L-v] \ / \ [s^{(L+1)} - (L+1)s + L]. \quad (9)$$

With $\Delta H = -7$ kcal/mol, a fairly typical value for base pair formation, and a melting temperature (where s=1) of 80°C, P_v is typically of order 10^{-3} or less (Figure 3).

If for simplicity at least v base pairs must be open to form an intermolecular base pair, and that bond itself has v base pairs (v is 3-4 at room temperature from studies of oligonucleotides) then the intermolecular association constant is $K_v = s^v$. Assuming equal probability of occurrence of all four bases at any point of the sequence, the probability that any given open end will find its complement is $(1/4)^v$.

Then, if the total molar concentration of monomers in all states of aggregation is C_0, the fraction of material in the dimer form (assuming only a small amount is dimerized) is

$$f_2 = C_2/C_0 = (s/4)^v C_0 \ P_v^2. \qquad (10)$$

For 200 bp fragments at 10 mg/mL, $C_0 = 7.6 \times 10^{-5}$ M. With the values for ΔH and T_m proposed above, s ranges from 18.6 at 273°K to 3.6 at 313°K, the experimental temperature range. Thus f_2 is always $\ll 1$ (Figure 4), and the hypothesis that end melting leads to intermolecular basepairing and subsequent gelation through network formation appears to be untenable.

Regardless of whether end-to-end association of rodlike DNA fragments occurs by base stacking or base pairing, no theory exists that would enable confident prediction of the salt dependence. Qualitatively, it is clear that increasing salt concentration should facilitate the close approach of like-charged polyions, and that Mg^{++} which interacts strongly with the backbone phosphates, should be more effective than Na^+. Both of these predictions are in agreement with experiment.

The end-to-end model for gelation suffers from the obvious difficulty that scattering experiments should be able to detect the increased average molecular weight and decreased diffusion coefficient attendant on multimolecular association before gelation. It is conceivable that only very small extents of association are required to produce gelation, and that the gel itself has the same scattering power as the free molecules. Further work is clearly needed to ascertain the plausibility of the model.

Ordinary-Extraordinary Transition

At salt concentrations above about 0.01 M, the light scattering behavior of dilute solutions (1.5 mg/ml) of mononucleosomal DNA fragments accords with theoretical expectation (3). That is, as the ionic strength is lowered, the total scattering intensity (or apparent molecular weight) decreases, and the apparent translational diffusion coefficient D_{app} increases in reciprocal fashion. These trends are expected from repulsive polyelectrolyte interactions and the inverse relation between D_{app} and the scattering structure factor.

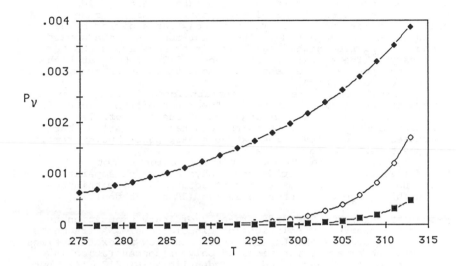

Figure 3. Probability of finding at least ν bases unpaired for 200 bp DNA with $T_m = 353°K$ and $\Delta H = -7$ kcal/mol. ν: ◆,4; ◊,5; ■,6.

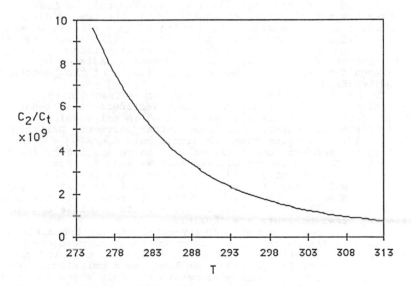

Figure 4. Mole fraction of dimers computed for $\nu = 4$ with the end-melting model as a function of T.

As the salt concentration continues to decrease, however, matters change dramatically (3). The total scattering intensity decreases more abruptly, and the QLS autocorrelation function, which has been a simple single-exponential decay, becomes markedly two-exponential. The two decay rates differ by as much as two orders of magnitude. The faster continues the upward trend of D_{app} from higher salt, and is thus assigned the term "ordinary". The slower, which is about 1/10 of D_{app} at high salt, and appears to reflect a new mode of solution dynamics, is termed "extraordinary".

Analysis of the relative contributions of the slow and fast decays to the total intensity, by "peeling" off the slower from the linear region of a semi-log plot of the autocorrelation function, indicates that it is the ordinary scattering that decreases in intensity. The extraordinary contribution remains roughly constant once it appears.

The solution in the extraordinary region is not birefringent, shows no evidence of physical phase separation, and shows no maxima or minima in the structure factor within the accessible range of scattering angles (30 to 135 deg).

Mechanistic Ideas. The ordinary-extraordinary transition has also been observed in solutions of dinucleosomal DNA fragments (350 bp) by Schmitz and Lu (12). Fast and slow relaxation times have been observed as functions of polymer concentration in solutions of single-stranded poly(adenylic acid) (13, 14), but these experiments were conducted at relatively high salt and are interpreted as a transition between dilute and semidilute regimes. The ordinary-extraordinary transition has also been observed in low-salt solutions of poly(L-lysine) (15), and poly(styrene sulfonate) (16,17). In poly(L-lysine), which is the best-studied case, the transition is detected only by QLS, which measures the mutual diffusion coefficient. The tracer diffusion coefficient (18), electrical conductivity (19), electrophoretic mobility (18,20,21) and intrinsic viscosity (22) do not show the same profound change. It appears that the transition is a manifestation of collective particle dynamics mediated by long-range forces; but the mechanistic details of the phenomenon are quite obscure.

It is worth noting that the ordinary-extraordinary transition in solutions of DNA fragments differs in at least one respect from the same transition observed in poly(lysine) or poly(styrene sulfonate). For these latter polymers, Drifford and Dalbiez (17) have formulated the simple rule $C_m b/2Ib_j = Z$ relating the monomer concentration C_m, charge spacing b, ionic strength I, Bjerrum length b_j, and salt valence Z. For double-stranded DNA at 1.5 mg/ml, this predicts that the transition will occur at I = 0.002 M, while in fact its midpoint is at 0.01 M NaCl. The reason for this discrepancy is not clear; one obvious difference is that DNA is a stiff wormlike chain, while the other polymers are flexible.

Both the gelation and ordinary-extraordinary transitions take place in the general range of concentrations predicted by the simple C $\approx (L^2 d)^{-1}$ argument based on the onset of rod-rod collisions. Stigter (23) has shown how, for a polyelectrolyte in low salt, the repulsive diameter may be strongly augmented by the diffuse ion atmosphere extending outward from the rod surface. However, even with this augmentation, the ordinary-extraordinary transition takes place at a concentration that is several-fold lower than predicted for the isotropic-anisotropic transition treated by Stigter. This is apparent from Figure 5, which shows

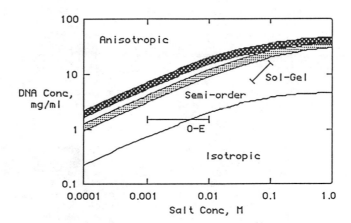

Figure 5. Regions of stability of isotropic and anisotropic
solutions of 150 bp DNA, calculated according to Stigter (23).
The light band corresponds to the coexistence region for fully
charged DNA, the dark band to DNA with 76% of charge neutralized
by counterion condensation. The salt/DNA concentration regions
where the gelation and ordinary-extraordinary transitions were
studied are indicated by brackets.

the ranges of salt and DNA concentration in which isotropic and
anisotropic solutions are expected to coexist. Separate
coexistence bands are computed for DNA with full charge, and for
DNA with charge reduced to 24% of the formal value by counterion
condensation.

Colloidal Crystal. One intriguing possibility is the formation
of a colloidal crystal stabilized solely by repulsive
electrostatic forces, as proposed originally by Wigner (24) for
electrons. The structure and dynamics of such electrostatically
stabilized ordered suspensions have been studied extensively with
polystyrene latexes with little or no added salt (e.g. 25), where
they give rise to Bragg scattering with visible light. A maximum
in the scattering structure factor, with concomitant minimum in
D_{trans}, has been seen in low salt solutions of poly(lysine) (26)
and poly(styrene sulfonate) (27); this is consistent with
formation of an ordered suspension.

A theoretical analysis of the stability of such colloidal
crystals of spherical latex particles has been carried out by
Marcelja et al (28). They employ the Lindemann criterion that a
crystal will be stable if the rms thermal displacement of the
particles about their equilibrium positions is a small fraction f
of the lattice spacing R. Comparison with Monte Carlo
simulations shows that f is about 0.1 for "hard" crystals, and
0.08 for "soft" crystals stabilized by long-ranged electrostatic
forces. This latter criterion translates into a critical ratio

$$\Gamma = (z_{eff}e)^2/\varepsilon Rk_BT = z_{eff}^2(b_{Bjerrum}/R) \tag{11}$$

where z_{eff} is the effective particle charge in units of the
proton charge e, ε is the dielectric constant, k_B is the Boltzmann
constant, T the temperature, and $b_{Bjerrum}$ the Bjerrum length in
the solution. Monte Carlo simulations show that a colloidal
crystal will be stable if $\Gamma > 155 \pm 10$. A similar analysis has
been carried out for flexible polyelectrolytes which can be
stiffened by electrostatic interactions, by De Gennes et al (29).

We have used the procedure of Marcelja et al (28) to compute
Γ for spherical molecules with the same charge and volume as 200
bp rodlike DNA. Each molecule is at the center of a Wigner-Seitz
cell of volume $(4/3)\pi R^3$ with bulk salt concentrations spanning
the experimental range (3). The nonlinear Poisson-Boltzmann
equation is solved numerically with appropriate boundary
conditions at the particle surface and the cell boundary. The
results are that $\Gamma = 155$ at about 3 mg/mL DNA (twice the
experimental concentration) with no added salt, but Γ is always <
155 for added salt in the experimental range. For NaPSS, with dp
= 3800 at $1-4 \times 10^{-2}$ mg/mL, $\Gamma > 300$, consistent with the
observation of a structure factor maximum.

While these results fall short of predicting stability for
our DNA solutions, they are close enough to encourage further
exploration. The obvious next step is to model the particles as
rods with various orientations at the lattice positions, to
compare the total electrostatic repulsion between linear and
spherical (effectively point) charge distributions.

Diffusional Dynamics. If the colloidal crystal is stable, does
it explain the extraordinarily slow diffusional behavior? While
some detailed theories of the dynamics of colloidal crystals have
been constructed (25,30), they are difficult to apply to our DNA
solutions. Therefore, it is of interest to present a much
simpler semiquantitative approach.

We start with the familiar Einstein diffusion equation, $\langle x^2 \rangle$ =2Dt, which is to be solved for $D = D_{xtal}$ in the colloidal crystal. The rms displacement can be estimated from the Lindemann criterion as $\langle x^2 \rangle^{1/2}$ = fR, if t is the period of a lattice vibration, $2\pi/\omega_0$. The characteristic frequency ω_0 can be estimated from the standard expression $\omega_0 = \sqrt{(k/m)}$, where k is the force constant and m the effective particle mass.

For charged particles on a lattice interacting through screened Coulomb forces, differentiation of the force law with respect to interparticle distance gives

$$ k = \frac{(Z_{eff}e)^2}{\varepsilon} \frac{(1+\kappa R)e^{\kappa R}}{\kappa R^3} \qquad (12) $$

where κ is the reciprocal Debye-Huckel length. In the absence of knowledge of the effective mass, we simply set it equal to the DNA molecule mass. Then, substituting numerical values gives $\omega_0 \approx 3.3 \times 10^5/s$, so $D_{xtal} \approx 8 \times 10^{-11}$ cm^2/s, compared with $D_{self} \approx 2 \times 10^{-7}$ cm^2/s. Thus it appears that colloidal crystal formation bears further investigation as a source of extraordinarily slow diffusion coefficients in low salt polyelectrolyte solutions.

Other mechanistic ideas The most obvious problem with the colloidal crystal model is that it is hard to reconcile with the tracer diffusion experiments on poly(lysine) (18) that do not detect any long-lived, slowly diffusing aggregates. While this type of experiment has not yet been done with DNA, it is reasonable to expect that the same result would be found.

Schmitz et al (31) have proposed that the discrepancy between QLS and tracer diffusion measurements can be reconciled by considering the effects of small ions on the dynamics and scattering power of the polyelectrolyte. In this model, the slow mode arises from the formation of "temporal aggregates". These arise as the result of a balance between attractive fluctuating dipole forces coming from the sharing of small ions by several polyions, and repulsive electrostatic and Brownian diffusion forces. This concept is attractive, but needs to be formulated quantitatively before it can be adequately tested.

Schmitz and Lu (12) have also considered coupling of translational and rotational modes for rigid rods in congested solutions as an explanation for the extraordinary diffusion regime. They concluded that, for 350 bp dinucleosomal DNA, the coupled ion model gave better agreement with the data. Since our DNA molecules are even shorter, 150 bp, the coupled translation -rotation model can seemingly be ruled out.

Conclusions

A good deal of systematic experimental work, varying DNA concentration and length, phosphorylation of the ends, salt composition, temperature, and other solvent conditions will be required before more extensive confrontation with theory can take place. It would also be desirable to detect putative end-to-end aggregates directly under gelation conditions, perhaps by tracer diffusion studies. Such a program, taking advantage of the ability of plasmid sequencing and restriction enzyme technology to produce substantial amounts of monodisperse DNA over a range from 100 to 1000 base pairs, is currently under way in our laboratory.

Acknowledgments

I am indebted to Drs. Andrew Fulmer, Julyet Aksiyote-Benbasat,
and Michael Fried for their experimental work on these systems,
and to Prof. Wilmer Miller for the use of his Rheometrics
apparatus. This research was supported by NIH grants GM 17855
and GM 29803.

Literature Cited

1. Fried, M .G.; Bloomfield, V. A. Biopolymers 1984, 23,
   2141-55.
2. Rill, R. L., Hillard, P. R. and Levy, G. C. J. Biol. Chem.
   1983, 258, 250-56.
3. Fulmer, A. W.; Benbasat, J. A.; Bloomfield, V. A. Biopolymers
   1981, 20, 1147-59.
4. Gosule, L. C.; Schellman, J. A. Nature 1976, 259, 333-35.
5. Wilson, R. W.; Bloomfield, V. A. Biochemistry 1979, 18,
   2192-96.
6. Widom, J.; Baldwin, R. L. J. Mol. Biol. 1980 144, 431-53.
7. Thomas, T. J.; Bloomfield, V. A. Biochemistry 1985, 24,
   713-19.
8. Doi, M.; Edwards, S. F. J Chem Soc Trans Faraday Soc II 1978,
   74, 918-32.
9. Sinclair, M.; Lim, K. C.; Heeger, A. J. Phys Rev Lett 1983,
   51, 1768-71.
10. Davis, R. C.; Tinoco, I., Jr. Biopolymers 1968, 6, 223-42.
11. Brahms, J.; Maurizot, J. C.; Michelson, A. M. J. Mol. Biol.
    1967, 25, 481-95.
12. Schmitz, K. S.; Lu, M. Biopolymers 1984, 23, 797-808.
13. Mathiez, P.; Weisbuch, G.; Mouttet, C. Biopolymers 1979, 18,
    1465-78.
14. Mathiez, P.; Mouttet, C.; Weisbuch, G. Biopolymers 1981, 20,
    2381-94.
15. Lin, S-C.; Lee, W. I.; Schurr, J. M. Biopolymers 1978, 17,
    1041-64.
16. Koene, R. S.; Mandel, M. Macromolecules 1983, 16, 973-78.
17. Drifford, M.; Dalbiez, J-P. Biopolymers 1985, 24, 1501-14.
18. Zero, K.; Ware, B. R. J Chem Phys 1984, 80, 1610-16.
19. Shibata, J.; Schurr, J. M. Biopolymers 1979, 18, 1831-33.
20. Wilcoxon, J. P.; Schurr, J. M. J Chem Phys 1983, 78, 3354-64.
21. Schmitz, K. S.; Ramsay, D. J. Macromolecules 1985, 18,
    933-38.
22. Martin, N. B.; Tripp, J. B.; Shibata, J. H.; Schurr, J. M.
    Biopolymers 1979, 18, 2127-33.
23. Stigter, D. Biopolymers 1979, 18, 3125-27.
24. Wigner, E. P. Phys. Rev. 1934, 46, 1002-11.
25. Hurd, A. J.; Clark, N. A.; Mockler, R. C.; O'Sullivan, W.J.
    Phys. Rev. A 1982, 26, 2869-81.
26. Ise, N.; Okubo, T.; Yamamoto, K.; Matsuoka, H.; Kawai, H.;
    Hashimoto, T.; Fujimura, M. J. Chem. Phys. 1983, 78, 541-45.
27. Drifford, M.; Dalbiez, J-P. J. Phys. Chem. 1984, 88, 5368-75.
28. Marcelja, S.; Mitchell, D. J.; Ninham, B. W. Chem. Phys.
    Lett. 1976, 43, 353-57.
29. DeGennes, P. G.; Pincus, P.; Velasco, R. M. Journal de
    Physique 1976, 37, 1461-73.
30. Hurd, A. J.; Clark, N. A.; Mockler, R. C.; O'Sullivan, W. J.
    J. Fluid Mech. 1985, 153, 401-16.
31. Schmitz, K. S.; Lu, M.; Singh, N.; Ramsay, D. J. Biopolymers
    1984, 23, 1637-46.

RECEIVED April 3, 1987

Chapter 14

Thermally Reversible Gelation of the Gelatin-Water System

Madeleine Djabourov and Jacques Leblond

Laboratoire de Physique Thermique, ESPCI 10, rue Vauquelin,
75231 Paris Cedex 05, France

The gelation mechanisms of gelatin aqueous solutions
are examined with the help of several experimental techniques ; optical rotation, electron microscopy and [1]H
nuclear magnetic resonance are used for the structural
investigation. The rheological study of the sol-gel
transition is undertaken with a Weissenberg Rheogoniometer, in oscillatory shear. The conformational coil —>
helix transition of the protein chains is responsible
for the gel formation. Optical rotation measurements reveal that the collagen triple helix is partially rena-
tured. The kinetics of helix growth is analyzed as a
two step process, which does not lead to an equilibrium
configuration within 10^3 hours. The first electron micrographs that we realized by adapting a quick freezing
and deep etching technique show the replica of the fibrous network of the gels. Variable mesh sizes are observed. The rheological parameters at the sol-gel transition have a critical behaviour with respect to the
helix amount. The analysis that we propose is consistent with the predictions of the percolation model.

The aim of this work is to elucidate the mechanisms of gelation of
the gelatin gels and to establish the relations between the microscopic structure and the rheological properties.

The aqueous gelatin gels are well known in the industrial field
for their remarkable ability to gelify. For a wide range of polymer
concentrations (a few percent to fifty percent g cm^{-3}), of pH, of ionic force... the gelatin + water solutions cooled to room temperature
form homogeneous, transparent, mechanically stable gels. The gels recover their fluidity when the temperature is raised back to about
40°C.

Gelatin is a biopolymer : it is denatured collagen. Due to its
natural origin, differences exist between the molecular composition

0097–6156/87/0350–0211$06.00/0
© 1987 American Chemical Society

of gelatins coming from different sources. Moreover the molecular
weight distribution is related also to the method of preparation.

Thus a full investigation of the properties of gelatin gels has
to be done on samples issued from the same batch, to allow quantitative comparisons of the results.

We have concentrated our studies on the influence of thermal
treatments both on the structure of the gels and on their mechanical
properties, in particular around the sol-gel transition.

In this paper, we first briefly recall the main features of the
collagen molecule, then we describe the structure of the gels, using
different experimental techniques (optical rotation (O.R.), electron
microscopy, proton nuclear magnetic resonance (N.M.R.)) for different
thermal treatments. A phenomenological and a microscopic interpretation of the mechanisms of gel formation is suggested.

The rheological properties, during the sol-gel transition, are
investigated with a Weissenberg rheogoniometer in oscillatory shear
(linear behaviour).

The relation with the microscopic structure is pointed up. An
analysis of the sol-gel transition in terms of a critical phenomenon
is proposed.

The collagen molecule

Chemical composition and native conformation. The protein collagen is
issued from animal tissues and bones. In the formula of the polypeptide -(NH-CHR-CO)$_n$-, R represents the lateral group of an amino-acid.
There are as many as twenty different amino-acids in collagen but the
sequences are repeated with a special periodicity. Sequences of the
type -(Gly-X-Pro)- or -(Gly-X-Hypro)- are often observed (X is a different amino-acid). Glycine (Gly) is regularly located every three residues. Ramachandran (1) has shown that the particular composition of
this protein is responsible for its conformation in the native state.
Indeed, the native collagen is a triple helix rod of 270 nm length.
Each chain in the triple helix is a left handed helix with a pitch of
0.9 nm, while the triple helix is a right handed helix with a pitch
about ten times longer, i.e. 8.6 nm. The structure is stabilized by
hydrogen bonds involving CO and NH groups of adjacent chains. Water
molecules placed inside the triple helices also establish   hydrogen
bonds with the proteic chains. The molecular weight of one chain is
around 100.000.

When the collagen rod can be extracted in the native form it is
soluble in acidic solutions, at room temperature. If the solutions are
heated, the collagen is denaturated ; the chains lose their helical
conformation. The characteristic temperature of this helix → coil
transition is around 36°C. The solution then contains principally single chains, but also some double and triple chains which were initially covalently bound and some sub-units of the single chains. This product is gelatin.

Renaturation in solution. When the hot (40°C) solutions are cooled
again the helices are renaturated. The presence of the left handed helices can easily be detected by measuring the optical rotation of the
solutions.

Several mechanisms have been proposed in order to explain the re-

lation between the helix renaturation and the gel formation. They are
summarized in Figure 1.
- Harrington and Rao (2) suggest that in semi-dilute solutions the renaturation of the helices proceeds via the growth of triple helices
  associating different chains. The helical sequences are interrupted
  by loops having coil conformation. One chain being thus involved
  into several helical junctions, a connected network appears (C>0.5%
  g cm^{-3})(see Figure 1-a).
- Eagland et al. (3) propose a different scheme. The helix formation
  is compared to a first order reaction concerning only individual
  chains. In the first step the helices are nucleated and stabilized
  by the solvent. Next, the chains slowly fold back and the helical
  sequences associate by hydrogen bonds. Van der Waals interactions
  or entanglements between the folded chains are responsible for the
  gel gormation (see Figure 1-b).
- Finally, for Godard et al (4), gelation is a crystallization phenomenon. The junctions of the network are fibers made of helices which
  first grow longitudinally. According to their interpretation (the
  fringed micelle model), the diameters of the fibers lie between 5
  and 15 nm, depending on the concentration and on the temperature
  (see Figure 1-c).
    Thus, the mechanisms of gelation determine the structure of the
network, and consequently, the rheological properties of the gels.
    We have tried to explore the gel structure at several microsco-
pic scales : the left handed helix conformation, the supramolecular
structure, showing the kind of helix association (triple helices, fibers, aggregates, ...), the role of the solvent.
    The details of the sample characterization and preparation have
been given elsewhere (5). We concentrate here on the main results.

Structure of the gels

The optical rotation measurements (5) can be used to determine the
amount X of left handed helices present in solution, which is given
by :

$$X = \frac{\text{number of residues in the helical conformation}}{\text{total number of residues in solution}} \tag{1}$$

(a residue is an amino-acid monomer).
    The helix amount is a function of the thermal treatments. We have
done a systematic investigation of this effect in two different ways :
lowering and raising the temperature at constant rates (cycles) or
quenching the hot solutions at different temperatures (T<36°C) and
measuring the time dependence of the helix amount. The second method
was preferred (5).

Gel formation. We plot in Figure 2 the helix amount versus time (in
hours), for quenching and annealing experiments at different temperatures (C=4,7% g cm^{-3}). In Figure 2-a, the time is reported in a linear
scale, while in Figure 2-b it is in a logarithmic scale (up to 10^3
hours). In the first figure, the helix amount seems to tend towards an
asymptotic limit, which is temperature dependent, but in the second
one one sees clearly that no limit exists, one may suppose, until all
the residues would be in a helical conformation (X=1). The transformation is not completed within periods of observation of the order of
10^3 hours.

The phenomenological analysis (6) of the increase of the helix amount X, shows a two step process : the first step is exponential, the second one is logarithmic with time. These two steps can be considered either independent or related to each other.

a- If the two steps are independent, then we may write :

$$X(t,T) = X_o(T)(1-e^{-t/t_R}) + X_1(T)Log(t/t_S+1) \qquad (2)$$

$X_o(T)$ determines the amplitude of the first process, t_R its characteristic time (rapid process), $X_1(T)$ defines the slope versus log t of the second process, t_S is the characteristic time for which the second (slow) process appears.

b- If the two steps are related to each other and the second process realises the maturation of the helices created during the first one, then :

$$X(t,T) = X_o(T)(1-e^{-t/t_R})$$
$$+ X_1(T) \int_o^t d/dt'(1-e^{-t'/t_R})Log\big[(t-t')/t_S+1\big]dt' \qquad (3)$$

We have adjusted the parameters X_o, X_1, t_R, t_S in order to obtain the best fit with the experimental points (the numerical values are given in Ref (6). In Figure 2-b, one can see that both hypothesis seem to be in a reasonable agreement with the experiments. The phenomenological analysis is unable to give an indication of the microscopic mechanisms involved. Further information on the structure is necessary. Some is provided by the melting behaviour of the gels.

Melting behaviour. When the gels are slowly heated (at the rate of 0.05°C/min) we can follow the "melting" of the helices (which means the helix $\rightarrow$ coil transition) by O.R. measurements. The curves giving X versus T, for increasing temperatures, have a sigmoïdal shape ; their derivatives with respect to the temperature determine the mean melting temperatures from the peak position (analogous to the endotherms obtained by differential scanning calorimetry (4)). In Figure 3, we have plotted the melting temperature T_m as a function of the quenching temperature T_q, for gels of concentrations 1 and 4.7% g cm^{-3} which were annealed during 120 to 150 hours. The error bars around the points represent the width of the melting peak. It is of the order of $\Delta T_m \sim$ 10°C for gels prepared at T_q=5°C, which indicates a wide spread of thermal stabilities among the helices which are formed at this temperature. When the solutions are quenched at higher temperature (26 or 28°C), the peak is narrower ($\Delta T_m \sim 5$°C) and it is also shifted to a higher temperature. A secondary peak also appears which has the stability of the collagen rod in the native state ($T_m \cong 36$°C).

We conclude from these experiments that the melting temperature of the gels is an increasing function of the quenching temperature. The best thermal stability which is observed does not exceed that of a collagen rod. This allows us to assume that, at these concentrations (a few percent), strong lateral interactions between the collagen rods do not exist. Such interactions would enhance the thermal stability, compared to the single collagen rod (7) leading to a crystalline structure of the gel.

The difference of thermal stability of the helices is not yet understood : it may come from the length of the helical sequences.

Using these arguments, and some others which will be developed elsewhere, the microscopic model of helix formation that we propose (8) is a molecular mechanism which is close to the scheme proposed by Harrington and Rao (2), summarized on Figure 1-a.

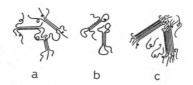

Figure 1. Mechanisms of gelation proposed in the literature :
1-a) triple helix growth (according to ref. (2)); 1-b) single
chain folding (according to ref. (3)) ; 1-c) crystallization model
(according to ref. (4)).

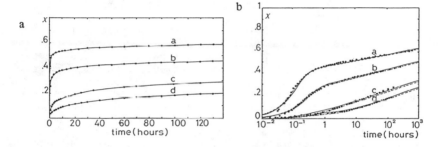

Figure 2. Kinetics of helix growth at different quenching temperatures : a) T = 10°C ; b) T = 20.5°C ; c) T = 26.5°C ; d) T = 28°C
(C = 4.7 %gcm^{-3}). In figure 2-a, time is given in a linear scale,
in hours. In figure 2-b, time is in a logarithmic scale, up to 10^3
hours. The continuous line is calculated using eq. (2), the dotted
line is calculated using eq. (3).

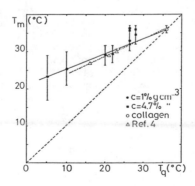

Figure 3. Melting temperature versus quenching temperature for
gels. The collagen melting temperature in dilute solutions is also
quoted.

Supramolecular structure. The observation of the supramolecular structure is of a primary importance both for elucidating the mechanisms of
helix growth and defining the parameters of the network.

Electron microscopic techniques can be used in order to visualize
the architecture of the network. We have adapted (P. Favard, N. Favard,
M. Djabourov, J. Leblond, to be published) a method recently proposed
by Heuser (9) (1978), for the observation of biological cells and tissues.

It consists first of quickly freezing the sample by pushing it
against a copper plate, previously cooled with liquid helium (10K).
Close to the gel surface very high rates of cooling $(2-3.10^4 K/S)$ are
achieved, which vitrify water over a depth of 10 to 20μm. The growth
of ice crystals being avoided, the polymer network structure is preserved. Then the amorphous water is sublimated and a replica of the
network is obtained by evaporating Pt and C over the rotating sample.
Stereoscopic images of the replica give the three dimensional organization of the network.

The first micrographs that we obtained for dilute gels (C=0.5%
g cm^{-3}) show a dense filamentous network of variable mesh sizes (see
Figure 4). A quantitative estimation of its parameters is not yet possible. The replicas show filaments with various diameters, corresponding to a minimum of 1.5 or 2nm (diameter of a triple helix) the Pt/C
coating thinckens the filaments. On some micrographs however larger
(10nm) filaments appear, but the conditions could not be reproduced
yet. A systematic investigation of the factors which play a role in
the process of replication, is under way. So, we intend to visualize
the network, at different stages of maturation, in well controlled
thermal conditions of gelation.

Role of the solvent in the gel formation. By proton NMR we have shown
(10) that water participates to the helix formation. A modification
of the relaxation times of water protons was observed during gelation.
While the spin-lattice relaxation time, T_1, is unaffected by the gelation process (depends only on temperature and concentration), a pro-
gressive decrease of the spin-spin relaxation time T_2 is noticed during quenching experiments, suggesting that an increasing fraction of
protons is incorporated into a rigid structure. In the gel state,
three water populations can be defined : free water, which is characterized by a relaxation time $T_2 \sim 2s$; bound water, which interacts
with the polypeptide in the coiled conformation, $T_2 \sim 300ms$; structural water which has a much shorter relaxation time, $T_2 \sim 0,2ms-1ms$. Within the assumption of a rapid exchange between the various proton
populations, the inverse of the relaxation time T_2 is proportional to
the fraction of structural water. Indeed, we have shown, for quenching
experiments, that the relaxation rate T_2^{-1} is proportional to the helix amount X, measured independently by O.R., for the same conditions.
The theoretical interpretation of the data that we propose (10) is
consistent with the models known for the collagen rod stabilization
by hydrogen bonds including water molecules (cf. the collagen structure (1)).

We conclude the structural analysis by stressing on two points.
First, the disorder of the structure appears both from the melting
behaviour and from the micrographs inspection. This character inhe-
rently belongs to the gel state, which is not an equilibrium state.

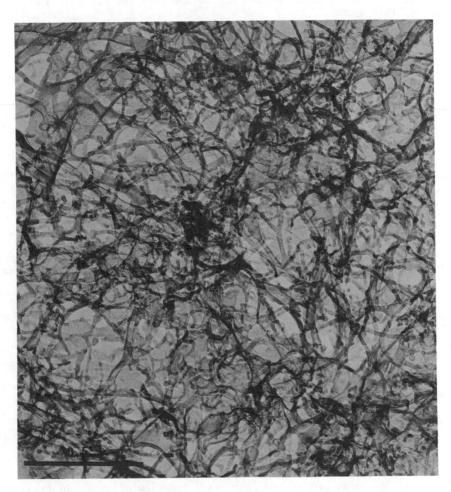

Figure 4. Replica of a gelatin gel of concentration c = 0.5 % g cm^{-3}, matured at room temperature, during fifteen days. The bar represents 0.5 μ. A dense fibrous network of variable mesh sizes is observed.

The gel continuously proceeds towards the stable equilibrium, but does not reach it within reasonable periods of observation. Second, the solvent mobility is modified by the gel formation. Water is included into the structure and stabilizes the helices. These two features seem to be common to a great number of physical polymer gels.

We show in the next section how we analyzed the sol-gel transition of this system.

Sol-gel transition

When the helix amount increases the medium changes from a viscous liquid (sol) to an elastic solid (gel). The kinetics of gelation depends strongly on the quenching temperature. The rheological measurements that we performed are particularly focused on the sol-gel transition and on the definition of the "gel point". The greatest difficulty encountered is due to the weakness of the bonds which can easily be destroyed by the mechanical stress.

We measured the shear modulus G(f) with a Weissenberg rheogoniometer with a cone and plane geometry, in oscillatory regime. The strain, ε, is given by the ratio of the angular deformation of the lower plate to the cone angle, the stress σ is proportional to the angular displacement of the upper plate (the cone). The shear modulus G is given by :

$$G^* = \sigma/\varepsilon \qquad (4)$$

It is a complex quantity. The phase lag ϕ between the stress and the strain determines the real part G' (the elastic component) and the imaginary part G" (the loss component) :

$$G^* = |G|[\cos\phi + i\sin\phi] = G'+iG''$$
$$|G| = \sqrt{G'^2 + G''^2} \qquad (5)$$

G' and G" are generally frequency dependent. We varied the frequency f between :

$$10^{-2} < f < 1\text{Hz}$$

The strain was kept as low as possible ($\sim$10%) to avoid disturbances.

The stress and strain signal were recorded and analyzed using a numerical oscilloscope (Nicolet 4094).

Gelation at different temperatures. We have followed the kinetics of gelation during quenching experiments, at temperatures $24 < T_q < 28°C$ and a concentration of 4.7% g cm^{-3}. We represent on Figure 5-a, the modulus, $|G|$, measured at f=0.15Hz, as a function of time (up to 400min), for seven temperatures. One can notice that the kinetics is extremely sensitive to the temperature ; the slope of $|G|$ versus time decreases by a factor 10, when the temperature is raised by only 4°C. On Figure 5-b, we plot the helix amount, deduced from O.R. measurements, in the same thermal conditions. Finally, the shear modulus versus the helix amount is given on Figure 5-c. For all the gelation temperatures, the kinetics condense nearly on a single curve (small discrepancies may come from the accuracy of the temperature measurement which is of the order of 0.1°C).

The relation between the shear modulus and the helix amount is not a linear one : for helix amounts below 6%, $X<6\%$, the moduli are

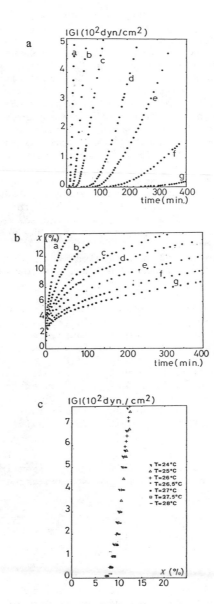

Figure 5. The sol gel transition. Figure 5-a : the shear modulus
|G| measured at f = 0.15 Hz as a function of time during quenching
experiments at several temperatures : a) T = 24°C ; b) T = 25°C ;
c) T − 26°C ; d) t = 26.5°C ; e) T = 27°C ; f) T = 27.5°C ; g) T =
28°C (C = 4.7 % g cm^{-3}). Figure 5-b : the helix amount measured by
O.R. in the same conditions. Figure 5-c : the shear modulus as a
function of the helix amount at the beginning of gelation.

small ($|G| \sim 1$ to 10 dyn.cm^{-2}) and are essentially of a viscous nature. Viscoelastic effects appear in the range $6 < X < 8\%$, which need a precise frequency dependence analysis. Above $X \sim 8\%$, the shear moduli are almost independent of the frequency : the medium behaves like an elastic solid ($G'' \cong 0$). In this range, up to $X \sim 15\%$, the elastic modulus increases sharply with the helix amount. The value of 2000 dyn.cm^{-2} corresponds to a helix amount $X \sim 15\%$.

Several conclusions can be drawn from these observations :
- In the range of temperatures investigated, the same structures are nucleated and grow, during quenching experiments, for $X < 15\%$;
- The helix amount appears as the "key" parameter for the gel formation. As for chemical gelation, the temperature influences only the kinetics of the reaction, but not the structure. However, in our case, a temperature increase slows down the process.
- There is a threshold between the sol and gel states determined by the helix amount. It is situated around $X = 7\%$, for a gel of concentration 4.7% g cm^{-3}. The elastic modulus increasing with the number of bonds between chains, we may assume that the junctions are due to the helical sequences.

All these arguments led us to analyze the sol-gel transition as a critical phenomenon, following the ideas put forward by the percolation models (11)(12).

Critical exponents. During gelation, while the modulus $|G|$ increases, the phase lagϕ between stress and strain shifts progressively from $\pi/2$, which corresponds to a newtonian liquid, to almost 0, which characterizes an elastic solid. In the whole viscoelastic range we have determined the frequency dependence of $G''(f)$ and of $G'(f)$, at different instants of gelation. This analysis (8) allowed us to propose a general method to determine the "gel point" which is the moment when a static shear modulus appears. Applying this criterion to the kinetics of gelation at T=27.4°C, we could define the critical helix content corresponding to the "gel point", with a fairly good approximation

$$6,95\% < X_c < 7,1\%$$

The modulus G' measured at f=0,015Hz is given in Figure 6 as a function of the distance to the gel point, evaluated by the helix amount $\dfrac{X - X_c}{X_c}$

The plot is in a log-log scale.

Close to the gel point, in the range $\Delta X / X_c < 0.1$, the static modulus cannot be measured. Strong relaxation effects are present even at the lowest frequency which could be used, to be consistent with the kinetics (one period of oscillation = 67s). Beyond this range for $\Delta X / X_c > 0.1$, G' (0,015Hz) corresponds to the static relaxed modulus. A critical exponent for the relaxed modulus can be determined by using the equation :

$$G \sim \left(\frac{X - X_c}{X_c}\right) t \tag{6}$$

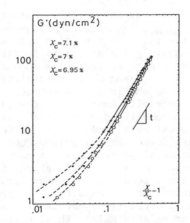

Figure 6. The log-log plot of the shear modulus G' measured at f = 0.015 Hz, versus $(X - X_c)/X_c$. The slopes of the continuous lines give the critical exponents t.

where t=1.82±0.15, the modulus increasing from 10 to 100 $dyn.cm^{-2}$ for
a helix amount :

   $0.1 < \Delta X/X_c < 0.4$

The values of t are in agreement with the predictions of the percolation model (12) for the electrical conductance of a random network.

Conclusion

The process of gelation of gelatin gels is closely connected to the
conformational transition of the protein chains. When the solutions
are cooled below 36°C, the collagen triple helix association is partially recovered. The structure of the gels depends on the whole thermal history : the equilibrium configuration does not settle, for a given temperature. The kinetics studies show that helix growth in quenching experiments is a two-stage process. The interpretation of a microscopic mechanisms for each stage has to be clarified by direct
structural measurements (X ray and neutron scattering experiments are
underway).

     The rheology of the sol-gel transition was undertaken with spe-
cial care in order to avoid gel disruption. A critical behaviour for
the shear modulus with respect to the helix amount, is noticed. A
simple relation between the rheological parameters and the degree of
helix formation is pointed out in a limited range of helix amounts
(X<15%). These experiments will continue on the fully matured gels.

     Physical gels, as exemplified by gelatin gels, exhibit many com-
mon features with chemical gels. Among them, we found the topological
disorder of the network formed by the polymer chains, and the formal
similarity of the process of gelation with a percolation problem.

     The great difference comes from the nature of the bonds : the
hydrogen bound gels have a much more complexe structure than a chemical network. The junctions of the physical gels are finite domains,
which can either be of a crystalline nature or a multi-chain association (triple helix, for gelatin gels). Thus, physical gels may have
very different architectures. Our efforts will be devoted now to the
precise analysis of the network geometrical parameters, in order to
explain the origin of elasticity for the gelatin gels.

Literature cited

1. Ramachandran,R.N., "Treatise on collagen", N.Y. Academic Press,
    1967, chap. III.
2. Harrington, W.F. ; Rao, N.V., Biochemistry, 1970, 9, 3714.
3. Eagland, D. ; Pilling, G. ; Weeler, R.G., Farad. Disc. Chem. Soc.
    1974, 57, 181.
4. Godard, P. ; Biebuyck, J.J. ; Daumerie, M. ; Naveau, H. ; Mercier,
    J.P., J. Polym. Phys. Ed., 1978, 16, 1817.
5. Djabourov, M. ; Papon, P., Polymer, 1983, 24, 539.
6. Djabourov, M. ; Maquet, J. ; Theveau, H. ; Leblond, J. ; Papon,
    P., Brit. Polym. J., 1985, 17, 169.
7. Flory, P. ; Garrett, R.R., J. Am. Chem. Soc. 1958, 80, 4836.
8. Djabourov, M., thèse d'Etat, Paris, 1986.

9.   Heuser, J., J. Cell. Biol., 1978, <u>79</u>, 224a.
10. Maquet, J. ; Theveneau, H. ; Djabourov. M. ; Leblond, J. ; Papon, P., Polymer, 1986, <u>27</u>, 1103.
11. Stauffer, D., J. Chem. Soc. Farad. Trans. 1976, <u>72</u>, 1354.
12. De Gennes, P.G., "Scaling concepts in polymer physics", Cornell University Press, 1979.

RECEIVED March 5, 1987

Chapter 15

In Vitro Polymerization of Complex Cytoplasmic Gels

Ralph Nossal

Physical Sciences Laboratory, Division of Computer Research and Technology, National Institutes of Health, Bethesda, MD 20892

Solutions are obtained to kinetic equations that pertain to a theoretical model having features similar to those of polymerizing cytoplasm. The effects of various factors on network formation and elasticity, including chain dissociation, the activity of capping proteins, initial monomer concentration, and the presence of crosslinking proteins are investigated. Assays for studying properties of reconstituted cytoplasmic networks are analyzed, and criteria for effective use of gel fraction determinations, gelation time assays, and elasticity measurements are investigated.

All eucaryotic cells contain various proteins in their cytoplasm that interact to form mechanically stabilizing structures. The amounts of these proteins differ with cell type, and the structural elements - collectively referred to as the cytoskeleton - can be very labile. Labile transformations of cytoskeletal networks are involved in such essential biological phenomena as chromosome movement and cell division, intracellular material transport, shape changes relating to tissue development, and amoeboid-like locomotion (1-3). A great deal of work in recent years has led to the biochemical characterization of numerous cytoskeletal proteins(4) and the elucidation of their spatial localization within a cell(2). However, few quantifiable models yet exist that are appropriate for incorporating that information into notions of shape transformation and cell movement(5-8).

Several mathematical theories concerning in vitro nucleation and polymerization of cytoskeletal proteins into linear polymeric structures have been developed. Particularly notable is the work of Oosawa and collaborators(9) on the rate limiting cooperative nucleation of actin monomers, and that of Wegner(10) on the asymmetric ATP-driven addition and dissolution

of monomers from both ends of linear molecules ('treadmilling').
In contrast, although various molecules are known to effect the
formation of cytoplasmic networks through the crosslinking or
bundling of filaments(11,12), almost no theoretical work has
been done to relate the gelation of such structures to specific
characteristics of their constituent proteins.

The principal cytoskeletal proteins in non-muscle cells are
actin, tubulin, and the components of 'intermediate filaments'.
Actin can exist either as monomers ('G-actin') or polymerized
into ~70 Å diameter double filament ('F-actin'). Polymerized
actin usually is localized at the margins of the cells, linked
by other proteins to the cell membrane. In contrast, tubulin
forms hollow filaments, approximately 250 Å in diameter, that
are distributed within a cell in association, generally, with
cell organelles. Stabilized microtubule structures are found in
the flagella and cilia of eucaryotic cells; however, in other
instances - examples being the mitotic apparatus and the cytoskeletal elements arising in directed cell locomotion - the
microtubules are temporal entities. Intermediate filaments,
which are composed of keratin-like proteins, are approximately
100 Å thick and form stable structural elements that impart
rigidity, for example, to nerve axons and epithelial cells.

The work that follows pertains primarily to actin networks.
Many proteins within a cell are known to associate with actin.
Among these are molecules which can initiate or terminate
polymerization, intercalate with and cut chains, crosslink or
bundle filaments, or induce network contraction (i.e., myosin)
(4,11,12). The central concern of this paper is an exploration
of the way that such molecular species interact to form complex
networks. Ultimately we wish to elucidate the biophysical
linkages between molecular properties and cellular function
(like locomotion and shape differentiation) in which cytoskeletal structures are essential attributes. Here, however, we
examine the in vitro formation of cytoplasmic gels, with an
emphasis on delineating quantitative assays for network constituents. Specific attention is given to gel volume assays,
determinations of gelation times, and elasticity measurements.
We hope, too, that insights gained from in vitro studies will
serve in the design of new experiments involving intact cells.

Any study of this kind naturally involves making
assumptions and compromises. We first need to choose a
tractable model of nucleation and polymerization, then a model
for the crosslinking of filaments. Finally, decisions have to
be made regarding those aspects of gelation and elasticity that
are central to the analysis, and those which can be ignored
until later. In the next section we discuss a model for
reversible elongation of linear polymers which allows for the
conversion of "active" to "capped" chains. A set of kinetic
equations is devised and solved for the case that filament
nucleation is very rapid compared with chain elongation and
termination. The analytical expressions that are obtained for
average chain length then are used to assess the information
that can be obtained from gelation assays involving crude,
unfractionated cytoplasmic extracts(13). The possibilities of

relating gelation time to network characteristics also are
examined. Finally, we investigate how network elasticity can be
used to measure the concentrations of crosslinking proteins and
other constituents in complex reactive mixtures. The discussion
mostly is limited to illustrative examples, our intention being
to present details and elaborations in other publications.

Model for Reversible Chain Elongation (Linear Growth)

The scheme shown in Figure 1 represents a polymerization process
where i_0 actin monomers associate with a nucleation site n to
form a protofilament to which subsequent actin monomers can add
and elongate a strand. Pure actin solutions are
self-nucleating, in that three or four actin monomers spontane-
ously interact to form a site to which other actin monomers then
add individually(9). The spontaneous nucleation of actin chains
is an unfavorable process, and generally is the limiting step in
polymerization reactions which involve only actin monomers
(G-actin). However, if a G-actin solution is 'seeded' with
small F-actin fragments, the latter act as nuclei and polymerization then is very rapid. Under certain conditions
actin-associated proteins such as gelsolin also initiate actin
filament growth(14) and, within cells, actin filament growth
probably is initiated by specific entities linked to the cell
surface(15,16). Moreover, for present purposes it is sufficient
to note that polystyrene latex beads, when covered with anionic
polypeptides, can nucleate actin filament growth(17). Thus, we
neglect the complications that accompany self-nucleation, and
assume that the formation of nuclei is irreversible and
instantaneous. The subsequent addition of monomer occurs with
an association constant $K_a \equiv k^+/k^- \equiv 1/K_a^-$, where the rate
constants k^+, k^- can be affected by the presence of nucleotides,
salts, and other factors(9,14,18). At each step a "capping
molecule", e, can bind and terminate chain growth, with an
association constant $K_e \equiv k_e^+/k_e^- \equiv 1/K_e^D$ (K_a^D and K_e^D signify
dissociation constants.)

If $C_1(t)$ indicates the number of free monomer units in the
assembly (e.g., G-actin), a kinetic equation for the depletion
of free monomer may be written, in accordance with the scheme
shown in Figure 1, as

$$dC_1/dt = -(k^+C_1 - k^-)N \tag{1}$$

where N is the total number of uncapped chains. We assume that
$C_1(t=0) = C_0$, in which case Equation 1 has the solution

$$C_1(t) = K_a^D + (C_0 - K_a^D) e^{-k^+ \int_0^t N(s)ds} \tag{2}$$

If we assume, also, that the nuclei and capping molecule
concentrations are fixed at the start of the experiment (t=0)
then, by virtue of our assumption that nucleation is rapid
compared with chain elongation, an equation for N(t) is given as

$$dN/dt = -k_e^+ eN + k_e^- (n_0 - N) \tag{3}$$

$$= -k_e^+ [(e_0 - n_0 + K_e^D)N + N^2 - K_e^D n_0] \tag{3'}$$

where n_0 now signifies the total number of chains, both 'active' and 'capped'. (To obtain Equation 3' we note that $e = e_0 - (n_0 - N)$). A solution to the above equation is easily obtained, but for illustrative purposes we consider the special case where e_0 is in excess, so that the free capping protein concentration e is approximately constant (i.e., $\rho \equiv n_0/e_0 \ll 1$). In this case Equation 3' as the form

$$dn/dt \approx - k_e^+ [(e_0 + K_e^D) N - K_e^D n_0] \tag{4}$$

which has the solution

$$N(t) = N_0 e^{-k_e^+(e_0+K_e^D)t} + K_e^D n_0(e_0+K_e^D)^{-1} (1-e^{-k_e^+(e_0+K_e^D)t}) \tag{5}$$

Thus, from Equations 2, 4, and the relationship that the average chain length $\langle r \rangle_t$ is given as the total amount of monomer incorporated into polymer $\Delta C(t)$ divided by the number of chains $N(t) = n_0$, one finds

$$\langle r \rangle_t = [C_1(0) - C_1(t)]/n_0$$

$$= n_0^{-1}(C_0 - K_e^D) [1 - \exp(-n_0 k^+ f(t)/k_e^+ e_0)] \tag{6}$$

where $\bar{K}_e^D \equiv K_e^D/e_0 = k_e^-/(k_e^+ e_0)$, and $f(t)$ is defined as

$$f(t) = (1+\bar{K}_e^D)^{-2} \{1 - \exp(-k_e^+ e_0(1+\bar{K}_e^D)t\} + (1+\bar{K}_e^D)^{-1} k_e^- t.$$

If capping is irreversible, i.e., $\bar{K}_e^D = 0$, Equation 6 takes the relatively simple form

$$\langle r \rangle_t = n_0^{-1}(C_0 - K_a^D) \{1 - \exp(-n_0 k^+(k_e^+ e_0)^{-1} (1 - e^{-k_e^+ e_0 t}))\} \tag{7}$$

so that in the long-time limit one finds

$$\langle r \rangle_{t=\infty} = n_0^{-1} (C_0 - K_a^D) \{1 - \exp(-n_0 k^+(k_e^+ e_0)^{-1})\}, \quad (\text{if } K_e^D = 0.) \tag{8a}$$

In contrast, if $K_e^D \neq 0$ the average chain length tends to a value which depends only on the kinetic parameters for chain elongation, viz.,

$$\langle r \rangle_{t=\infty} = n_0^{-1}(C_0 - K_a^D), \quad\quad (\text{if } K_e^D \neq 0.) \tag{8b}$$

Gel Fraction Assay

When concentrated solutions of cytoplasmic extracts of certain cells are warmed to room temperature, the proteins form gels

which can be separated from the solution by low speed
centrifugation(13). The amount of the protein in the gel, as a
function of the concentration of protein in the extract, appears
as seen in Figure 2a. We now show how the shape of such curves
can be explained and related to parameters of network formation.

We again utilize the model discussed in the previous
section, viz., a network composed of chains whose average length
is <r> monomeric units, where r depends on various parameters
related to nucleation, polymerization, and capping. We need,
also, to make an assumption about the manner in which the chains
are crosslinked. For illustration, we assume that our gels are
crosslinked by "actin binding protein"(19), which forms
tetrafunctional junctions between actin strands. In such
instance the fraction of all monomers which are in the gel
network, g, is given as the solution of the following
equation(20)

$$(1 - g) = (1 - \alpha g)^r \tag{9}$$

where $\alpha < 1$ is the fraction of all units which participate
directly in crosslinking.

The solutions to Equation 9 are those values of g for
which the functional $f=(1-g)^{1/r}$ intersects the functional
$\bar{f}=(1-\alpha g)$, where $r=fcn[C_0,k^+,k^-,n_0,e_0,k_e^+,k_e^-]$ and α in general
also is a function of the same variables. Actin binding protein
(ABP) joins contiguous chains and α therefore depends on strand
density and network topology in addition to the intrinsic rate
constants for attachment of ABP to an available binding site.
If A_0 is the total concentration of ABP in the assembly (both
free and bound), then, to first order, the amount of ABP that is
incorporated into the network (after a stationary state is
achieved) is given as

$$A_\infty = A_0/(1 + (K_X S_X)^{-1}) \tag{10}$$

where S_X is the concentration of binding sites and K_X is an
appropriate association constant. (Equation 10 follows from a
simple mass-action equation.) ABP is believed to bind two actin
filaments only when their orientation is such that they cross
approximately at right angles(21). Chain polarity, too, may be
important, so S_X may be a rather complicated function of spatial
orientation. However, the concentration of overlap points
primarily depends on the amount of monomer which is incorporated
into the chains, viz.,

$$S_X \sim (\Delta C)^\beta \equiv \gamma(\Delta C)^\beta \tag{11}$$

where $\beta=2$ has been calculated by mean field theory and $\beta=9/4$ by
a scaling theory which takes into account excluded volume(22).
The coefficient γ is unknown, and we here consider it to subsume
those topological factors upon which S_X might depend.

The crosslink fraction α is related to the number of
crosslinked sites and the amount of polymer as

$$\alpha = 2A_\infty/(C_0 - C_1(\infty)) = 2A_\infty/\Delta C_\infty \tag{12}$$

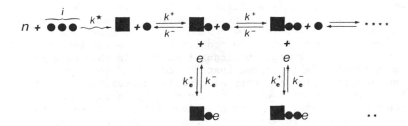

Fig. 1: Kinetic scheme used to approximate polymerization
of linear capped actin filaments.

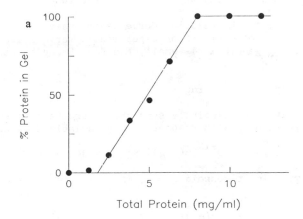

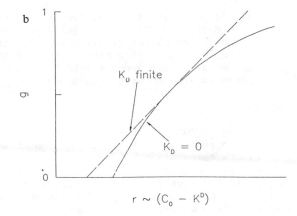

Fig. 2: a) Results of gel fraction assay on cytoplasmic
extracts of Ehrlich ascites cells (after Ishiura
and Okada(13)).
b) Solution of Equation 9 for r=50, chosen for
purpose of illustration.

where we here signify a stationary state (i.e., $t \rightarrow \infty$). The assay shown in Figure 2a involves varying the amount of crude cell extract, for which the concentration of crosslinking molecules always changes in proportion to the concentration of actin and other cytoplasmic constituents. In this case it is not unreasonable to assume that the amount of monomer incorporated into filaments also varies approximately as the total amount of extract, so that $\alpha \approx A_0/C_0$ is approximately constant, whatever the concentration of the crude extract. It is easy to solve Equation 9 to obtain results which are qualitatively shown in Figure 2b. A gelation threshold exists which, by this model, is independent of any special nucleation kinetics for filaments. Thus, the requirement that the monomer concentration exceed a critical value, noted for pure actin solutions, is not in any way implied by the results of these gelation assays.

The slope of the gelation curve can be used to learn about the dependences of $\underline{\alpha}$ or $\langle r \rangle$ on experimental variables. Because the product $\underline{\alpha g}$ generally is small, Equation 9 can be rewritten as

$$\ln (1-g) \approx - r\alpha g \tag{13}$$

from which it is a relatively straightforward task to show that the derivative of $\underline{g}$ with respect to any variable $\underline{X}$ is given by

$$g^{-1}[(1-g)^{-1} + g^{-1} \ln(1-g)] \, dg/dX = d(\alpha r)/dX \tag{14}$$

Near the gelation threshold (i.e., if $g \ll 1$) one finds the yet simpler form

$$(1-g)^{-1} \, dg/dX = d(\alpha r)/dX \tag{15}$$

Equation 15 can aid in designing gel fraction assays for differing tasks. In certain instances the gel fraction will vary in proportion to the amount of crosslinking protein. However, if, for example, the capping protein concentration is varied, $(1-g)^{-1} \, dg/de$ can change according to Equation 8a as the product of an exponential and inverse square power of $\underline{e}_0$.

Gelation Time Assay

Rather than measuring the amount of material in the gel fraction, it might be easier to determine the time at which gelation of a network takes place. (For example, one could focus a laser beam on a sample and note when the speckle interference pattern 'freezes'.) Gelation occurs in a developing network if the crosslink fraction α exceeds a critical value α_c, given as[23]

$$\alpha_c = 2[(f_w-2)(r-1)]^{-1} \tag{16}$$

where f_w is the average functionality of the network junctions
(i.e., the number of strands joined at a junction). Two
fundamentally different situations should be considered: in one
instance preformed chains are used and the gel time depends
solely on crosslinking kinetics; the other is the case where
actin filaments polymerize while gelation takes place.
   The mathematics again must be tailored to specific
applications but, as an illustration, we consider the case that
chains polymerize while being crosslinked by ABP, the latter
forming tetrafunctional junctions ($f_w = 4$). We assume that
binding of ABP occurs sufficiently fast that network formation
is limited only by chain growth kinetics, so that the condition
$\alpha \geq \alpha_c$ implies $(2A/\Delta C) \geq (\langle r \rangle - 1)^{-1}$, and (cf. Equation 10)

$$2A_0 (1 + (K_X S_X)^{-1}) \geq n_0 \tag{17}$$

where S_X implicitly is a function of $\Delta C(t)$. (To obtain
Equation 17 we note that $(\langle r \rangle_t -1) \sim \langle r \rangle_t) = \Delta C(t)/n_0$.) If we
manipulate Equation 17 and use the relationship given by
Equation 11, it follows that gelation occurs when $t=t^*$, where t^*
is given as the solution of

$$\Delta C(t^*) = \{\bar{K}_X [2A_0/n_0 -1]\}^{-1/\beta} \tag{18}$$

where $\bar{K}_X$ is defined as $\bar{K}_X \equiv \gamma K_X$.
   Suppose, for example, that capping protein is in excess and
that capping is irreversible. Then, by Equations 7 and 18,
we readily find that the time to gelation is given as

$$t^* = -(e_0 k_e^+)^{-1} \cdot$$
$$\cdot \ln\{1+k_e^+ e_0 (n_0 k^+)^{-1} \ln[1-(C_0 -K_a^D)^{-1}[\bar{K}_X(2A_0/n_0-1)]^{-1/\beta}]\} \tag{19}$$

Equation 19 appears to be a complicated function of many kinetic
constants. However, if the ratio A_0/n_0 is sufficiently large,
the expression given in Equation 19 becomes

$$t^* \approx (n_0 k^+(C_0 -K_a^D))^{-1} [\bar{K}_X(2A_0/n_0)]^{-1/\beta} \tag{20}$$

In this case one could calibrate an assay with a known
concentration $A_0^{stand.}$ and determine unknown quantities A_0
according to the simple relationship

$$t^*/t^*_{stand.} \approx (A_0/A_0^{stand.})^{-1/\beta} \tag{21}$$

Elasticity Assays

Elasticity measurements already have been used to detect the
presence of crosslinking proteins in cytoplasmic extracts(24).
If preformed actin chains are employed, assessment of the
rheological state of a network directly provides information
about the parameters of crosslinking. Moreover, chain growth
can be studied, although indirectly, through the effects of C_0,
n_0, K_a^D,...etc. on the concentration of crosslinking sites S_X.

Beyond the gel point, the shear modulus is related to the number of primary network chains n_0 and the crosslink fraction α as(23)

$$G^{asymp} \approx (\alpha_0)^{-1} (\alpha-\alpha_0) \, n_0 \psi k_\beta T/V_0 \tag{22}$$

where k_B is Boltzmann's constant, T is the temperature, V_0 is the volume of the unstressed network, and ψ is a factor (of order unity) which depends on network topology(23). α_c is given by Equation 16. The term α_0 is proportional to α_c, being given as (23,25)

$$\alpha_0 \approx \alpha_c \, [\textstyle\sum_{j=2}^{\infty} jw_j - 1]/[1-\sum_{j=2}^{\infty} w_j/j], \text{ (large <r>)} \tag{23}$$

where w_j is the fraction of junctions having functionality $2j$. When a network is crosslinked only by ABP, one discerns from Equation 23 that α_0 is related to α_c as $\alpha_0 \sim 2\alpha_c$ and finds from Equations 12 and 22 that $\underline{G}$ is related to $\underline{A}$ and n_0 as

$$G^{asymp} \approx (A-n_0)\psi k_\beta T/V_0 \tag{24}$$

Strictly speaking, Equation 23 pertains to networks of Gaussian chains which interact only at junctions; chain entanglements and intrachain molecular interactions have been neglected. Note that $\underline{G}$ is the zero (low) frequency storage modulus.

We again consider a network crosslinked by actin binding protein. The number of crosslinks that are formed, $\underline{A}$, is given by Equation 10, and a plot of $\underline{G}$ vs $\underline{A_0}$ (the total amount of added ABP) is shown, schematically, in Figure 3. Both the slope and the intercept $\underline{A_0}^*$ provide information about the kinetic parameters of network formation. Elasticity determinations clearly can be used to assess the amount of crosslinking protein in an assembly: if all other conditions are kept constant, $\underline{G}$ varies linearly with $\underline{A_0}$; consequently, after appropriate calibration (in principle with only two data points), elasticity measurements could be used for quantitative assessment of the efficacy of biochemical purification procedures. Parenthetically, we note that if conditions can be arranged such that $K_X S_X >> 1$, $\underline{A_0}^*$ gives a direct measure of the number of nuclei $\underline{n_0}$.

Generally, however, $\underline{A}$ depends implicitly on other network parameters. The dependencies can be assessed by investigating the slope of $\underline{G}$ as experimental conditions are changed. For example, if capping is irreversible ($\bar{K}_e = 0$), $\underline{G}$ varies with the amount of capping protein as (cf. Equation 24)

$$(\psi V_0^{-1} k_\beta T)^{-1} \, \partial G/\partial e_0 = \partial A/\partial e_0$$

$$= -\beta \gamma A_0 (\Delta C)^{\beta-1} K_X (1+K_X S_X)^{-2} (C_0-K_a^D) n_0 k^+ (k_e^+ e_0^2)^{-1} \exp(-n_0 k^+/k_e^+ e_0) \tag{25}$$

In this instance $\underline{G}$ changes as an inverse power of $\underline{e_0}$

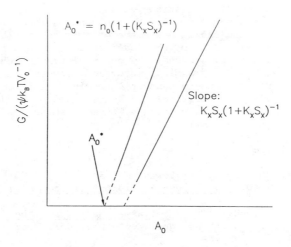

Fig. 3: Schematic representation of the way that the shear modulus G varies with changes in the amount of crosslinking protein.

(approximately as $e_0^{-(\beta+1)}$). In contrast, if capping is rever-
sible (i.e., $K_e^D \neq 0$), $\underline{G}$ will be insensitive to changes in $\underline{e}_0$
(cf. Equation 8b).

Comments

The examples that are presented above are meant to illustrate
the possibilities and limitations of various assays for
constituents of complex networks. Although analytical
expressions in general may be rather complicated, conditions
frequently can be found that considerably simplify the results.
Thus, appropriate mathematical models can yield important
insights into assay design.
        Various elaborations of our analysis certainly need to be
developed. In addition to assuming special models for polymerization and crosslinking, the present investigation is incomplete
in that the fundamental equations, Equations 9, 16 and 22,
involve approximations commonly made in applications of polymer
theory. Still to be examined are the effects of spatial
segregation on gelation, and the modifications to elasticity
theory necessitated by stiffness of polymer strands, chain
entanglements, and the dynamical nature of network elements.
Perhaps persons who usually concern themselves with simpler,
'chemical', gels will be stimulated to use their considerable
expertise to elucidate properties of these fascinating and
important natural systems.

Literature Cited

1. Alberts, B.; Bray, D.; Lewis, J.; Raff, M.; Roberts, K.;
    Watson, J. D. The Molecular Biology of the Cell; Garland:
    New York, 1983.
2. Porter, K., Ed.; The Cytoplasmic Matrix and the Integration
    of Cellular Function; supplement to J. Cell Biol. 1984,
    99(1,Pt.2), 3s-248s.
3. Allen, R. D. Ann. Rev. Biophys. Chem. 1985, 14, 265-290.
4. Korn, E. D. Physiol. Rev. 1982, 62, 672-737.
5. Oster, G. F.; Odell, G. M. Physica 1984, 12D, 333-350.
6. Odell, G. M. J. Embryol. Exp. Morph. 1984, 83(Suppl.),
    261-287.
7. Oster, G. F. J. Embryol. Exp. Morph. 1984, 83(Suppl.),
    329-364
8. Dembo, M.; Harlow, F. Biophys. J. 1986, 50, 109-121.
9. Oosawa, F.; Asakura, S. Thermodynamics of the
    Polymerization of Protein; Academic: New York, 1975.
10. Wegner, A. J. Mol. Biol. 1976, 108, 139-150.
11. Weeds, A. Nature 1982, 296, 811-816.
12. Stossel, T. P.; Chaponnier, C.; Ezzell, R.; Hartwig, J. H.;
    Janmey, P. A.; Lind, S. E.; Smith, D. B.; Southwick, F. S.;
    Yin, H. L.; Zaner, K. S. Ann. Rev. Cell Biol. 1985, 1,
    353-402.
13. Ishiura, M.; Okada, Y. J. Cell Biol. 1979, 80, 465-480.
14. Stossel, T. P. J. Cell Biol. 1984, 99(1,Pt.2), 15s-21s.

15. Geiger, B.; Avnur, Z.; Rinnerthaler, G.; Hinssen, H.; Small, J. V. J. Cell Biol. 1984, 99(1,Pt.2), 83s-91s.
16. Mangeat, P.; Burridge, K. J. Cell Biol. 1984, 99(1,Pt.2), 95s-103s.
17. Brown, S. S.; Spudich, J. A. J. Cell Biol. 1979, 80, 499-504.
18. Pollard, T. D.; Mooseker, M. S. J. Cell Biol. 1981, 88, 654-659.
19. Hartwig, J. H.; Stossel, T. P. J. Biol. Chem. 1975, 250, 5696-5705.
20. Flory, P. J. Principles of Polymer Chemistry; Cornell: Ithaca, NY, 1953; p. 379.
21. Niederman, R.; Amrein, P. C.; Hartwig, J. J. Cell Biol. 1983, 96, 1400-1413.
22. de Gennes, P.-G. Scaling Concepts in Polymer Physics; Cornell: Ithaca, NY, 1979; pp 77ff.
23. Pearson, D. S.; Graessley, W. W. Macromolecules 1978, 11, 528-533.
24. Stossel, T. P.; Hartwig, J. H.; Yin, H. L.; Zaner, K. S.; Stendahl, O. I. Cold Spring Harbor Symposium XLVI, 1982, p.569.
25. Nossal, R. Macromolecules 1985, 18, 49-54.

RECEIVED April 3, 1987

Chapter 16

Thermally Reversible Hydrogels

Swelling Characteristics and Activities of Copoly(N-isopropylacrylamide–acrylamide) Gels Containing Immobilized Asparaginase

Liang Chang Dong and Allan S. Hoffman

Chemical Engineering Department, Center for Bioengineering, FL-20, University of Washington, Seattle, WA 98195

Hydrogels synthesized from polymers and copolymers of N-isopropyl acrylamide (NIPAAm) shrink or swell as the temperature is raised or lowered through their lower critical solution temperature (LCST). We show here that when an enzyme is immobilized within such gels it may be "switched" on and off reversibly as the temperature is cycled. Such catalytic hydrogels may be used to control reactions by a thermal feedback mechanism.

Hydrogels may be synthesized by polymerizing or copolymerizing a variety of mainly hydrophilic monomers with minor amounts of crosslinking agents (1). If the monomers chosen are precursors of water soluble polymer or copolymer backbones which exhibit a phenomenon known as a lower critical solution temperature (LCST), (2) then the gel made from them will shrink significantly over a relatively narrow temperature range as the temperature is raised to the LCST and above (3-6). One can change the LCST of the gel, the rates of shrinking and swelling, and the permeation rates of substances within these hydrogels by copolymerizing the LCST monomer with more hydrophilic or more hydrophobic monomers (7-9).

Since the deswelling and shrinking occur over a relatively narrow temperature range, one may release or "deliver" at these specific temperatures, substances which have been previously absorbed into the gel. The reverse process is also possible, wherein substances in the solution are absorbed into the gel when it is cooled and reswells. In such a manner, thermally reversible gels have been applied for delivery (4) or separation (4,6) of substances to and from the surrounding aqueous medium. Drug delivery from uncrosslinked thermally reversible copolymers has also been studied, where the copolymer contains hydrophobic segments which act as "crosslinkers" and prevent it from dissolving in aqueous solutions (10). Specific binding pair ligands, such as antibodies, antigens and haptens may be immobilized on the polymer backbones used to prepare the gels (4,11-14). Then one can selectively bind and remove from the surrounding medium, substances which are specifically bound to the immobilized ligand. An immunodiagnostic assay has been developed on this principle (12,14). One can subsequently deliver these same substances to a surrounding medium when it contains an eluting solute (4,13).

In this paper we have immobilized an enzyme within a thermally reversible hydrogel. Immobilized enzymes have been used in a variety of applications, ranging from treatment of diseases to sensors, assays, and industrial processes (15-20). When an enzyme is immobilized within a gel which exhibits reversible shrinking and swelling as the temperature is raised and lowered through the LCST of the gel matrix polymer, the enzyme may be switched off and on as the substrate diffusion rate is regulated by the gel pore size (5). In addition to enzymes, a variety of catalysts, cocatalysts or reactants may be immobilized within LCST hydrogels. We propose that such catalytic, thermally reversible gels may be used to control reactions rates and temperatures by a thermal feedback mechanism.

We report here on copolymer hydrogels of N-isopropyl acrylamide (NIPAAm) and acrylamide (AAm) which are crosslinked with methylene-bis-acrylamide (MBAAm) and which contain the enzyme asparaginase immobilized within the gel.

Materials and Methods

Materials

N-isopropyl acrylamide (NIPAAm) was obtained from Eastman Kodak. Acrylamide (AAm, electrophoresis grade), methylene-bis-acrylamide (MBAAm, electrophoresis grade), tetramethylethylenediamine (TEMED), and ammonium persulfate were obtained from Aldrich. L-asparaginase amidohydrolase (asparaginase) derived from *Escherichia Coli* was obtained as ELSPAR from Merck & Co., Inc. Asparagine, Trizma base (tris(hydroxymethyl)aminomethane) and Sigma Ammonia Color Reagent (Nessler reagent) were obtained from Sigma, and Triton X-100 was procured from Packard Instrument Company. All chemicals were used as received, and solvents used were reagent grade. PD-10 Sephadex columns were purchased from Pharmacia.

Methods

The methods of gel synthesis, immobilization of monomer conjugated enzyme, assay of enzyme activity, and determination of gel water content have been published elsewhere (4,5). A schematic of the synthesis is shown in Fig. 1. The gel compositions are identified as "NA-100" (100% NIPAAm), "NA-95" (95% NIPAAm, 5% AAm), "NA-90" (90% NIPAAm, 10% AAm) and "NA-85" (85% NIPAAm, 15% AAm); all are based on mole percents of monomers. Total monomer concentration was always 1.75 M. The experiment to determine the temperature dependence of enzyme activity was carried out after the enzyme reversibility experiment.

Results and Discussion

Poly(NIPAAm) has been previously shown to have an LCST ca. 31-33° (21) while copolymers of NIPAAm and AAm have LCST's which rise as the AAm content increases (5, 7-9). At a sufficiently high content of AAm, the LCST phenomenon is no longer observed. Figure 2 illustrates the temperature dependence of relative gel water contents for copolymer gels of NIPAAm and AAm. The sharpest drop in water content with temperature is seen for the 100% NIPAAm gel. As the AAm content increases, the drop becomes flatter, and occurs at higher temperatures.

Figures 3 and 4 show the kinetics of water deswelling of the NA-100 and NA-95 gels. It can be seen that as little as 5% AAm has a significant effect on both the rate and extent of deswelling at temperatures between ca. 34° and 40°. This is the region where collapse of the poly(NIPAAm) gel would be occurring due to the 31-33° LCST of poly(NIPAAm). The LCST of a copolymer of 95% NIPAAm/5% AAm has an LCST around 34-38°, as estimated from Fig. 2. Relatively rapid collapse of this gel would be expected only above 40°, as seen in Fig. 4.

The specific enzyme activities of the gels are shown in Fig. 5 as a function of increasing temperature. It can be seen that the enzyme activities parallel the water contents of the gels seen in Fig. 2. All enzyme gel activities rise with temperature, as expected, until the gel LCST region is reached. These data indicate that the activity of an immobilized catalyst (enzyme) may be "shut off" by raising the temperature above a critical temperature. This is happening because shrinkage of the gel with loss of pore water will both retard or eliminate diffusion of reactants (substrates) into the gel and products out of the gel, as well as change the microenvironment of the enzyme. A rise in temperature in some reaction systems (including the body) could be undesirable and the ability of such a solid phase enzyme gel to shut off a reaction over a narrow temperature range may be useful for control of reaction rates and temperatures by this feedback mechanism.

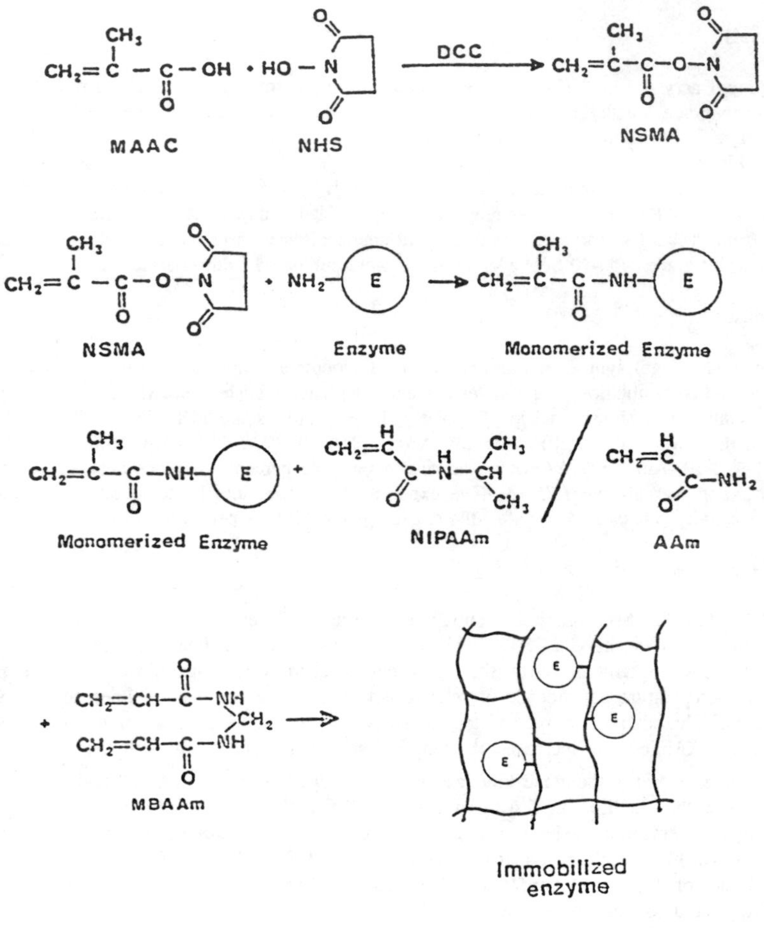

Figure 1. Schematic of synthesis of enzyme immobilized within hydrogel exhibiting thermally reversible shrinking and swelling.

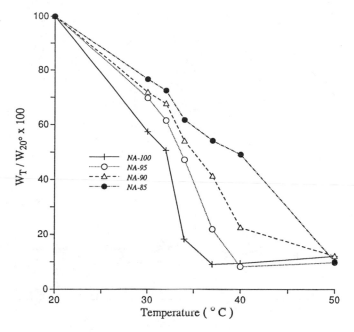

Figure 2. Deswelling ratios for NIPAAm-co-AAm hydrogels at different temperatures (24 hr. equilibration at each temperature).

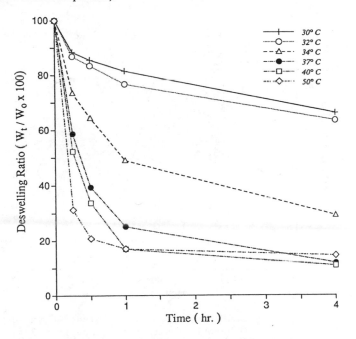

Figure 3. Water deswelling kinetics of NA-100 gel.

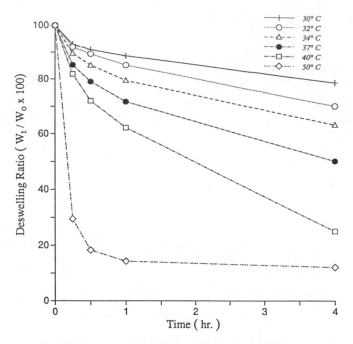

Figure 4. Water deswelling kinetics of NA-95 gel.

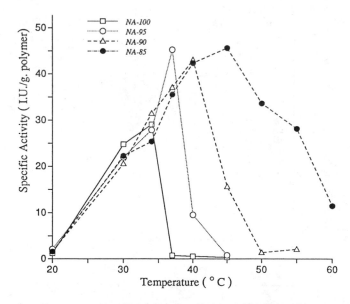

Figure 5.   Temperature dependence of immobilized enzyme activity
in LCST hydrogels.   (Reproduced with permission from Ref. 5.
Copyright 1986 Elsevier Science.)

For a catalytic gel to be most useful for such reaction control, it must act reversibly. We have also studied the specific enzyme activities of the gels by cycling them between 30°C and 40°C. Figure 6 is a schematic of the protocol used. The results are shown in Figs. 7-10. It is evident that the enzyme activity is reversible in all of these gels. In addition, there is an especially dramatic drop in gel enzyme activity in going from 30° to 40° for the NA-100 and NA-95 gels in all three cycles. This is in sharp contrast to the NA-90 and NA-85 gels which show a rise in activity for the same temperature changes, again in all three cycles. This is expected, because the NA-90 and NA-85 gels are still below their LCST's at 40°. The data in Fig. 8 suggest that the level of enzyme activity at 40° for all of the NA gels may be in proportion to the "free pore water". The data also suggest that as much as 30-35% water is "bound" by the polymer chains within the gel matrix and not available as "pore" water. Thus the enzyme may be difficult to reach or even unavailable to substrate in the NA-100 and NA-95 gels at 40°. In addition, diffusion of the aspartate product molecules out of the gel would also be retarded.

It can also be noted that all of the gels rise in enzyme activity at 30° as the number of 30°-40° cycles increases. (Compare Fig. 7 to Fig. 9 to Fig. 10) This may be due to scission of some crosslinks as the gels swell and shrink during the temperature cycling and/or to relative movements of the enzyme and polymer segments within the gel which provide more rapid access of substrate (asparagine) to the enzyme as well as more rapid diffusion of product (aspartate) away from the enzyme, with increasing number of cycles.

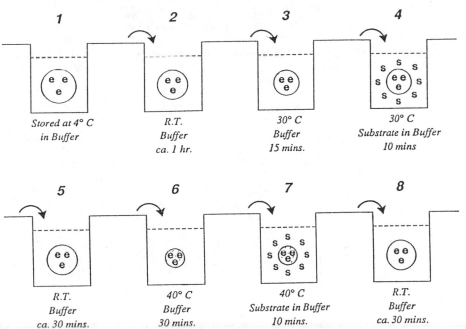

Repeat cycle from steps 3 to 8 two more times

Figure 6. Schematic of temperature cycle protocol used to measure reversibility of immobilized enzyme activity in LCST hydrogels. (Reproduced with permission from Ref. 5. Copyright 1986 Elsevier Science.)

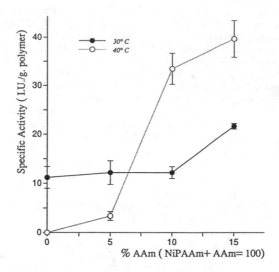

Figure 7. Dependence of immobilized enzyme activity on composition of LCST hydrogels at 30° and 40°: first temperature cycle.

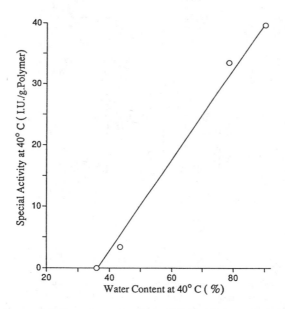

Figure 8. The change of enzyme activity at 40°C in the NA series of gels (first cycle) as a function of the gel water contents at 40°C.

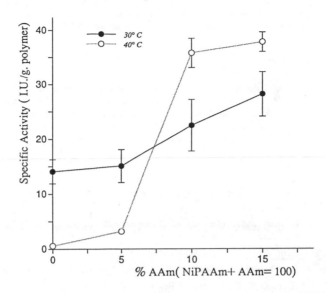

Figure 9. Dependence of immobilized enzyme activity on composition of LCST hydrogels at 30° and 40°: second temperature cycle.

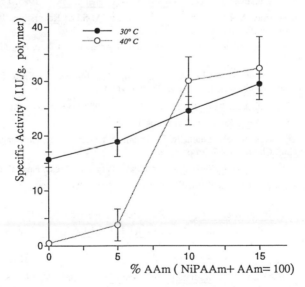

Figure 10. Dependence of immobilized enzyme activity on composition of LCST hydrogels at 30° and 40°: third temperature cycle.

In summary, we have shown for the first time that catalysts such as enzymes may be immobilized within LCST hydrogels. These gels may be warmed above their LCST's, significantly reducing the enzyme activity of the gel. We have also shown that this phenomenon is reversible. We propose that such gels may be used to control reaction rates and temperatures by a feedback mechanism.

Acknowledgments

We would like to acknowledge the support of Genetic Systems Corporation (GSC). In addition, one of the authors (ASH) is grateful for many stimulating discussions he has had with GSC personnel, especially Nobuo Monji, Carole Ann Cole, John Priest, John Plastino and Karen Auditore-Hargreaves. We also want to thank Ali Afrassiabi, Sara Shoemaker and Cheryl Kruesel for their help on the manuscript, and Wu-Xiao-Ying for her help in the laboratory.

Literature Cited

1.   Ratner, B. D.; Hoffman, A. S.; in Hydrogels; Andrade, J. D., Ed.; ACS Symposium Series, 1976; No. 31, p 1.

2.   Franks, F.; Chemistry and Technology of Water Soluble Polymers, Finch, C. A., Ed.; Plenum Press: New York, 1983; Chapter 9.

3.   Tanaka, T.; Scient. Amer., 1981, 224, 124-138.

4.   Hoffman, A. S.; Afrassiabi, A.; Dong, L. C.; J. Contr. Release, 1986, 4, 213-222.

5.   Dong, L. C.; Hoffman, A. S.; J. Contr. Release, 1986, 4, 223-227.

6.   Freitas, R. F. S.; Cussler, E. L.; Chem. Eng. Sci., (in press).

7.   Chiklis, C. K.; Grasshoff, J. M.; J. Polym. Sci., 1970, A2, 1617-1626.

8.   Taylor, L. D.; Cerankowski, L. D.; J. Polym. Sci (Polymer Chem.), 1975, 13, 2551-2570.

9.   Priest, J. H.; Murray, S. L.; Nelson, R. J.; Hoffman, A. S.; in Reversible Gelation of Polymers, (Published in this Symposium volume.)

10. Okano, T.; Bae, Y. H.; Kim, S. W.; Presentation at Amer. Chem. Soc. Mtg.: New York, NY, April 14-18, 1986.

11. Cole, C. A.; Schreiner, S. M.; Priest, J. H.; Monji, N.; Hoffman, A. S.; in Reversible Gelation of Polymers, (Published in this Symposium volume.)

12. Monji, N.; Hoffman, A.S.; Appl. Biochem. Biotech., 1987 (to appear in April, 1987 issue.)

13. Hoffman, A.S.; J. Contr. Rel., 1987 (in press).

14. Auditore-Hargreaves, K.; Houghton, R. L.; Monji, N.; Priest, J. H.; Hoffman, A. S.; Nowinski, R. C.; Clin. Chem., 1987 (in press).

15. Guilbault, G. G.; Enzymatic Methods of Analysis, Pergamon Press: New York, 1970.

16. Hoffman, A. S.; Schmer, G.; Kraft, W.; Harris, W., Trans. Amer. Soc. Artif. Internal Organs, 1972, 18, 10.

17. Zaborsky, O.R.; Immobilized Enzymes, CRS Press: Cleveland, OH, 1973.

18. Messing, R. A., Ed.; Immobilized Enzymes for Industrial Reactors, Academic Press: New York, 1975.

19. Maugh, T. H.; Science, 1984, 223, 474-486.

20. Dong, L. C.; Hoffman, A. S.; Radiation Phys. and Chem., 1986, 28, 177-182.

21. Heskins, M.; Guillet, J.E.; J. Macromol. Sci. - Chem., 1968, A2, 8, 1441-1455.

RECEIVED June 15, 1987

Chapter 17

N-Isopropylacrylamide and N-Acryloxysuccinimide Copolymer

A Thermally Reversible, Water-Soluble, Activated Polymer for Protein Conjugation

Carol-Ann Cole[1], Sigrid M. Schreiner[1], John H. Priest[1], Nobuo Monji[1], and Allan S. Hoffman[2]

[1]Genetic Systems Corporation, 3005 1st Avenue, Seattle, WA 98121
[2]Chemical Engineering Department, Center for Bioengineering, FL-20, University of Washington, Seattle, WA 98195

A copolymer capable of reaction with biologically active proteins was synthesized by a free radical polymerization in tetrahydrofuran (THF) under anhydrous conditions using azobisisobutyronitrile as the thermal initiator. Longer chain polymers were prepared using benzene instead of THF to avoid chain transfer. The thermally reversible phase transition properties of the copolymers suggested potential applications to the technologies of product isolation and pollutant removal. Conjugation of a monoclonal immunoglobulin to the copolymer is described and utilized in a novel antigen capture fluorescence immunoassay for human IgG.

Poly(N-isopropylacrylamide) (polyNIPAAM), formed by a free radical polymerization of N-isopropylacrylamide, is a water soluble, temperature sensitive polymer. In aqueous solution, it exhibits a lower critical solution temperature (LCST) in the range of 30–35°C depending on the concentration and the chain length of the polymer. Thus, as the solution temperature is raised above the LCST, the polymer undergoes a reversible phase transition characterized by the separation of a solid phase which redissolves when the solution temperature is lowered below the LCST. Its physicochemical properties have been investigated by several laboratories (1-3).

This thermally reversible precipitation suggested potential applications to the technology of reaction product isolation. It could be used as a tool to allow isolation of a specific product from a totally soluble reaction by raising the temperature.

The first step in the process was to covalently incorporate biologically active protein molecules into this polymer. Methods analogous to previous reports (4-6) involved first adding a functional group to the protein that would provide it with the ability to polymerize, such as a vinyl or substituted vinyl group, followed by copolymerization with the N-isopropylacrylamide monomer in aqueous solution using N,N,N',N'-tetramethylethylenediamine and

ammonium persulfate as redox initiators. The disadvantages of this
procedure were first, that the protein was subjected to two
reactions which could result in diminution of the biological
activity and second, the results were difficult to control.
Therefore the preparation of an activated, preformed polymer which
was capable of reacting directly with the protein molecules in
solution provided a less traumatic one-step incorporation of the
protein into the polymer. This new method retained the biological
activity of the attached protein and was more reproducible. As one
possible application of our technology, the development of a novel
immunoassay is also described here.

EXPERIMENTAL

General. All chemicals and biochemicals were obtained from Sigma
Chemical Company or Aldrich Chemical Company unless otherwise
mentioned. N-Isopropylacrylamide was purchased from Eastman Kodak
Company. Azobisisobutyronitrile was purchased from Polysciences,
Inc. Organic solvents were AR or HPLC grade. THF was pretreated to
control peroxide formation (7). Water was deionized and distilled
using a Corning MP-6A still. Nitrogen was prepurified grade. Mouse
monoclonal antibodies, 2HI (anti-human kappa, IgG_2) and 3F6
(anti-human gamma, IgG_2), were produced and purified by
Dr. Edward Clark, Immunology Department, Genetic Systems
Corporation. The hydroxylapatite used was DNA-Grade, Bio-Gel HTP,
Bio-Rad Laboratories. Pierce Protein Assay Reagent was used to
determine the protein concentrations of the copolymer/Ig conjugates.

N-Acryloxysuccinimide. Prepared as described by Pollak et al. (4)
and used without recrystallization. Melting point (68.5-70°C),
FT-IR and NMR agreed with the literature values.

Anhydrous Copolymerization of NIPAAM and N-Acryloxysuccinimide
(NASI). In a modification of the procedure of Pollak et al., (4),
NIPAAM (5 g, 44 mmol), NASI (0.372 g, 2.2 mmol) and
2,2' azobisisobutyronitrile (AIBN, 0.021 g, 0.13 mmol) were
dissolved in 50 ml of dry tetrahydrofuran. The magnetically stirred
solution was degassed, heated to 50°C for 24 hours under positive
nitrogen pressure, and allowed to cool. The reaction mixture was
filtered (0.45 µ teflon filter) and the filtrate volume reduced by
half. Ether was added with mixing to precipitate the copolymer.
The precipitate was filtered off, washed with ether, and dried under
vacuum to yield 4.7 g of dry product (A-poly-2). Thin layer
chromatography on silica gel using dichloromethane/methanol (93:7)
showed only a trace of free monomer. This activated copolymer was
soluble in water, THF, CH_2Cl_2 and DMF. It was reproducibly
prepared in good quantity and stored in the solid state for months,
protected from moisture, without loss of activity.

Anhydrous PolyNIPAAM Homopolymer (A-poly-1). This homopolymer was
prepared by the method described for A-poly-2 except that no NASI
was added to the reaction.

Anhydrous NIPAAM Homopolymers and NIPAAM-NASI Copolymers using
Benzene as solvent. The procedure was the same as described for

A-poly-2 except benzene or benzene/THF mixtures were used as the reaction solvent. After polymerization, the reaction mixture was allowed to cool. If solid polymer was present, the solvent was removed by syringe and replaced with THF (50 ml). The mixture was stirred at room temperature (anhydrous conditions, positive nitrogen pressure) until all solids had dissolved. This solution was filtered through glass wool and the filtrate was added to ethyl ether (200 ml) with vigorous stirring to precipitate the polymer which was isolated as previously described. If no solid was present, the reaction mixture was filtered through glass wool and precipitated in ether.

Aqueous PolyNIPAAM Homopolymer (PolyNIPAAM). To 20 mg NIPAAM dissolved in phosphate buffered saline, 2.3 mg of ammonium persulfate and 9.3 mg of N,N,N',N'-tetramethylethylenediamine (TEMED) was added to initiate the free radical polymerization. The mixture was then incubated for 3 hours at room temperature. The polyNIPAAM was isolated by precipitation in 14.3%, by volume, saturated $(NH_4)_2SO_4$. After removal of residual $(NH_4)_2SO_4$ by ion exchange chromatography (Bio-Rad AG501-X8D), polyNIPAAM was stored as the lyophilized solid.

LCST. We determined the lower critical solution temperature (LCST) of the polymer at various concentrations by visual observation of the temperature at which turbidity first appeared in a solution immersed in a silicone oil bath with the temperature raised at the rate of 3°C/hour.

Estimation of Polymer Sizes by Gel Permeation Chromatography. The copolymer (1 mg) was dissolved in 1 ml of phosphate buffered saline (PBS), pH 7.4, and applied to a column of Sephacryl S-300 (1 x 108 cm) or Sephacryl S-400 (1 x 114 cm). The column was eluted with PBS at a flow rate of 0.2 ml/min. The elution profile of the copolmer was monitored by its absorbance at 214 nm. Bovine serum albumin (BSA) was chromatographed for comparative purposes and polyacrylamide standards (Modchrom, Inc.) were used.

Conjugation of Immunoglobulin (Ig) to the Activated Copolymer and Isolation of Copolymer/Ig Conjugate by Hydroxylapatite Chromatography. A monoclonal immunoglobulin (2 mg) dissolved in 2.0 ml of 0.1 M HEPES (N-2-hydroxyethylpiperazine-N'-ethanesulfonic acid) buffer, pH 7.5, was added to 100 μl of DMF containing 20 mg of activated copolymer. After thorough mixing, the solution was incubated for 2 hours at room temperature. The volume of solution was adjusted to 3.0 ml with distilled water and 0.5 ml of saturated $(NH_4)_2SO_4$ was added to precipitate both the copolymer and copolymer/Ig conjugate, leaving unconjugated Ig in the solution. The precipitate was collected by centrifugation at 1500 xg for 15 min. at 20°C. Unconjugated Ig was removed by repeated precipitation of the copolymer/Ig conjugate in 14.3% by volume of saturated $(NH_4)_2SO_4$. The final pellet was completely dissolved in 6 ml of 0.01 M phosphate buffer, pH 6.8. This solution was then applied to a column (1.5 x 1.0 cm) of hydroxylapatite (HA) equilibrated with 0.01 M phosphate buffer, pH 6.8 (conditions under which only the

copolymer/Ig conjugate binds). The column was eluted with 0.01 M
phosphate until no more copolymer and/or protein was detectable in
the eluate. The elution buffer was then changed to 0.3 M phosphate,
pH 6.8, to elute the bound conjugate. The eluted fractions which
contained Ig were pooled together. The yield of Ig as a copolymer
conjugate was about 80% (1.6 mg protein).

Antigen Capture Fluorescence Immunoassay for Human IgG. A series of
human IgG standards were prepared in phosphate buffered saline
containing 1% (W/V) bovine serum albumin (PBS/BSA) to the following
concentrations: 0, 0.19, 0.38, 0.75, 1.5, 3.0 µg/ml. An
A-poly-2/anti-human kappa monoclonal antibody (designated 2H1)
conjugate (MAb unlabeled) was prepared as described above. A
monoclonal antibody specific for the gamma chain of human IgG
(designated 3F6) was labeled using fluorescein isothiocyanate (Fl).
    The assay was performed as follows: To 300 µl of PBS/BSA was
added the following reagents: 50 µl of A-poly 2/2H1 conjugate
(4.5 µg MAb), 50 µl of 1% of polyNIPAAM (as a co-precipitating
agent), 50 µl of IgG standard and 100 µl of 3F6/FL (1 µg
MAb). The reaction mixture was incubated for 60 minutes at room
temperature to allow specific binding to occur. The temperature was
then raised to 45°C for ten minutes to precipitate the polymer. The
resultant precipitate was pelleted by centrifugation at 4,000 xg for
5 minutes at 37°C. The supernatant was withdrawn and the
precipitate was redissolved in 1 ml of ice-cold PBS. The
temperature was again raised to 45°C to precipitate the polymer, the
resultant precipitate was pelleted by centrifugation, the
supernatant was withdrawn, and the pellet redissolved in 200 µl of
ice-cold PBS. A 150 µl aliquot if the resultant solution was
diluted into 1,350 µl of PBS and the fluorescence measured in a
fluorimeter (λ_{ex} 495 nm, λ_{em} 520 nm).

RESULTS AND DISCUSSION

Activated Copolymer. Using procedures and modifications of
procedures described by Pollak et al. (4) we synthesized
N-acryloxysuccinimide and copolymerized it with
N-isopropylacrylamide in anhydrous tetrahydrofuran at 50°C using
azobisisobutyronitrile (AIBN) as thermal initiator (Figure 1). The
result was a watersoluble, activated copolymer in which the
N-acryloxysuccinimide provided functional groups which readily
reacted with by the amino groups of lysine residues in proteins. We
designated this particular activated copolymer where the molar
reaction ratio was 20 NIPAAM/1 NASI as A-poly-2.
    Unlike the polyNIPAAM homopolymer prepared in aqueous solution
which has an apparent molecular weight of about 130,000, the
apparent size of the anhydrous copolymer (A-poly-2) was much
smaller. A-poly-1, an anhydrous homopolymer and all the copolymers
prepared using THF as the reaction solvent, gave the same
chromatographic profile and apparent molecular weight as A-poly-2
using Sephacryl S-400. These results are indicative of the
chain-transfer activity of the solvent, THF, which was also noted by
Pollak et al. (4). Gel permeation chromatography comparisons with
protein using Sephacryl S-300 and PBS showed that A-poly-2 coeluted
with bovine serum albumin (BSA) which has a molecular weight of

about 70,000. An absolute molecular weight analysis (performed by Modchrom, Inc., Mentor, Ohio, using GPC/SEC detected by differential viscometry) of the activated copolymer, which had a 40 NIPAAM/1 NASI molar reaction ratio, gave: Intrinsic viscosity = 0.092 dl/g and MW_N = 400, MW_p = 1865, MW_w = 2,725 and MW_z = 7,400.

To provide higher molecular weight polymers, we prepared a polyNIPAAM homopolymer and some NIPAAM/NASI activated copolymers at various molar reaction ratios using benzene as the reaction solvent, thus avoiding the chain-transfer activity of tetrahydrofuran (Figure 2). These polymers from benzene were even larger than the polymers from aqueous solutions, and we then prepared a range of homopolymers and activated copolymers using various benzene/tetrahydrofuran solvent ratios, thus providing a range of polymer size as choices for different applications.

Co-existence curves of the A-poly-2 copolymer before and after the hydrolysis of active ester groups indicated that, in both water and PBS, the copolymer with intact active esters had an LCST a few degrees lower (29 ä 31°C) than that of the hydrolyzed copolymer (31 ä 34°C).

When Ig was conjugated to A-poly-2 at a reaction ratio of 2 mg protein to 20 mg A-poly-2, about 80% of the added Ig was conjugated to A-poly-2 (Figure 3). The thermal phase separation characteristics of these conjugates were quite different from those of the unconjugated copolymer. Aggregation of the copolymer/Ig conjugate was not visually detectable at or above the LCST, due to the submicron size of the aggregated particles. When laser light scattering was employed for measurement of particle aggregation, however, we found that the LCST of the copolymer/Ig conjugate was about the same as that of the hydrolyzed A-poly-2. These studies indicated that, although the physical characteristics of the aggregated particle changed due to protein conjugation, the LCST of the copolymer attached to the protein remained the same.

Application. Using the copolymer-Ig conjugate, we developed a novel polymer-based immunoassay utilizing the demixing behavior of polyNIPAAM at or above the LCST as the separation technique. Briefly, essential features of the method in a double antibody antigen capture assay include: (a) admixing in solution the polymer/first antibody (specific to one epitope of an antigen) conjugate, the biological fluid sample suspected of containing the antigen and the second antibody (specific to a different epitope of the antigen)/signal conjugate at a temperature below the LCST to form a "sandwich"-type immune complex in the solution; (b) raising the temperature of the solution above the polymer's LCST to cause the polymer/immune complex sandwich to precipitate; (c) measuring the amount of signal found in the precipitate to determine the concentration of the antigen. A brief sketch of our assay is shown in Figure 4. In this paper we have used an antigen capture fluorescence immunoassay for human IgG to demonstrate the utility of this system (Figure 5).

Immunoassays have found wide applications in the field of clinical diagnostics for the detection and measurement of drugs, vitamins, hormones, proteins in general, metabolites, microorganisms, and other substances of interest in biological

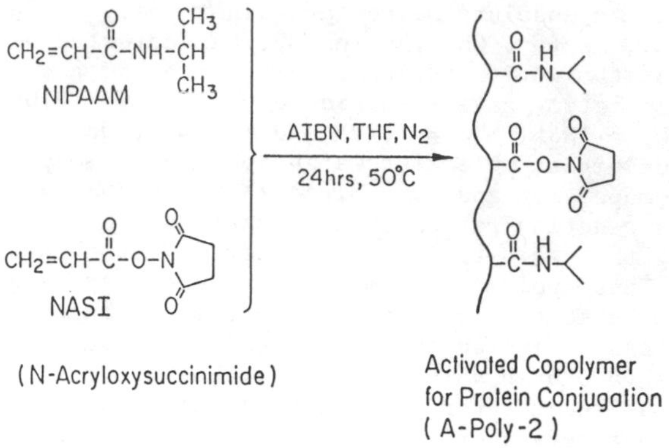

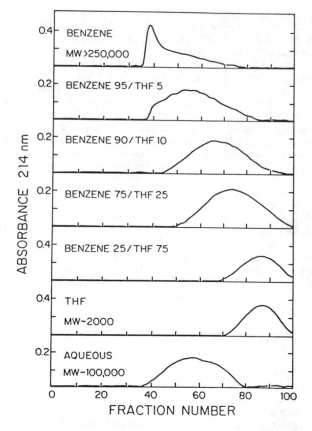

Figure 1.   Anhydrous preparation of activated copolymer.

Figure 2.   Sephacryl S-400 (PBS) chromatographic profiles
of polyNIPAAM homopolymers prepared in various reaction
solvents.

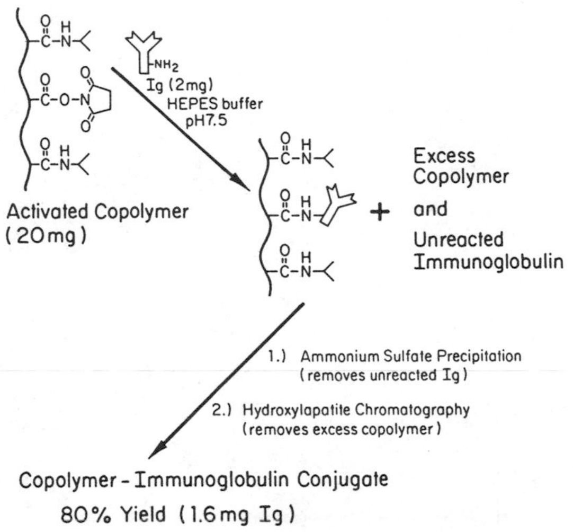

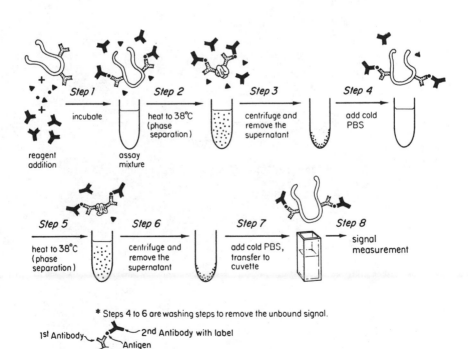

Figure 3.   Conjugation of activated copolymer to immuno-globulin.

Figure 4.   Thermally induced precipitation immunoassay procedure.

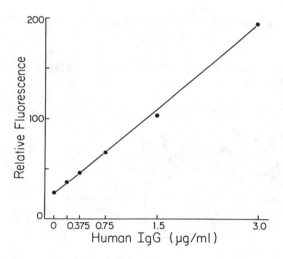

Figure 5.   Antigen capture fluorescence immunoassay for human IgG.

fluids as well as in process streams and environmental waters
(8–10). Immunoassays can be divided into two general categories,
homogeneous and heterogeneous. In a homogeneous immunoassay, the
signal emitted by the specifically bound, labeled reactant is
different from the signal emitted by the free labeled reactant.
Hence, bound and free can be distinguished without physical
separation. Homogeneous immunoassays have the advantages of being
rapid, easy to perform, and rapidly amenable to automation. Their
principle disadvantages are that they are relatively prone to
interferences, generally limited in sensitivity, and mainly limited
to lower molecular weight analytes (11). In a heterogeneous
immunoassay on the other hand, the signal emitted by the bound
labeled reactant is indistinguishable from the signal emitted by the
free-labeled reactant; therefore, a separation step is required to
distinguish between the two. Most of the heterogeneous immunoassays
employ at least one reactant immobilized on a solid phase. Since
the kinetics of reaction between an immobilized antibody (or
antigen) and its binding site tend to be slower than the kinetics of
the same reaction occuring in solution, long incubation times are
frequently required. Heterogeneous assays also tend to be
time–consuming and labor–intensive due to the requirement of
multiple wash steps. However, they are generally more sensitive
than homogeneous assays, less prone to interferences and can be used
with both low and high molecular weight analytes. Numerous
separation methods are described in the literature and have been
used in heterogenous immunoassays (9, 11).

   Our thermally induced phase separation immunoassay offers
several advantages over other heterogeneous immunoassays. First,
the specific binding reactions occur in solution rather than on a
solid phase. Hence the reaction kinetics are more favorable,
leading to reduced induction times. Second, non–specific binding or
entrapment is very low. This is probably related to the fact that
the polymers which may be used are water soluble and thus reasonably
hydrophilic, unlike conventional solid phase systems (ex., latex)
which utilize polystyrene, or other hydrophobic polymers. Third,
the signal may be concentrated by redissolving the precipitated
polymer in a substantially smaller volume than the original volume
of the assay (e.g., in the assay described in this paper the final
pellet was redissolved into a 200 μl volume of PBS instead of the
original 500 μl volume). In addition, in this paper we have used
centrifugation in our assay; however, other methods such as
filtration are equally possible.

   Finally, it should be noted that this general technique may be
used for a wide variety of separation processes in addition to
immunoassays, where the isolation of a specific component in a
biological fluid, industrial process stream or body of water is
desired. Thus, product recovery and/or toxin or pollutant removal
processes are possible with this methodology.

Acknowledgments

We thank Dr. George B. Benedek and Dr. George Thurston, Department of Physics, Massachusetts Institute of Technology, and Dr. J. M. Schurr, Department of Chemistry, University of Washington, for light scattering measurements and interpretations.

Literature Cited

1. Wooten, W. C.; Blanton, R. B.; Coover, H. W., Jr. J. Polym. Sci. 1957, 25, 403–412.
2. Heskins, M.; Guillet, J. E. J. Macromol. Sci. 1968, A2(8), 1441–1455.
3. Hirokawa, Y.; Tanaka, T. J. Chem. Phys. 1984, 81, 6379–6380.
4. Pollak, A.; Blumenfeld, H.; Wax, M.; Baughn, R. L.; Whitesides, G. M. J. Am. Chem. Soc. 1980, 56, 6324–6336.
5. Plate, N. A.; Valuev, L. I.; Chupov, V. V. Pure and Appl. Chem. 1984, 56(10), 1351–1370.
6. Nowinski, R. C.; Hoffman, A. S. U. S. Patent 4 511 478, 1985.
7. Burfield, D. R. J. Org. Chem. 1982, 47, 3821–24.
8. Langone, J. J.; Van Vunakis, H., Eds.; Immunochemical Techniques. Part B. Methods in Enzymology, 1981, Vol. 74; Academic Press: New York.
9. Langone, J. J.; Van Vunakis, H., Eds.; Immunochemical Techniques. Part C. Methods in Enzymology, 1981, Vol. 74; Academic Press: New York.
10. Langone, J. J.; Van Vunakis, H., Eds.; Immunochemical Techniques. Part D. Methods in Enzymology, 1982, Vol. 84; Academic Press: New York.
11. Miyai, K. Adv. Clin. Chem. 1985, 24, 61–110.

RECEIVED January 24, 1987

Chapter 18

Lower Critical Solution Temperatures of Aqueous Copolymers of *N*-Isopropylacrylamide and Other *N*-Substituted Acrylamides

John H. Priest[1], Sheryl L. Murray[1], R. John Nelson[1], and Allan S. Hoffman[2]

[1]Genetic Systems Corporation, 3005 1st Avenue, Seattle, WA 98121
[2]Chemical Engineering Department, Center for Bioengineering, FL-20, University of Washington, Seattle, WA 98195

High polymers of N-isopropyl acrylamide (NIPAAM) exhibit a lower critical solution temperature (LCST) in phosphate buffered saline: above 31°C precipitation occurs, with minimal concentration dependence. Copolymers of NIPAAM with acrylamide (AAM), N-methyl acrylamide (NMAAM) and N-ethyl acrylamide (NEAAM) exhibited LCSTs elevated in proportion to their comonomer content. As expected acrylamide was the most effective at elevating the LCST of the copolymer formed. However, NEAAM was more effective than NMAAM. The reason for this is not clear. In contrast, copolymers of NIPAAM with N-t-butyl acrylamide (NTBAAM) exhibited LCSTs that were lowered as a linear function of the comonomer input ratio. Copolymers with N-n-butyl acrylamide (NNBAAM) displayed similar behavior up to 40% NNBAAM, but then the LCST dropped abruptly fron 17°C to below zero. The use of these copolymers in diagnostics and bioseparations is discussed.

The water solubility at room temperature of polymers of N-substituted acrylamides changes abruptly as the N-alkyl substituent is changed from ethyl to butyl. PolyAAM,* polyNMAAM and polyNEAAM are all soluble in water, while polyNNBAAM and polyNTBAAM are insoluble in water under ambient conditions. It is interesting to note that polyNIPAAM is positioned in this series at the border between the very soluble and the very insoluble, and it exhibits a lower critical solution temperature (LCST) in water at 31–33°C (1-3). Below the LCST, a 20% solution of polyNIPAAM can be prepared. Above the LCST the solubility of polyNIPAAM is less than 10^{-3}%. The dramatic solubility difference below and above the LCST allows the quantitative removal from solution of the polymer and any material specifically bound to it. This phenomenon has been exploited for a number of uses, among them the delivery or separation of biomolecules to or from aqueous solutions (4, and references therein) and in an immunoassay (5,6).

Assays based solely on polyNIPAAM to cause quantitative
separations lack the flexibility for choosing the assay temperature,
since the polymer precipitates at or near 31°C. For many
immunoassays it is desirable to incubate the antibody with the
sample at 37°C or above (7). For others it may be desirable to
incubate at low temperatures, such as overnight at 4°C, followed by
precipitation at room temperature. The latter avoids the necessity
of heating a centrifuge above 22°C. A third application of the LCST
phenomenon to diagnostics is in assays based upon the binding of a
DNA probe to its complementary sequence in a sample to detect, for
example, viral or bacterial nucleic acids, or hereditary diseases
such as sickle cell anemia or ß thallasemia (8). However, these
hybridization assays require incubation at 50–60°C in high salt
(9). The ability to fine-tune the LCST of polyNIPAAM–based
copolymers extends the potential of this technology.

The purpose of this study was to prepare a series of random
copolymers of NIPAAM with predictable and well defined temperatures
of precipitation covering the range of 0 to 45°C, as well as some
that precipitate above 55°C under the conditions of high salt used
in DNA hybridization assays. The N-substituted acrylamides offer
the greatest chemical similarity to NIPAAM and therefore should
copolymerize randomly with the latter (10). Thus, copolymers of
NIPAAM with AAM, NMAAM, NEAAM, NNBAAM and NTBAAM were prepared at
selected monomer ratios and their aqueous solution behavior was
evaluated.

EXPERIMENTAL

Materials NMAAM, (Pfaltz and Bauer), NEAAM, NNBAAM, NTBAAM
(Monomer–Polymer and Dajac Laboratories, Inc., Trevose, PA), NIPAAM
(Eastman Kodak Company, Rochester, NY), AAM, ammonium persulfate
(Bio-Rad Laboratories, Richmond, CA) and TEMED (Sigma Chemical Co.,
St. Louis, MO) were used as received. NEAAM was also obtained from
Polysciences. Sephacryl S-400 was obtained from Sigma. All other
chemicals were reagent grade or better.

Polymerizations Where possible, polymers and copolymers were
prepared in normal saline buffered with 10 mM sodium phosphate
(PBS), pH 7.4, by room temperature initiation of 1% monomer
solutions using 40 mM TEMED (HCl) and 5 mM ammonium persulfate.
However, due to poor solubility, 0.2% solutions of NTBAAM and
proporationately lower initiator concentrations were used.
PolyNEAAM was also synthesized by polymerization in tetrahydrofuran
as described by Cole et al. (5).

Lower Critical Solution Temperatures LCSTs were determined from
plots of optical density at 600 nm versus temperature for 0.03%
solutions of each polymer in PBS and were defined as the temperature
at which $A_{600} = 0.1$. Temperatures were raised at less than 0.3°C
per minute and were measured with a thermometer that had been
calibrated against an NBS primary standard thermometer. LCSTs for
Figure 6 were determined from the cloud points of 0.01% solutions.

Gel Permeation Chromatography   The relative molecular weights of the copolymers were compared by chromatography on a 1.0 x 116 cm Sephacryl S-400 column with detection by absorbance at 214 nm. This also enabled the determination of the relative efficiency of polymerization reactions via integration of the total column volume (V_t) peak. This was possible because the monomers are the predominant species of small molecules that absorb at 214 nm.

Analysis of the Copolymerizabilities of Monomers   The composition of the copolymers formed was determined by measuring the relative amounts of each monomer, NIPAAM and AAM, that remained in solution after a copolymerization. Copolymerizations were terminated by addition of 1 ml of reaction mix to 9 ml of 0.1% phosphoric acid at 50°C, followed by centrifugation of a 0.4 ml aliquot at 6,500 x g for 5 minutes in an Eppendorf microfuge. After 100 fold dilution of an aliquot of the supernate, 200 μl of this was injected onto an IBM reversed phase C_{18} HPLC column pre-equilibrated with 2% acetonitrile in 0.1% aqueous phosphoric acid and the eluent monitored at 214 nm. The monomers were eluted using a 0.1% aqueous phosphoric acid (solvent A): acetonitrile (solvent B) gradient as follows: for 5 minutes the solvent was 98% solvent A and 2% solvent B, followed by a linear gradient to 80% A and 20% B over 10 minutes. After 5 more minutes at 80% A and 20% B, the solvent was returned to 98% A and 2% B.

RESULTS

The LCSTs of copolymers of NIPAAM with AAM, NMAAM or MEA were elevated as a regular function of their comonomer input ratio (Figure 1.) As expected, acrylamide was the most effective at raising the LCST of the copolymer formed, but surprisingly NEAAM was more efficient than NMAAM. Since substitution of isopropyl groups with methyl groups has less effect than substitution with ethyl groups, one might expect polyNMAAM to exhibit an LCST. Below 95°C it did not, but polyNEAAM exhibited an LCST between 85°C and 90°C. This was true whether the NEAAM is polymerized using TEMED-persulfate or AIBN, ruling out an initiator effect on the LCST. Copolymers of NIPAAM with AAM, NMAAM and NEAAM were also analyzed by gel permeation chromatography both for molecular weight of the copolymers and for polymerization efficiency. A representative chromatogram is illustrated in Figure 2. The results of the analysis indicated no significant differences in the polymerization reactions which would explain the greater effectiveness of NEAAM over NMAAM at raising the LCST of the copolymer formed (Table I). The gel permeation chromatogram of polyNEAAM was also not significantly different from that of polyNIPAAM.

Additional tests of the randomness of the copolymers were conducted. Plots of absorbance at 600nm versus temperature for the polymer and the copolymers did not reveal any differences indicative

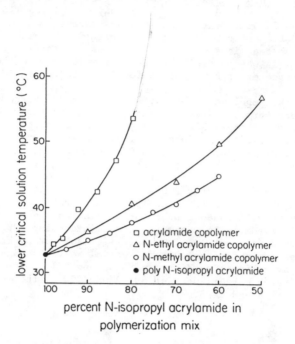

Figure 1.   Lower critical solution temperatures of copolymers of
N-isopropyl acrylamide with other N-alkyl acrylamides as a function
of monomer input ratios.

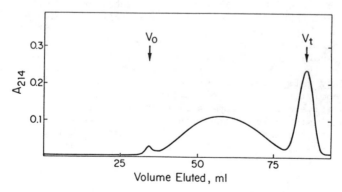

Figure 2.   Sephacryl S-400 Chromatogram of Acrylamide/N-isopropyl
Acrylamide (10/90) Copolymer.

Table I. Results of Gel Permeation Chromatographic
Analysis of Copolymers of NIPAAM

Polymer	Kav^1	Residual Monomer (%)
polyNIPAAM	0.42	5.3
polyNIPAAM-AAM	0.45	7.9
polyNIPAAM-NMAAM	0.40	5.6
polyNIPAAM-NEAAM	0.40	5.1

$$^1K_{av} = \frac{V_e - V_o}{V_t - V_o}$$

where
V_e = elution volume of the polymer
V_o = column void volume
V_t = total column volume

of heterogeneity (Figure 3). However, the randomness of the copolymers of NIAPAAM and AAM was best supported by measurement of the copolymerization reactivity ratios for the two monomers. Figure 4 shows the results for a 10 minute reaction, after which at least 87% of the monomers had polymerized. These results indicated that the copolymerization was almost perfectly random ($r_1=r_2=1.0$). This high extent of polymerization usually accentuates deviations from random copolymerization using this protocol, but none was seen even after 3 hours (data not shown).

Copolymerization of NIPAAM with NTBAAM proved to be an effective method for producing material with an LCST that was lowered in direct and apparently linear proportions to the amount of NTBAAM added (Figure 5). The poor water solubility of NTBAAM was apparently not a problem. Likewise NNBAAM demonstrated a similar dependence of LCST on co-monomer input ratio up to a point. Copolymers containing 40% or more NNBAAM, however, would not redissolve in PBS at any of several temperatures including -2 and -4°C. Thus it was not possible to produce copolymers of NIPAAM and NNBAAM that precipitate between 0 and 17°C. Beyond a critical number of n-butyl side chains per polymer molecule water solubility virtually disappears.

As observed for other copolymers that exhibit an LCST ($\underline{3}$), sodium chloride depresses the LCST of NIPAAM copolymers (Figure 6). The difference appears to be very large for NIPAAM copolymers in 0.9 M sodium chloride versus PBS (15 to over 20°C). These studies indicated that the NIPAAM-AAM copolymer that precipitated most efficiently above 55°C and below 65°C in 0.9M NaCl contained 67% NIPAAM and 33% AAM.

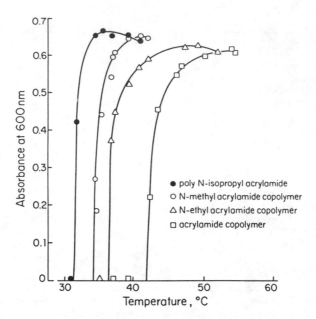

Figure 3.   Turbidity versus Temperature Curves for poly-N-isopropyl
acrylamide and its copolymers.

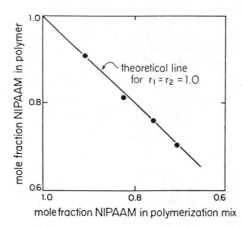

Figure 4.   Copolymerization plot for acrylamide and N-isopropyl
acrylamide (NIPAAM).

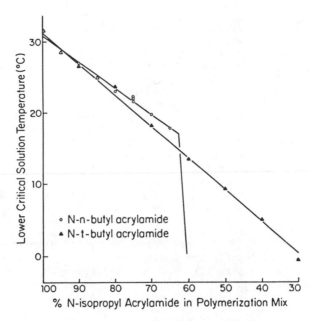

Figure 5. Lower Critical Solution Temperatures of Copolymers of N-isopropyl Acrylamide and N-n- and N-t-butyl Acrylamide as a Function of Monomer Input Ratios.

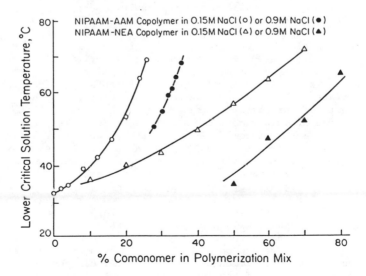

Figure 6. Lower Critical Solution Temperatures of Copolymers of NIPAAM and NEA or AAM in 0.15 M and 0.9 M NaCl.

DISCUSSION

Using N-isopropyl acrylamide and acrylamide or other N-substituted
acrylamides it is possible to design copolymers that will
precipitate at any desired temperature between 0 and 65°C. It is
not surprising that acrylamide is the most effective comonomer in
raising the LCST.
    However, the greater effectiveness of NEAAM over that of NMAAM
at raising the LCST of the copolymer is difficult to explain. If
the NEAAM had contained a larger amount of polymerization inhibitor
than the other monomers, which would have lowered the molecular
weight of the polymer formed, the LCST might have been higher. This
would also have lowered the extent of polymerization. Less than 1%
of this kind of impurity could have these effects and still meet the
purity specifications of the manufacturer. This was found not to be
the case by the two criteria of polymer molecular weight and extent
of polymerization. In addition, while the discrepancy between the
literature values for the LCST for polyNEAAM (74°C) (3) and those
determined in our laboratories (85-90°C) also points to the NEAAM as
the cause, the relatively poor efficiency by which NMAAM raises the
LCST of its NIPAAM copolymers indicates that the latter is the
abnormal monomer (Figure 1). For our purposes acrylamide appeared
to be the best choice for a comonomer for the synthesis of high LCST
copolymers, especially since it can be obtained in very high purity.
    For these copolymers to be used in immunoassays, an antibody
specific for the analyte of interest must be covalently bonded to
them. This can be accomplished by the synthesis of an activated
polymer followed by conjugation to an antibody (5). However, one may
also accomplish this via the aqueous copolymerization (or
terpolymerization) of an antibody-monomer conjugate with the free
monomer (or monomers) by methods previously described (11-13). Due
to the necessity to efficiently incorporate antibody into these
copolymers, a high extent of polymerization was desirable. This
does not significantly change the LCSTs of copolymers of NIPAAM and
AAM (3). However the determination of copolymerizability of the two
monomers by the classical method of analysis of the polymer
composition is usually not valid at high extents of polymerization.
While deviations from random copolymerization are obscured by
measurements of the polymer composition at high conversion, they
are amplified by measurement of the residual monomers. The finding
of almost perfectly random behavior by these two monomers indicated
to us that they had passed a critical and sufficient test. While
our copolymerization reactivity ratios for NIPAAM and AAM disagree
with those of Chiklis and Grasshoff (10), the extent of the
disagreement is relatively small. Similar disagreements are often
found in the literature for other pairs of monomers (14). Thus the
discrepancies could easily be due to the differences in
polymerization conditions, such as pH, initiators and
concentrations, monomer concentrations, etc.
    Many immunoassays are performed at 37°C or above (7). An
advantage of the novel immunoassay methodology disclosed in the
previous paper is that it avoids a significant problem encountered
with many heterogeneous immunoassays, that of slow kinetics when
binding of a molecule in solution to a solid surface is involved.

The ability to incubate a AAM–NIPAAM copolymer–antibody conjugate with the sample at 37°C should further improve this advantage.

The effect of the butyl side chains on the LCST's of copolymers of NIPAAM is interesting, especially in the case of the n–butyl copolymer. One hypothesis is that the n–butyl groups associate and precipitate more readily than the less flexible t–butyl groups do. This is consistent with the observation that poly–N–n–propyl acrylamide is insoluble at room temperature in water (3).

For use in immunoassays, copolymers that precipitate at 0 to 17°C are difficult to synthesize by this method, especially when considering a third monomer component such as an antibody–monomer conjugate. Perhaps a better method in this case is the conjugation with activated copolymers (5), or the use of copolymers of AAM and NNBAAM.

Another application of this methodology is to use several different copolymers to detect multiple analytes in a single sample. Each polymer would have a different antibody attached and be precipitated at a different temperature. This appears to be possible since one copolymer that precipitates at a lower temperature does not appear to remove a copolymer with a higher LCST from solution. (J. H. Priest, unpublished observations). It is also conceivable that a DNA probe–based assay could be included with a panel of immunoassays. After removal of the various antibody–copolymer conjugates at lower temperature sodium chloride would be added, the hybridization would be performed at 55°C and the DNA–copolymer conjugates precipitated at 65°C.

Acknowledgments

We wish to thank Dr. Niels H. Andersen and associates of the Department of Chemistry, University of Washington, for many NMR, infrared and mass spectral analyses.

Abbreviations

AAM, acrylamide; NMAAM, N–methyl acrylamide; NEAAM, N–ethyl acrylamide; NNBAAM, N–n–butyl acrylamide; NTBAAM, N–t–butyl acrylamide; NIPAAM, N–isopropyl acrylamide; LCST, lower critical solution temperature; TEMED, Tetramethylethylenediamine; PBS, phosphate–buffered saline; AIBN, 2,2' azobis(isobutyronitrile).

Literature Cited

1. Heskins, M.; Guillet, J. E. J. Macromol. Sci. Chem. 1968, A2 (8), 1441.
2. Haas, H. C.; MacDonald, R. L.; Schuler, A. N. J. Polymer Sci. 1970, 8 (part A–1), 3405.
3. Taylor, L. D.; Cerankowski, L. D. J. Polymer Sci. 1975, 13, 2551.
4. Hoffman, A. S.; Afrassiabi, A.,; Dong, L. C., this symposium.
5. Cole, C–A.; Schreiner, S. M.; Priest, J. H.; Monji, N.; Hoffman, A. S., this symposium.
6. Jones, T.; Houghton, R. L. Clin. Chem. 1986, 32, 1067.

7. Tsang, V. C. W.; Wilson, B. C.; Peralta, J. M. In Immunochemical Techniques; Longone, J. J.; Van Vunakis, H., Eds.; Methods in Enzymology Vol. 9, part E Academic Press, Orlando, Florida, 1983.
8. Meinkoth, J.; Wahl, G.   Anal. Biochem. 1984, 138 267-284.
9. Young, B. D.; Anderson, M. L. M.   In Nucleic Acid Hybridization, A Practical Approach; Hames, B. D.;Higgins S. J., Eds.; IRL Press, Washington D.C., 1985.
10. Chiklis, C. K.; Grasshoff, J. M. J. Polymer Sci. 1970, 8, 1617.
11. Pollak, A.; Blumenfeld, H.; Wax, M.; Baughn, R. L.; Whitesides, G. M. J. Am. Chem. Soc. 1980, 56, 6324-6336.
12. Plate, N. A.; Valuev, L. I.; Chupov, V. V. Pure and Appl. Chem. 1984, 56(10), 1351-1370.
13. Nowinski, R. C.; Hoffman, A. S. U.S. Patent 4 511 478, 1985.
14. Young, L.J.   In Polymer Handbook, (Brandrup, J.; Immergut, E. H., Eds.) p.II-105. 2nd Edition, John Wiley ∂ Sons, New York, 1974; II-105.

RECEIVED April 24, 1987

Chapter 19

Polymer Network Studies Using Paramagnetic Probes: Cu(II) in Cross-Linked Polyacrylamide Gels

Gary C. Rex and Shulamith Schlick

Department of Chemistry, University of Detroit, Detroit, MI 48221-9987

The microstructure of water as the swelling fluid in crosslinked polyacrylamide gels has been studied using hydrated Cu(II) as the paramagnetic probe. The Electron Spin Resonance spectrum of the probe indicates a distribution of the $g_{//}$ and hyperfine splitting $A_{//}$ from the ^{63}Cu nucleus along the symmetry axis of the hydrated cation. The widths $\delta g_{//}$ and $\delta A_{//}$ of these distributions in the swollen network were evaluated for network pore diameters in the range .7 to 6 nm. The method is based on ESR measurements at X-band (9GHz) and S-band(2.4GHz), between 77K and 300K. The distribution widths were found to increase with pore size but a plateau is approached for pore diameters larger than ~3 nm. This result can be related to the degree of "strain" or fluctuations in the environment of the paramagnetic cation when the amount of water in the pore increases. It appears that a continuous variation exists in the bonding parameters between the central ion and the oxygen ligands with increasing swelling of networks. The residual width, excluding broadening by the $g_{//}$ and $A_{//}$ distributions, increases in pores larger than ~3nm. Substitution of part of the paramagnetic Cu(II) ions by diamagnetic Zn(II) ions results in line narrowing in these large pores. This result indicates that the residual linewidth increase can be attributed to dipolar broadening between paramagnetic ions. A distance of 1.8 nm between the ions is deduced. An important conclusion of this analysis is that the amount of Cu(II) ions hydrated by "bulk" water is negligible in gels with pore diameters in the range studied.

Surface interactions between water and polymer networks have a profound effect on the water structure. The properties of water in these and other heterogeneous systems are sensitive to the size of the network pores and have been described by the two-phase model which assumes partition of the water between the "bulk" and the "bound" water phases[1,2]. Evidence for this partition has been obtained in several proton NMR studies[3-6] and also in ESR studies of paramagnetic probes in zeolites[7], silica gels[8] and in water containing polymers[9].

Although this model has been successful for interpretation of results in a variety of systems, recent studies indicate that it represents an oversimplification[1]. For instance dilatometry, specific conductivity and differential scanning calorimetry results obtained on networks swollen by water can be better descrobed if three types of water are assumed: bound, interfacial and bulk water[10,11]. While the properties of bulk water and to some extent of bound water are reasonably well understood, the interfacial water phase is poorly defined, probably due to the fact that it might represent a wide range of structures which depend on and are sensitive to the local environment and to the specific interactions in the system studied.

Metal ions in heterogeneous systems are expected to be solvated by the different types of water, leading to a partition of the ions between the various phases present. If the guest is paramagnetic, its solvation can be studied using the technique of Electron Spin Resonance (ESR) and used to derive information on the network-solvent interactions.

In a recent publication[12] we have presented evidence that binding of Cu(II) in crosslinked polyacrylamide (PAA) gels depends on the pore size of the gel. In crosslinked networks prepared from a high concentration of the monomers, a bimodal distribution of pore size was deduced, based on the detection of two Cu(II) sites in ESR spectra: in one site the cation is hydrated by water and bound to the polymer network through one nitrogen ligand; in the second site Cu(II) is fully hydrated by water molecules from the water pool of the pore. Gels prepared from lower monomer concentrations have pore diameters larger than 0.7 nm. In these networks only the fully hydrated Cu(II) ion is detected.

In this report we analyze the binding of hydrated Cu(II) in pores of diameter in the range 0.7 to 5.8 nm, based on ESR spectra measured at X-band (9 GHz) and S-band (2.4 GHz), in the temperature range 77 K to 300 K. It will be shown that the results obtained in this study can best be rationalized in terms of cation solvation by water whose properties vary gradually, as a function of the distance from the polymer network. No evidence was observed for the presence of measurable amounts of bulk water in pores of diameter in the range studied. Some preliminary results have already been reported[13].

Experimental

Crosslinked polyacrylamide gels were obtained by free radical polymerization of acrylamide in the presence of the tetrafunctional monomer N,N'-methylene-bis(acrylamide) (BIS) at 288 K. Gels with pore sizes in the range of interest in this study were prepared by varying the total monomer concentration in the polymerization mixture. The procedure has been described in detail[12]. Normal copper is a mixture of magnetic isotopes ^{63}Cu and ^{65}Cu in a ratio of 2:1. In this study magnetically dilute samples of Cu(II) in PAA gels were prepared using isotopically enriched ^{63}Cu in order to obtain maximum spectral resolution. ^{63}Cu (98%) as CuO was purchased from the Oak Ridge National Laboratory and was reacted with a stoichiometric amount of H_2SO_4 in order to obtain the $CuSO_4$ used for doping of the gels. The copper concentration in the gels varied between ~100 and 500 acrylamide units for each cation, depending on the water content of the gels.

ESR spectra at X-band in the temperature range 77 K-300 K were measured with Varian E-9 and Bruker ER 200D-SRC spectrometers operating at 9.3 GHz and 9.7 GHz, respectively. Spectra at 77 K were taken in a liquid nitrogen Dewar inserted in the ESR cavity. Above this temperature the Bruker Variable Temperature unit ER 4111 VT was used. The S-band spectra at 2.4 GHz and 120 K were measured at the National Biomedical ESR Center in Milwaukee, Wisconsin using a spectrometer equipped with a loop gap resonator cavity[14]. The X-band spectra were checked at 120 K and found identical to those obtained at 77 K. The absolute value of the magnetic field was measured using a Bruker ER 035M NMR Gaussmeter. Calibration of g-values was based on 2,2-diphenyl-1-picrylhydrazyl (DPPH) (g=2.0036) and Cr(III) in MgO (g=1.9800). The scan was calibrated by using a $^{55}Mn(II)$-doped MgO single crystal. A width of 433.5 G for the total separation of the ^{55}Mn sextet was used.

Spectra were simulated by a Burroughs 6800 mainframe computer at the University of Detroit and plotted on a Hewlett-Packard 7470A digital plotter.

Results

ESR spectra of Cu(II) in crosslinked PAA at X-band and 77 K for pore diameters of 1.3 and 4.0 nm are shown in Figure 1. All spectra are identical in the perpendicular region, with $g_\perp$ = 2.0081 and $A_\perp$ = 10x10^{-4} cm^{-1}. $A_\perp$ was evaluated by dividing the width of the perpendicular signal by three; $g_\perp$ was take at the magnetic field where the perpendicular signal crossed the baseline. The low field quartet of lines are centered at $g_{||}$ = 2.403. The hyperfine splitting $A_{||}$ = 135x10^{-4} cm^{-1} is due to the ^{63}Cu nucleus (I=3/2). In the parallel orientation at a given pore size we observe a gradual increase in the linewidths corresponding to m_I values of -3/2, -1/2, 1/2 and 3/2. For a given m_I value, the linewidth increases with pore size. The linewidth at half maximum intensity of the m_I = -3/2 and m_I = -1/2 transitions as a function of pore diameter can be measured directly from the ESR spectra[15] and are given in Table I.

In many systems ESR linewidths of Cu(II) depend on the microwave frequency. It was shown in some early papers that lines are broader at Q-band (35 GHz)[16] and narrower at S-band[17], compared with those at X-band. This was our initial motivation for

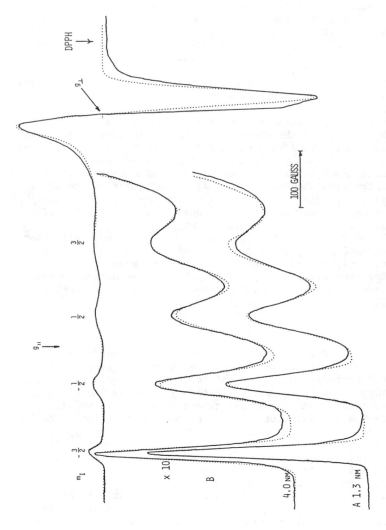

Figure 1. ESR spectra of Cu(II) at X-band and 77 K in chemically cross-linked polyacrylamide gels with pore diameters of 1.3 nm (A) and 4.0 nm (B). Solid lines are experimental spectra; dotted lines are spectra calculated using the appropriate values of ΔH^R, $\delta A_{\parallel}$, and $\delta g_{\parallel}$ given in Table I and with $g_{\parallel} = 2.408$, $g_{\perp} = 2.080$, $A_{\parallel} = 0.0134$ cm^{-1}, $A_{\perp} = 0.0009$ cm^{-1}, and $\Delta H^R_{\perp} = 30.0$ Gauss.

Table I

Variation of the experimental linewidth ΔH at X-band and S-band, the residual width ΔH^R, the width of the $g_\|(\delta g_\|)$ and the $A_\|(\delta A_\|)$ distributions as a function of pore diameter of the network

Pore Diameter (nm)	ΔH(Gauss) S-band		ΔH(Gauss) X-band		ΔH^R(Gauss)	$\delta g_\|$	$\delta A_\|$(cm^{-1}) x10^4	$\delta A_\|/\delta g_\|$ (cm^{-1})
m_I	-3/2	-1/2	-3/2	-1/2				
.7	22.3	11.3	19.2	35.6	10.9	0.0390	22.7	0.0582
1.0	23.1	11.6	19.4	36.4	11.2	0.0400	23.5	0.0587
1.3	24.2	11.8	20.8	38.0	11.3	0.0420	24.7	0.0588
1.7	24.8	12.4	21.2	39.4	12.0	0.0432	25.3	0.0586
2.3	25.3	12.7	21.6	40.0	12.2	0.0439	25.7	0.0585
3.2	26.0	14.3	22.0	40.6	14.0	0.0440	25.7	0.0584
4.0	26.4	15.4	23.6	43.2	15.2	0.0465	26.2	0.0563
5.8	26.7	15.7	25.2	44.4	15.3	0.0474	26.4	0.0557

measuring ESR at S-band, in order to interpret the experimental variation of the linewidth with pore size and m_I values.

ESR spectra of Cu(II) in crosslinked PAA at S-band and 120 K, for pore diameters of .7 nm and 3.2 nm are shown in Figure 2. Similar to the X-band spectra is the increase in linewidth for a given value of m_I as the pore diameter of the network increases. The variation of the linewidth in one type of gel as a function of the m_I value is however markedly different at S-band, compared to that observed at X-band: the linewidth corresponding to $m_I = 1/2$ is the narrowest line observed in this system. The linewidths corresponding to the $m_I = -3/2$ and $-1/2$ transitions at S-band were measured directly from the spectra and are included in Table I, together with the widths measured at X-band.

The results presented in Figures 1 and 2 are typical of Cu(II) complexes with tetragonal symmetry and can be interpreted in terms of an axial spin Hamiltonian.

$$\mathcal{H} = \beta \left[g_{||} H_z S_z + g_{\perp}(S_x H_x + S_y H_y) \right] + A_{||} S_z I_z + A_{\perp}(S_x I_x + S_y I_y) \quad (1)$$

Solution of the spin Hamiltonian to second order gives the magnetic field for the allowed transitions.

$$H(m_I, \theta) = \frac{h\nu}{g\beta} - \frac{Km_I}{g\beta} + \frac{A_{\perp}^2(A_{||}^2 + K^2)\left[I(I+1) - m_I^2\right]}{4g\beta h\nu \, K^2}$$

$$- \frac{g_{||}^2 g_{\perp}^2 (A_{||}^2 - A_{\perp}^2)^2 \cos^2\theta \sin^2\theta m_I^2}{2g^5 \beta h\nu \, K^2} \quad (2)$$

In this expression θ is the angle between the magnetic field and the symmetry axis while g and K are defined below.

$$g^2 = g_{||}^2 \cos^2\theta + g_{\perp}^2 \sin^2\theta \quad (3)$$

$$K^2 g_{||}^2 = g_{||}^2 A_{||}^2 \cos^2\theta + g_{\perp}^2 A_{\perp}^2 \sin^2\theta \quad (4)$$

Eqs. 2, 3 and 4 can be used to simulate a powder spectrum, taking into consideration the correction for the transition probability necessary in a field-swept ESR spectrum[18]. In most cases an orientation dependent linewidth is assumed in generating the spectrum:

$$\Delta H^2 = \Delta H_{||}^2 \cos^2\theta + \Delta H_{\perp}^2 \sin^2\theta \quad (5)$$

The experimentally observed variation of the linewidths with m_I and with the microwave frequency presented in Figures 1 and 2 cannot be reproduced by eqs. 2-5. An m_I variation similar to that presented here has been observed before for Cu(II) in frozen glasses and treated phenomenologically[19], by assuming an explicit m_I dependence of the linewidth ΔH, or by generating a powder spectrum through superposition of spectra with different values of the $g_{||}$ and hyperfine coupling constants[20-22].

A model proposed by Francisz and Hyde[23] has satisfactorily

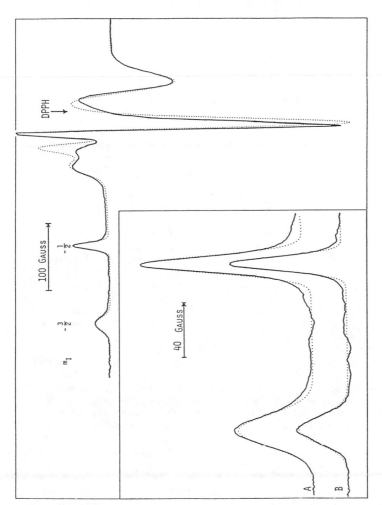

Figure 2. ESR spectra of Cu(II) at S-band (2.4 GHz) and 120 K in chemically cross-linked polyacrylamide gels with pore diameter of 3.2 nm. The inset shows the two low field lines of the parallel quartet for pore diameter of 3.2 nm (A) and 0.7 nm (B). Solid lines are experimental spectra; dotted lines are spectra calculated using the appropriate values of ΔH^R, $\delta A_{//}$, and $\delta g_{//}$ given in Table I, and with $g_{//} = 2.408$, $g_\perp = 2.080$, $A_{//} = 0.0133$ cm^{-1}, $A_\perp = 0.0005$ cm^{-1}, and $\Delta H^R_\perp = 16.5$ Gauss.

explained both the m_I and the microwave frequency dependence of the
linewidths. The model is based on the assumption that small site
fluctuations of molecular bonding parameters affect the range of
values for $g_{||}$ and $A_{||}$. According to this model, the linewidths
measured in the parallel orientation can be described by the
distribution parameters $\delta g_{||}$ and $\delta A_{||}$ and are frequency dependent.
We will interpret our results in terms of this theory.

The linewidth at half maximum intensity $H_{||}$ is composed of the
residual width $\Delta H_{||}^R$ and a contribution from the distribution δH, as
shown in eq. 6.

$$\Delta H^2 = (\Delta H^R)^2 + (\delta H)^2 \qquad (6)$$

The width due to the distribution depends on the m_I value, on the
microwave frequency ν and on the distribution parameters $\delta g_{||}$ and $\delta A_{||}$

$$(\delta H)^2 = (m_I \, \delta A \,)^2 + (\frac{h\nu \, \delta g_{||}}{g_{||}^2 \beta})^2 + \frac{2\varepsilon \, m_I \, h\nu}{g_{||}^2 \beta} \, \delta g_{||}, \, \delta A_{||} \qquad (7)$$

In eq. 7 ε is a parameter which indicates the extent of correlation
between $\delta g_{||}$ and $\delta A_{||}$. If $\varepsilon = 1$, these distributions are "perfectly
correlated", in the sense that all complexes studied have the same
ratio $\delta A_{||}/\delta g_{||}$.

The last term in the expression for the linewidth, eq. 7,
depends on the microwave frequency and can be either positive or
negative. For negative values of m_I, there is one value of m_I
which, due to cancellation of terms in eq. 7, results in the
narrowest line observed. In the system we studied, the narrowest
line is observed at $\nu = 2.4$ GHz and $m_I = -1/2$, as seen in Figure 2.

The four parameters which are involved in eqs. 6 and 7, $\delta A_{||}$,
$\delta g_{||}$, $\delta H_{||}^R$ and ε, have been calculated from the experimental values
of the linewidths corresponding to $m_I = -3/2$ and $-1/2$ at X- and
S-bands, using a least squares fitting program. The values
obtained are given in Table I and the variation of the calculated
$\delta g_{||}$ and $\delta A_{||}$ values with the pore diameter is plotted in Figure 3.
Based on these parameters, the variation of the linewidth with
frequency for networks with pore size of .7 nm was calculated and
plotted in Figure 4. It is seen that for $m_I = -1/2$ the narrowest
line is expected at a microwave frequency of ~ 2 MHz, as observed
experimentally at S-band in the system studied. The width of this
line is very close to the residual width $\Delta H_{||}^R$ deduced for this
network and given in Table I. For $m_I = -3/2$ the narrowest line is
expected to be measured at a microwave frequency of ~ 6 GHz.

In all networks studied we found $\varepsilon = 0.97 \, 0.02$; we can therefore
assume that in all complexes studied the variations in $g_{||}$ and $A_{||}$
values are perfectly correlated.

In order to check further the correctness of this procedure,
we used the deduced values for the distribution parameters and the
residual linewidth to simulate the experimental spectra at X-band
and S-band, using an expression which specifically includes the
linewidths dependence on the distribution parameters. An
orientation dependent linewidth was used, eq. 5, with $H_\perp = H_\perp^R$.
The effect of the $g_{||}$ and $A_{||}$ distributions on the linewidth was
included only for the parallel orientation[23].

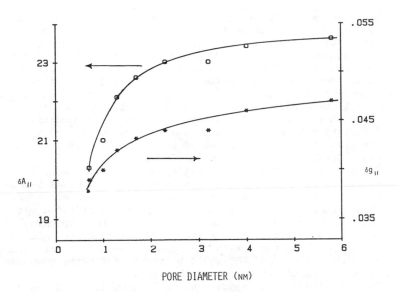

Figure 3. Values of $\delta A_{\parallel}$ and $\delta g_{\parallel}$ for Cu(II) in polyacrylamide gels as a function of pore diameter, deduced from experimental spectra at X-band, 77 K and at S-band, 120 K.

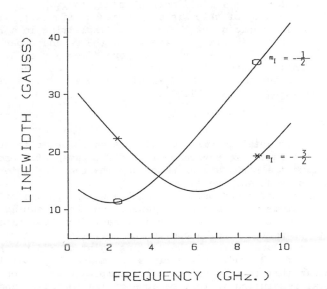

Figure 4. Variation of the linewidth of the parallel signal for Cu(II) in crosslinked polyacrylamide gels of pore diameter 0.7 nm as a function of the microwave frequency, for $m_I = -3/2$ and $-1/2$. The solid line is calculated from the values of ΔH^R, $\delta A_{\parallel}$ and $\delta g_{\parallel}$ given in Table I. Measured values are indicated.

The results of the simulations are shown in Figures 1 and 2, superimposed on the experimental results. The agreement between calculated and experimental spectra is very good. Numerous simulations were performed in order to assess the effect of the various parameters. The results indicate that the simulated spectra are very sensitive to the choice of the distribution parameters and to the values of the residual widths $\Delta H_{//}^R$ and $\Delta H_{\perp}^R$. Given the limited possibilities of measuring ESR spectra at S-band, we believe that computer simulations are a viable alternative. We also feel that the error margin in the parameters deduced by computer simulation can be decreased if ESR spectra of isotopically enriched ^{63}Cu are measured and simulated[24].

The parameters used for simulation of the absorptions in the perpendicular region, $\Delta H_{\perp}^R$ and $\Delta A_{\perp}$, were slightly lower at S-band, compared with X-band. A plausible reason for this effect might be a rhombic distortion in the local symmetry of the hydrated cation. The result would be an additional splitting in the perpendicular direction which is expected to be more evident at higher microwave frequencies. If the assumption that axial symmetry is maintained, larger values for $\Delta A_{\perp}$ and $\Delta H_{\perp}^R$ would be required for the computer simulation at X-band, as we indeed observed.

The variation of the spectra above 77 K up to 310 K was measured for pore diameters of 0.7, 1.7, 4.0 and 5.8 nm. The temperature variation is very similar for all the network studied. Typical results are shown in Figure 5 for 0.7 nm pores. The most important effect of the increase in temperature is the appearance of a signal centered at a field corresponding to g_{iso} = 2.1910 at ~245 K. The intensity of this signal increases with temperature and indicates the isotropic quartet due to Cu^{2+} splitting in a hydrated complex in which the tumbling is averaging the g- and hyperfine coupling anisotropy. In networks with pore diameters of 5.8 nm the isotropic signal is observed even at 225 K. The best resolution of the isotropic quartet is observed in all networks studied at ~275 K and we obtain A_{iso} = 12 x $10^{-4}cm^{-1}$.

Discussion

The results obtained will be interpreted in order to obtain details on the immediate environment of the paramagnetic probe and used to define the structure of water and the range of interactions between the solvent and the network.

The concept of bound or non-freezable water appears often in studies of systems which are heterogeneous on the molecular level. The term applies to water which is different from bulk water because its properties show a continuous variation as it warms up from low temperatures through the melting point of 273 K. From a large number of ESR studies of various paramagnetic probes it becomes clear that in bulk water at low temperatures, around 77 K, the spectral resolution is lost because of ice formation and aggregation of the paramagnetic probes which results in dipolar broadening. In such systems a broad (~300 G) line is the only signal observed[25,26]. Therefore in many cases various salts are added in order to obtain a glass in which ice formation and ionic aggregation are prevented.

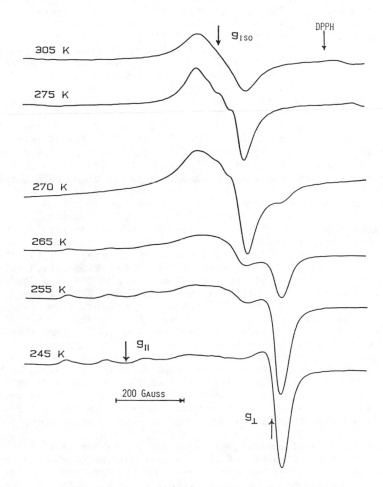

Figure 5. ESR spectra of Cu(II) at X-band in chemically cross-linked polyacrylamide gels with pore diameter of 0.7 nm as a function of temperature. The appearance of the quartet centered at g_{iso} is visible above 245 K.

For Cu(II) in water adsorbed on silica gels it was reported[25] that in gels with small pores isolated hydrated ions are detected at 77 K; in pores larger than ~4 nm a broad signal is superimposed on the spectrum of isolated ions. The appearance of the broad signal indicates aggregation of cations and the presence of bulk or freezable water. In a recent publication the Cu(II) probe was used to test the possibility of ice formation in microemulsions[27]. Ice formation was detected in one of the microemulsions studied for very slow cooling rates from ~300 K to 77 K.

Examination of the ESR spectra measured in this study, Figures 1 and 2, shows no indication of the dipolar broadened line at 77 K in the networks studied even when the samples were cooled to 77 K from ambient temperature during more than four hours. We particularly checked the S-band spectra for this line. We expect the dipolar broadening to be the same at the two frequencies but much more conspicuous at S-band because the spectrum from isolated ions is spread over a smaller range of magnetic fields at this microwave frequency. The absence of the broad line indicates that in all the networks measured Cu(II) hydrated by freezable, or bulk, water is not detected. These results are in agreement with those presented in ref. 25 which indicate the absence of bulk water in water absorbed on silica gels with pores smaller than 6 nm.

The conclusions from these ESR studies can be compared with the results of an NMR study of proton spin lattice relaxation in crosslinked polyacrylamide gels[6]. This NMR study reported various small (up to 6% of the total) amounts of bound water as a function of the length of the network between the crosslinking points which was taken as a measure of the pore size. Most of the gels studied[6] contained a high concentration of the crosslinker BIS and the resulting pore size was not calibrated. It has been shown in a study of gel filtration of model proteins that at high levels of BIS the pore size increases whereas a decrease in the pore size is expected if the results obtained at low levels of BIS are extrapolated[28]. A bimodal distribution of pore diameters is also a definite possibility. In networks prepared with high levels of BIS we have detected by ESR a bimodal distribution of pore size using the vanadyl ion, VO^{2+}, as a paramagnetic probe[29]. The large amount of bulk water reported in ref. 6 might therefore be due to the presence of very large pores which are swollen by large quantities of water.

In our system, because the amount of bulk water is negligible, we have a simpler problem and can consider only bound water within the picture of a two-phase system or bound and interfacial water if the three-phase model is adopted. Assuming as a first approximation that the pores are spherical and that the effective diameter of water is 0.03 nm[25], we can roughly estimate that the number of water layers in the pores studied ranges from 1, in the networks with pore diameters of .7 nm, to 10 in the largest pores studied. The absence of bulk water in these networks might indicate that the effect of the polymer interaction is felt through at least ten layers of water molecules. This conclusion might seem to be in contradiction with previous results which indicate that strong modification of the water structure is evident in the first two to three surface layers[27] and probably not beyond about six layers[25]. The contradiction can be rationalized in two ways.

First, the strength of the polymer-water interaction must diminish at larger distances from the network, and is clearly reflected in the distribution of the $g_{//}$ and $A_{//}$ values. As has been stated before, this distribution is due to local variation in the values of the in plane and to a smaller degree of the out-of-plane bonding parameters between Cu(II) and the oxygen ligands[23]. In the smallest pores studied most of the water is in the first two to three layers and is strongly affected by the proximity of the network, so that fluctuations in the bonding parameters are limited, if not impossible. The result is a relatively narrow distribution in the values of $g_{//}$ and $A_{//}$ and narrow observed lines. As the pores increase the ligands are less affected by the interaction with the network and wider fluctuations in the bonding parameters are observed. The deduced values of the distribution parameters increase significantly up to pore diameters of 2 nm and seem to approach a plateau for pores of diameter 3 nm, where approximately five to six layers of water exist in the pores. In order to visualize the distribution of water in the various layers, we have indicated in Figure 6 the cumulative fraction of water molecules in the first six layers, as a function of pore diameter. As seen from Figure 6, the number of layers in the largest pore is 10 but the fraction of molecules in the first 6 layers is .94, indicating that the increase in pore diameter does not increase proportionately the number of molecules of water distant to the network. The conclusion is that even if hydrated Cu(II) in layers remote from the network might be able to distort, their number is not large enough to contribute to the total signal intensity observed.

An alternative explanation for the plateau observed in the distribution parameters $\delta A_{//}$ and $\delta g_{//}$ is suggested by the deduced values of ΔH^R as a function of pore size.

In Table I we observe that the residual width changes very slightly up to and including networks with pore diameters of 2.3 nm but increases above pore diameters of 3.2 nm. We checked the source of the broadening by measuring ESR spectra of gels doped with a 1/1 mixture of Zn(II) and Cu(II) ions, for pore diameters of 0.7 and 5.8 nm. We chose to monitor the effect of this substitution by measuring the linewidth of the signal corresponding to the $m_I=-3/2$ parallel transition at X-band, which can be measured most accurately from experimental spectra. The Zn(II) substitution had no effect on the linewidth in networks with pore diameters of 0.7 nm. In the largest pores, however, the linewidth is reduced by 3 G. The increase of the residual linewidth with increase in pore diameters can therefore be assigned to dipolar broadening. Assuming that the distribution parameters do not change on Cu(II) substitution by Zn(II), we can calculate from eq. 7 the residual linewidth excluding dipolar broadening, $\Delta H_{//}^R(0)$. The result is $\Delta H_{//}^R(0)=10$ G. This value is, within experimental error, identical to the residual linewidth deduced in networks with small pores and is considered the limiting value of the linewidth in all pores, in the absence of dipolar broadening. The distance d between the cations in the large pores can be calculated by observing that the dipolar contribution $\delta(\Delta H)$ to the residual linewidth for large pores is 5.3

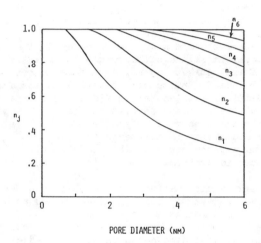

PORE DIAMETER (NM)

Figure 6. Cumulative fraction of water molecules n_j as a function of pore diameter. We have used

$$n_j = \sum_{i=1}^{j} n_i$$

and n_i as the fraction of water molecules in the ith layer.

G. Using the expression for the second moment of Gaussian lines, we can write[30]

$$\delta(\Delta H) = 2\left[\frac{3}{5} g^2 \beta^2 S(S+1)\right]^{\frac{1}{2}} d^{-3} \qquad (8)$$

If the isotropic value of g for the hydrated cation in eq. 8 above is used, we obtain the relation between the interion distance d (in nm) and the observed broadening.

$$\delta(\Delta H) = 27.193 \ d^{-3} \qquad (9)$$

We deduce that the intercation distance is 1.8 nm.

This value of d suggests that in the large pores, for example in pores with diameter of 5.8 nm, the cations are approximately at 2.0 nm from the network, not at 2.9 nm if only one cation per pore is measured. The presence of two cations per pore reduces even more the number of ions which are expected to be solvated by water removed from the polymer network. The result is that even though the pores increase in size, the distance between the cation and the network decreases.

It is possible that both explanations are valid and contribute to the observed results.

The gradual variation in the distribution parameters can be compared to the gradual change observed in the rate of proton transfer from the fluorescent probe pyranine in reversed micelles as a function of the size of the water pool[31]. The reaction rate reaches a limiting value for water pools of diameter 4 nm. In addition, a study of electron solvation in reversed micelles by pulse radiolysis indicates that both the width and the wavelength at maximum absorption vary gradually with the size of the water pool and reach limiting values in large water pools, typically of diameter 6 nm[32]. While the probes and the experimental measurements are quite different in these, and our, studies, we believe that the picture is consistent and points to an entire range of water properties, depending on the distance from network in crosslinking polymers or from the micelle boundary in reversed micelles. The picture of two or even three water phases in these systems seems to be an oversimplification indeed.

The variation of the spectra as a function of temperature in the range 77 K–310 K support the idea of the gradual change in the properties of water as the distance to the network changes. The isotropic signal indicates rapid tumbling on the ESR timescale, with a correlation time of $\sim 1 \times 10^{-8}$s. The width of the signal decreases and its intensity increases gradually above 235 K indicating a change in the mobility of the hydration water. In bulk water a sudden change is observed in the mobility around the melting point of 273 K. The fact that in the gels studied the isotropic signal is observed well below the melting point of ice indicates that the water is not "bulk" but rather bound or interfacial. At the temperatures where the isotropic signal was observed, an anisotropic signal, from hydrated Cu complexes with slower tumbling rates, is also observed. This might indicate hydration of the cation by water bound to the network (anisotropic signal) and by interfacial water (isotropic signal). The relative

intensity of the two signals changes with temperature, indicating a
temperature-dependent equilibrium. The fact that in networks with
pore diameters of 5.8 nm, the isotropic signal is detected at even
lower temperatures is very likely indicative of the larger amount
of interfacial water in these networks.

Conclusion

This report indicates that studies of polymer networks using
paramagnetic probes is capable of providing information on the
polymer-water interactions as well as on cation binding to the
polymer network.
Additional studies using paramagnetic probes in reversible
polyacrylamide gels are in progress.

Acknowledgments   This research was supported by a grant from the
Research Corporation and by an NSF equipment grant DMR-8501362 for
the purchase of the ESR spectrometer. Support of the ESR
measurements at S-band was provided by a grant NIH-RR-01008 to the
National Biomedical ESR Center. We thank Drs. J.S. Hyde and C.
Felix for their assistance with these measurements.

References

1. Fendler, J.H. Science 1984, 223, 888 and references therein.
2. Kuntz, I.D. In Magnetic Resonance in Colloid and Interface
    Science; Resing, H.A.; Wade, C.G. Eds.; ACS Symposium Series,
    Vol 34.
3. Creekmore, R.W.; Reilley, C.N. Anal. Chem. 1970, 42, 570 and
    725.
4. Fripiat, J.; Letellier, M. J. Magn. Reson. 1984, 57, 279.
5. Doskocilova, D.; Schneider, B.; Jakes, J. J. Magn. Reson. 1978
    29, 79.
6. Katayama, S.; Fujiwara, S. J. Am. Chem. Soc. 1978, 101, 4485.
7. Taarit, Y.B.; Naccache, C. Chem. Phys. Letts. 1971, 11, 11.
8. Martini, G.; Bindi, M.; Ottaviani, M.F.; Romanelli, M.
    J. Colloid Interface Sci. 1985, 108, 140.
9. Hamada, K.; Iijima, T.; McGregor, R. Polymer J. 1985, 17,
    1245.
10. Lee, H.B.; Jhon, M.S.; Andrade, J.D. J. Colloid Interface
    Science 1975, 51, 225.
11. O'Driscoll, K.F.; Mercer, D.G. In Contemporary Topics in
    Polymer Science; Shen, M. Ed.; Plenum Press: New York,
    1979; Vol. 3, p. 319.
12. Rex, G.C.; Schlick, S. J. Phys. Chem. 1985, 89, 3598.
13. Rex, G.C.; Schlick, S. Amer. Chem. Soc. Polym. Div. Preprints
    1986, 27, 339.
14. Froncisz, W.; Hyde, J.S. J. Magn. Reson. 1982, 47, 515.
15. Hubbell, W.L.; McConnell, H.M. J. Am. Chem. Soc. 1971, 93,
    314.
16. Aasa, R.; Aisen, P. J. Biol. Chem. 1968, 243, 2399.
17. Abdrachmov, R.S.; Ivanova, T.A. J. Mol. Struct. 1973, 19, 683.
18. Aasa, R.; Vanngard, T. J. Magn. Reson. 1975, 19, 308.
19. Bogomolova, L.D.; Jachin, V.A.; Lazukin, V.N.; Pavlushkina,
    T.K.; Shmuckler, V.A. J. Non-Cryst. Sol. 1978, 28, 375.

20. Griscom, D.L.; Friebele, E.J.; Siegel, G.H., Jr. Solid State Commun. 1974, 15, 479.
21. Taylor, P.C.; Bray, P.J. J. Magn. Reson. 1970, 2, 305.
22. Griscom, D.L. J. Non-Cryst. Sol. 1984, 64, 229.
23. Froncisz, W.; Hyde, J.S. J. Chem. Phys. 1980, 73 3123.
24. Cannistraro, S.; Giugliarelli, G. Chem. Phys. 1985, 98, 115.
25. Bassetti, V.; Burlamacchi, L.; Martini, G. J. Am. Chem. Soc. 1979, 101, 5471.
26. Narayana, P.A.; Li, A.S.W.; Kevan, L. J. Phys. Chem. 1982, 86, 3.
27. Bruggeller, P. J. Phys. Chem. 1986, 90, 1834.
28. Fawcett, J.S.; Morris, C.J.O.R. Sep. Sci. 1966, 1, 9.
29. Rex, G.C.; Schlick, S., to be published.
30. Abragam, A. Principles of Nuclear Magnetism; Oxford University Press: Oxford, 1983; Chapter IV, p.106.
31. Bardez,; Goguillo, B.-T.; Keh, E.; Valeur, B. J. Phys. Chem. 1984, 88, 1909.
32. Pileni, M.P.; Hickel, B.; Ferradini, C.; Pucheault, J. Chem. Phys. Lett. 1982, 92, 308.

RECEIVED January 24, 1987

INDEXES

Author Index

Audebert, Roland, 72
Berry, G. C., 129
Bloomfield, Victor A., 199
Blum, Frank D., 107
Candau, S. J., 33
Chung, B., 22
Cohen, Yachin, 181
Cole, Carol-Ann, 245
Cotts, P. M., 57
Djabourov, Madeleine, 211
Dong, Liang Chang, 236
Dormoy, Y., 33
Frost, Herbert H., 181
Guenet, J. M., 33
Hirsch, E., 33
Hoffman, Allan S., 236,245,255
Iliopoulos, Ilias, 72
Leblond, Jacques, 211
Magestro, Paul, 152
Miller, Wilmer G., 152
Möller, Martin, 87

Monji, Nobuo, 245
Mühleisen, Elke, 87
Murray, Sheryl L., 255
Mutin, P. H., 33
naNagara, Byaporn, 107
Nelson, R. John, 255
Nossal, Ralph, 224
Omeis, Jürgen, 87
Paul, C. W., 57
Priest, John H., 245,255
Quivoron, Claude, 72
Rex, Gary C., 265
Russo, Paul S., 1,152
Schlick, Shulamith, 265
Schreiner, Sigrid M., 245
Se, Kazunori, 129
Terech, P., 115
Thomas, Edwin L., 181
Wan, Wender, 46
Whittenburg, Scott L., 46
Zachariades, A. E., 22

Affiliation Index

Almaden Research Center, IBM, 22,57
Carnegie–Mellon University, 129
Centre d'Etudes Nucléaires
    de Grenoble, 115
Gen Corporation, 22
Genetic Systems Corporation, 245,255
Institut Charles Sadron, 33
Institut für Makromolekulare
    Chemie der Universität Freiburg, 87
Laboratoire de Physique
    Thermique, ESPCI 10, 211

Louisiana State University, 1,152
National Institutes of Health, 224
Unité Associée au Centre National
    de la Recherche Scientifique, 72
Université Louis Pasteur, 33
University of Detroit, 265
University of Massachusetts, 181
University of Minnesota, 152,199
University of Missouri—Rolla, 107
University of New Orleans, 46
University of Washington, 236,245,255

Subject Index

A

Acrylamide–N-isopropylacrylamide
copolymer chromatogram, 257,258f
    low critical solution
        temperature, 257,258f

N-Acryloxysuccinimide
    anhydrous copolymerization with
        N-isopropylacrylamide, 246
    preparation, 246
N-Acryloxysuccinimide–N-
        isopropylacrylamide copolymer
    anhydrous preparation, 248,250f

N-Acryloxysuccinimide-N-
  isopropylacrylamide copolymer—
  Continued
  chromatographic profiles, 249,250f
  conjugation to immunoglobulin, 249,251f
  molecular weight analysis, 248–249
Actin
  form in cytoskeletal proteins, 225
  interaction with molecules to form
    complex networks, 225–234
Actin binding protein, cross-linking
  gels, 228
Antibody bonding, of copolymers, 262
Antigen capture fluorescence immunoassay
  plot, 249,252f
  procedure for human IgG, 248
Apparent activation energy for flow,
  calculation, 68–69
Apparent molecular weight, concentration
  dependence, 95,97
Aqueous gelatin gels, properties, 211
Association of molecules with a sulfonate
  group at one chain end
  closed association model, 95
  effect of cyclohexanol on light
    scattering intensity, 91,93f
  g' ratios, 91,95f
  intrinsic viscosity vs. molecular
    weight, 91,94f
  reduced osmotic pressure vs.
    concentration, 91,92f
  sedimentation analysis, 95,96f
  temperature dependence, 91,93f
Atactic polystyrene–carbon disulfide gels,
  effect of temperature at
    gelation, 107–108
Atactic polystyrene–solvent gels,
  formation, 107
Atactic polystyrene–toluene gels
  relaxation times vs.
    temperature, 109,111f,112
  self-diffusion coefficient vs.
    temperature, 109,111f
  solvent mobility, 112–113
Autocatalytic model for physical gelation
  gel network growth mechanism, 125,126f
  kinetic small-angle neutron
    scattering, 125,127f

B

Ball-drop method, gel determination, 3
Base pairing at ends, for deoxyribonucleic
  acid gelation, 202,204,205f
Base stacking at ends, for deoxyribonucleic
  acid gelation, 202,203f
Birefringence decay, calculation, 35
Bound water, description, 274
Bulk water, electron spin resonance
  spectra, 274

C

Closed association model, concentration
  dependence of apparent molecular
  weight, 95,97
Coagulation
  process, 195,196f
  slow, *See* Slow coagulation
Coagulation of poly(1-phenylene-2-
  benzobisthiazole) solutions
  influencing factors, 144,146
  light scattering, 147
  nematic–isotropic phase
    transition, 147–149
  volume fraction, 146
Coagulation process, phase transition, 182
Coagulation studies
  diagram of phase separation, 134,135f
  process, 134
  rate measurement, 133–134
Collagen
  chemical composition, 212
  native conformation, 212
  renaturation, 212–213,215f
Collodial crystal formation
  critical ratio, 208
  dynamics, 208
  gelation of deoxyribonucleic acid
    fragment, 208
  problems with model, 209
Complexation between complementary
  macromolecules
  degree vs. polymer
    concentration, 83,84f,85
  schematic, 83,84f
Complexation equilibrium, of poly(acrylic
  acid), 74–75
Condensation polymerization of
  polyfunctional monomers, modelization of
  the systems, 83,84f,85
Cooperative diffusion, definition, 50
Copoly(N-isopropylacrylamide–acrylamide)
  gels
  change of enzyme activity vs. gel water
    contents, 241,242f
  deswelling ratios, 237,239f
  schematic of synthesis, 237,238f
  schematic of temperature, 237
  temperature dependence of immobilized
    enzyme activity, 237,240f
Copolymerabilities of monomers,
  analysis, 257
Copolymers
  antibody bonding, 262
  preparation, 256
Copolymers of N-isopropylacrylamide
  copolymerization plot, 259,260f
  gel permeation chromatographic
    analysis, 257,259t

Copolymers of N-isopropylacrylamide—
  Continued
  lower critical solution temperatures vs.
    monomer input ratio, 259,261*f*
  turbidity vs. temperature, 259,260*f*
Correlation function, calculation, 132–133
Critical exponents,
  measurements, 220,221*f*,222
Cross-linked polyacrylamide gels,
  preparation, 266–267
Cross-links in fishnet gels, 6
Crystallization, vs. gelation, 5–7
Cu(II) in cross-linked polyacrylamide gels
  dipolar contribution to residual line
    width, 277,279
  distribution parameters, 272,273*f*
  electron spin resonance spectra, 267,268*f*
  line width vs. pore size, 272,273*f*
  preparation, 267
  variations in experimental line
    width, 267,268*t*,270
Cu(II) in water adsorbed on silica gels
  dipolar broadening, 276
  ESR spectra, 276
Cyclohexane, physical gelation, 115–127
Cytoplasmic gels
  elasticity assays, 231–234
  gel fraction assay, 227–228,229*f*,230
  gelation time assay, 230–231
  reversible chain elongation
    model, 226–227,229*f*
Cytoskeletal proteins, mathematical theories
  concerning nucleation and
  polymerization, 224–225
Cytoskeletal proteins in nonmuscle cells,
  forms, 225
Cytoskeleton, definition, 224

D

Debye correlation function, calculation, 188
Degree of association, calculation for
  unimers and multimers, 98
Degree of complexation
  calculation, 75
  vs. concentration ratio, 75,76*f*
Density correlation function in the cross
  section plane, definition, 184,187
Deoxyribonucleic acid, preparation, 200
Deoxyribonucleic acid fragments
  condensation, 199
  factors influencing states, 199
  gelation, 200–205
  light-scattering behavior, 204,206
  stability, 208
  states, 199

Deuteron relaxation time, vs. temperature
  for atactic polystyrene–toluene
  gels, 109,111*f*,112
Diffusion coefficient
  application to
    non-θ conditions, 53–54,55*f*
    polymer gels, 54,55*f*
    ordinary–extraordinary transition, 54
    θ solvents, 52
  concentration dependence, 47,49*f*
  for polystyrene, 52–53
  general expression, 47–48,50,52
  microscopic expression, 52–53
Diffusion of probes through transient gels,
  analysis, 16
Diffusion rate, influencing factors, 46
Diffusional dynamics for deoxyribonucleic
  acid, semiquantitative approach, 208–209
Dipolar distribution, calculation, 277,279
Direct visualization methods of gels
  nonvisible microscopy, 14
  visible microscopy, 13–14
Dry-jet wet spinning processing,
  description, 182
Dynamic phase diagram, regimes, 47,48*f*
Dynamic probe methods, use in gel
  visualization, 16
Dynamic scattering, description, 15–16

E

Effectively cross-linked reversible gels
  characteristics, 88
  cross-link formation, 87–88
Einstein relation, expression, 50
Elasticity assays, application of elasticity
  measurements, 231–232,233*f*
Electron spin resonance (ESR) for
  steroid–cyclohexane
  amplitude variation, 120,122*f*
  gel-phase spectra, 120,122*f*
  vs. small-angle neutron
    scattering, 120,123
Electron spin resonance line width of
  Cu(II)
  distribution parameters, 272,273*f*
  effect of temperature on
    properties, 279–280
  effects of parameters, 274
  influence of microwave
    frequency, 267,270
  model for frequency dependence, 272
  pore size vs. temperature, 274,275*f*
  spectra at x-band, 267,268*f*
  variation, 270
  vs. pore size, 272,273*f*

Electron spin resonance spectra, experimental procedures, 267
Emission anisotropy of luminescent molecules
  calculation, 81
  reciprocal vs. concentration ratio, $81,82f,83$
End-to-end association for deoxyribonucleic acid gelation, model, $201-202,203f$
Equal time density correlation function, calculation, 51
Ethylene copolymer gels, gelation vs. crystallization, 6

F

Fishnet gels
  description, 7
  macroscopic examples, $8,10-11f$
  pictorial representation, $9,12f$
Fluorescence recovery methods, use in gel visualization, 16

G

Gel, definition, 3,22,171
Gel fraction assay
  amount of protein in gel vs. in extract, $227-228,229f$
  cross-linking of chains, 227
  factors influencing gel fraction, 230
  gelation threshold, 230
Gel permeation chromatography
  comparison of copolymer molecular weight, 257
  estimation of polymer sizes, 247
Gel point, definition, 220
Gel research, present strategies and future outlook, 9,13-17
Gel state, comparison to more common physical states, 4-5
Gelatin, description, 211-212
Gelation
  effect of temperature, $218,219f,220$
  mechanisms, $212-213,215f$
  vs. crystallization, 5-7
Gelation of deoxyribonucleic acid fragments
  base pairing at ends, $202,204,205f$
  base stacking at ends, $202,203f$
  effect on concentration, 201
  end-to-end association, 201
  gelation transition vs. solution conditions, 200-201
  mechanism, 201
  properties of gels, 200

Gelation of molecules with sulfonate groups at both chain ends
  effect of solvent, 100,103
  models, $100,102f$
  polymer volume fraction vs. concentration, $100,101f$
  zero shear viscosities, 103,104,105
Gelation time assay, determination, 230-231
Gels
  classification scheme, 5-7
  factors influencing formation, 5
  formation, $213-214,215f$
  melting behavior, $214,215f$
  problems in studying, 2
  role of solvent in formation, 216,218
  sol-gel transition, 218-222
  structure, 213-218
  study, 1
  supramolecular structure, $216,217f$
Green-Kubo relation, expression, 47

H

Hamiltonian, for Cu(II) complexes, 270
Helix growth
  kinetics vs. quenching temperature, $213,215f$
  two-step process, 214
Heterogeneous water systems
  Cu(II) binding in polyacrylamide gels, 266-280
  types of water, 266
High-angle light scattering photometry
  delay, completion, and duration times vs. quench, $158,161f$
  growth rate, $158,160f$
  intensification at various angles, 158
  typical set of envelopes, $158,159f$
Homopolymers, interactions, 73
Hydrogels, synthesis, 236
Hydroxylapatite chromatography, isolation of immunoglobulin-copolymer conjugate, 247

I

Immunoglobulin, conjugation to activated copolymer, $247-249,251f$
Immunoglobulin, human, antigen capture fluorescence immunoassay, 248
Immunoglobulin-copolymer conjugate
  application, 249
  isolation by hydroxylapatite chromatography, 247

Indirect visualization methods of gels
  dynamic probe methods, 16–17
  rheology, 17
  scattering, 14–16
Inhomogeneous binary mixture, free
  energy, 154
Intrinsic viscosity
  calculation, 63
  effect of aggregates, 63–64
  second viral coefficient data, 64t
  vs. solvent composition, 64,65f
Ionomers
  definition, 88
  ionic group at one end of chain, 89
  ionic groups at chain ends, 88
  random distribution of ionic groups, 88

                         K

Kerr constant, calculation, 36
Kinetic low-angle scattering envelopes
  Debye plot vs. time, 171,173f
  growth rate, 171,172f
  Guinier plot vs. time, 171,173f
  intensification during gelation, 171,172f
Kinetic model of physical gelation
  agreement with experimental
    data, 123,126f
  gel network growth mechanism, 125,126f
  kinetic small-angle neutron
    scattering, 125,127f
  phenomenological description, 123
  typical behavior, 123,124f,125

                         L

Lattice gels
  description, 7
  examples, 7
  macroscopic example, 8,10–11f
  sectorial representation, 12f
Light scattering
  apparatus for measurement, 156–157
  determination, 58–59
  effect of solvents, 61,62f,65f
  equation, 58
  measurement, 157
  plots for poly(vinylbutyral), 59,60f
Light scattering cells, description, 131–132
Light scattering from biphasic systems
  nonrandom systems, 154–156
  random systems, 153–154
Light scattering intensity
  analysis, 46
  concentration dependence, 97–98,99f

Light scattering measurements
  apparatus, 132
  correlation function calculation, 132
  photon correlation light scattering, 132
Light scattering studies, scattering vs.
  temperature, 134,136
Line width at half maximum intensity,
  calculation, 272
Local motion, measurements, 16–17
Longitudinal deuteron relaxation time, vs.
  temperature for atactic
  polystyrene–toluene gels, 109,111f,112
Low-angle light scattering photometry
  compositions and temperatures, 167,168t
  Debye plots, 158,162–165f
  Guinier intercept vs.
    temperature, 158,166f
  Guinier plots, 158,162–165f
  least-squares analysis of Guinier and
    Debye plots, 158,167t
Low molecular weight molecules,
  structure, 115–116
Lower critical solution temperatures
  determination, 247,256
  effectiveness of copolymers, 262
  vs. comonomer ratio, 257,258f
Lyotropic solutions of rigid polymers,
  properties of fibers and films, 181

                         M

Macroscopic lattice structure,
  examples, 8,10–11f
Melting behavior of gels, melting
  temperature vs. quenching
  temperature, 214
Microfibril diameter, average,
  calculated, 187
Microfibrillar morphology, effect of
  coagulation conditions, 195
Microfibrillar network, formation during
  coagulation, 182
Microfibrillar network in coagulation fibers
  and films
  electron micrographs, 184,185–186f
  SAXS measurements, 184–187
  structural model, 188
Mobility of polymer sequences
  calculation, 81
  vs. concentration ratio, 81,82f,83
Molecules with sulfonate groups at both
  chain ends, gelation, 100–105
Monomers, analysis of
  copolymerizabilities, 257
Mutual diffusion, definition, 50
Mutual diffusion coefficient,
  calculation, 51–52

N

N-substituted acrylamide polymers, effect of
  N-alkyl substituent on water
  solubility, 255
Nematic–isotropic phase transition
  disclinations in texture, 137,138*f*
  light transmission, 137,139*f*
  photon correlation function vs. reduced
    correlation, 140,143*f*,144
  photon correlation scattering, 149
  ring images, 137,138*f*
  scattering vs. temperature, 140,141*f*
  scattering vs. texture
    transition, 140,142*f*
  temperature dependence of
    scattering, 148–149
Nonassociated polymers
  characterization, 89,90*t*
  extinction vs. concentration, 90,92*f*
  functionalizations, 90–91
  synthesis, 89
Noncrystallizable polymers, gelation, 57
Nonrandom biphasic systems
  diffusion coefficient, 155
  growth rate, 155
  light scattering, 154–156
Nonvisible microscopy, use in gel
  visualization, 14
Normalized signal intensity,
  calculation, 108–109
Nuclear magnetic resonance measurements,
  experimental procedure, 108

O

Optical microscopy
  apparatus, 133
  measurements, 157
  micrograph of
    poly-γ-benzyl-DL-glutamate–
      dimethylformamide, 170*f*,171
    poly-γ-benzyl-DL-glutamate–
      toluene, 168,169*f*
Ordinary–extraordinary transition for
  deoxyribonucleic acid fragments
  colloidal crystal formation, 208
  diffusional dynamic, 208–209
  light scattering behavior, 204,206
  occurrence, 206
Osmotic pressure, concentration
  dependence, 98,99*f*

P

Particle radius, calculation, 37
Phase transition during coagulation, kinetic
  mechanism, 182

Photographic light scattering,
  measurement, 157
Polarized luminescence, for polymer
  complexes, 81,82*f*,83
Poly(acrylic acid)
  complexation, 83,84*f*,85
  degree of complexation vs.
    concentration, 75,76*f*
  effect of structure on
    conformation, 75,77*f*
  gain in viscosity vs. concentration
    ratio, 78,80*f*
  pH vs. concentration ratio, 75,76*f*
  polarized luminescence, 81,82*f*,83
  preparation, 73
  specific viscosity vs. concentration
    ratio, 75,77*f*,78,79*f*
  structure, 78,80*f*,81
Poly(benzobisthiazole) polymer
  coagulation, 133–137,144–147
  light scattering cells, 131
  light scattering studies, 134,136*f*
  nematic–isotropic phase
    transition, 137–144
  phase diagram, 144,145*f*
  preparation, 130–131
Poly(γ-benzyl-α-glutamate)
  apparatus for scattering
    measurements, 156
  high-angle light scattering
    photometry, 158,159–160*f*
  kinetic low-angle scattering
    envelopes, 171,172–173*f*
  low-angle light scattering
    photography, 168,170*f*,171
  low-angle light scattering
    photometry, 158,162–166*f*,167*t*
  optical microscopy, 167–168,169–170*f*,171
  phase boundaries, 152–153
  preparation, 156
Polyfunctional monomers, modelization
  of the system, 83,84*f*,85
Poly(*N*-isopropylacrylamide)
  anhydrous homopolymer, preparation, 246
  disadvantages for assay use, 256
  properties, 245
  solubility, 255
Polymer complexes, definition, 72
Polymer size estimation, by gel permeation
  chromatography, 247
Polymer–solvent ternary systems,
  behavior, 72
Polymers
  preparation, 256
  sources and molecular weights, 73,74
Poly(1-phenylene-2-benzobisthiazole)
  phase transitions, 129
  structure, 129–130
Poly(*p*-phenylenebenzobisthiazole)
  description, 181–182

Poly(p-phenylenebenzobisthiazole)—
  Continued
microfibrillar
    network, 184,185–186f,187–188
  scattered intensity, 184
  slow coagulation, 188–194
  structure, 183
  synthesis, 183
Poly(p-phenylenebenzobisthiazole) fibers
  differential scanning
    calorimetry, 189,193f
  electron micrographs, 189,192f
  optical micrographs, 189,191f
  X-ray diffraction, 189,194t
Poly(p-phenylenebisthiazole) fibers
  relationship between phase transformation
    and morphology, 194–195,196f
  schematic phase diagram of
    binary system, 194,196f
    ternary system, 195,196f
Polystyrene
  concentration dependence of diffusion
    coefficient, 46
  measurement of diffusion
    coefficient, 52–53
Polystyrene–toluene gels, atactic—See
  Atactic polystyrene–toluene gels
Poly(vinyl chloride)
  effect of starting concentration on
    aggregate structure, 43,45
  gelation vs. crystallization, 6
  preparation, 34
  quasi-elastic light scattering, 41–43
  transient electric birefringence, 36–41
Poly(vinylbutyral) (PVB)
  light scattering plots, 59,60f
  structure, 58,60f
  viscosity, 59
Potentiometry, of poly(acrylic
    acid), 74–75,76–77f
Proton spin–lattice relaxation in
  cross-linked polyacrylamide gels, 276
Pulsed-gradient spin-echo method,
  self-diffusion coefficient
  measurement, 108–109
Pulsed-gradient spin-echo nuclear
  magnetic resonance spectra
  behavior of toluene in atactic
    polystyrene vs.
    temperature, 109,110f
  self-diffusion coefficient of toluene in
    atactic polystyrene vs.
    temperature, 109,111f

Q

Quasielastic light scattering
  experimental procedure, 36
  scattering vector calculation, 36
  variance calculation, 36
  wavevector dependence, 41,42f,43,44f

R

Random biphasic systems, light
    scattering, 153–154
Relative viscosity, effect of
    concentration, 58
Relaxation time studies on toluene
  effects of experimental
    conditions, 112–113
  energy of activation, 112
Reverse micelle model,
    steroid–cyclohexane
    system, 118,121f
Reversible chain elongation
  average chain length, 227
  number of uncapped chains, 226–227
  polymerization scheme, 226,229f
  rate of nucleation, 226
  spontaneous nucleation, 226
Rheological measurement, gel
    identification, 3–4
Rheological observations of polyethylene
    pseudogels, deformation of the
    crystalline phase, 23,25f
Rheology, use in gel visualization, 17
Rodlike polymer gels
  binary phase diagram, 174,178f
  characteristics, 171,174
  initial growth, 177,178f
  rod diffusion, 174–177
Rodlike polymers
  behavior, 152–153
  characteristics, 152

S

Scattered intensity, measurement, 184
Scattering, use in gel visualization, 14–16
Scattering, invariant, calculation, 187
Scattering vector, measurement, 36
Scattering wavevector, calculation, 46
Second viral coefficients, effect of
    solvent, 61,63f
Self-diffusion, definition, 50
Self-diffusion coefficient
  effect of temperature, 109,111f
  measurement, 108–109
Slow coagulation
  differential scanning
    calorimetry, 189,193f
  electron micrographs, 189,192f
  optical micrograph of
    spherulites, 189,191f
Small-angle neutron scattering for
    steroid–cyclohexane system
  cross section intensity, 120
  curves for double helices, 116–117
  helices in dried gel network, 118,119f
  intensity vs. time, 120,121f

Small-angle neutron scattering
  for steroid–cyclohexane system—
  Continued
  scattering curves vs. time, 120,121*f*
  scattering intensity, 118,120
  vs. electron spin resonance, 120,123
Small-angle X-ray scattering (SAXA), for
  epoxy-impregnated poly(*p*-phenylene-
  benzobisthiazole), 187,190–191*f*
Sol–gel transition
  critical exponents, 220,221*f*,222
  effect of temperature, 218,219*f*,220
Solvent mobility in atactic
  polystyrene–toluene systems, rate, 112
Spherulites, optical micrographs, 189,191*f*
Spinodal decomposition, tests, 176
Static scattering, description, 14–15
Steady-state birefringence, vs. squared
  electric field, 37,41
Steroid–cyclohexane system
  electron spin resonance
    experiments, 120,122*f*,123
  kinetic behaviors, 123
  solidlike gel network, 116,118,119*f*
  temperature–concentration phase
    diagram, 116,117*f*
  zones of gel region, 123
Structure of gels
  amount of left-handed helices
    present, 213
  kinetics of helix growth vs. quenching
    temperature, 213–214,215*f*
  melting behavior, 214
  role of solvent in gel formation, 216,218
  supramolecular structure, 216,217*f*
Structure of polymer complex,
  cases, 78,81,82*f*
Supramolecular structure of gels
  micrographs, 216
  visualization by electron
    microscopy, 216

T

Thermally induced precipitation
  immunoassay
  advantages, 253,262–263
  applications, 253
Thermally reversible precipitation,
  disadvantages of procedures, 245–246
Thermoreversible gelation of poly(vinyl
  chloride) solutions, mechanism, 33–34
Transient electric birefringence
  decay curve, 37,40
  parameter for poly(vinyl chloride)
    solutions, 37,39*t*
  particle size, 37
  setup, 36

Transient electric birefringence—
  Continued
  steady-state variation vs. squared
    electric field, 37,41
  theory, 34–36
  time-dependent curves, 36–37,38*f*
Transient gel
  description, 8–9
  sectorial representation, 9,12*f*
Translational diffusion coefficient,
  calculation, 43
Transmittance, measurement, 133
Transport coefficient, calculation, 50–51
Transverse deuteron relaxation time, vs.
  temperature for atactic
  polystyrene–toluene
    gels, 109,111*f*,112
Tubulin, form in cytoskeletal proteins, 225
Two-phase model for heterogeneous water
  systems, evidence, 266

U

Ultra high molecular weight polyethylene
  preparation, 23
  pseudogels, 22
  structure, 22–23,24*f*
  viscoelastic behavior, 22–32
  X-ray scan, 23,26,27*f*

V

Variance, measurement, 36
Velocity correlation function,
  calculation, 51
Viscoelastic behavior of ultra high
  molecular weight polyethylene
  pseudogels
  analysis, 31–32
  deformability, 23,25*f*
  dynamic loss modulus vs. oscillation
    frequency, 26,28*f*
  dynamic storage modulus vs. oscillation
    frequency, 26,27*f*
  dynamic storage modulus vs.
    temperature, 26,29*f*
  effect of
    solution concentration, 26,30*f*
  effect of temperature, 26,28–29*f*
  rheological property measurements, 23
  rheooptical observations, 23
  studies, 26,31
Viscometry
  effect of molecular weight, 78,79*f*
  gain vs. concentration ratio, 78,80*f*

Viscometry—*Continued*
  intrinsic viscosity, 59
  viscosity of 12% PVB solutions, 59
  vs. concentration
    ratio, 75,77*f*,78,79*f*
Viscosity, measurement, 74
Viscosity of 12% PVB solutions
  effect of
    entanglements, 69
  effect of solvent composition, 68–69
  effect of structure, 69
  effect of temperature, 64,66–67*f*
  extent of aggregation, 68–70
Visible microscopy, use in gel
  visualization, 13–14

W

Water molecule fraction, vs. pore
  size, 277–278*f*
Water–polymer networks, effect of surface
  interactions on water structure, 266
Wavevector dependence
  calculation, 41
  effect of temperature, 43,44*f*

Z

Zero shear viscosities, vs.
  concentration, 103,104*f*,105

Production by Cara Aldridge Young
Indexing by Deborah H. Steiner
Jacket design by Carla L. Clemens

Elements typeset by Hot Type Ltd., Washington, DC
Printed and bound by Maple Press Co., York, PA
Dust jackets printed by Atlantic Research Corporation, Alexandria, VA

Recent Books

Personal Computers for Scientists: A Byte at a Time
By Glenn I. Ouchi
276 pp; clothbound; ISBN 0–8412–1000–4

The ACS Style Guide: A Manual for Authors and Editors
Edited by Janet S. Dodd
264 pp; clothbound; ISBN 0–8412–0917–0

Silent Spring Revisited
Edited by Gino J. Marco, Robert M. Hollingworth, and William Durham
214 pp; clothbound; ISBN 0–8412–0980–4

Chemical Demonstrations: A Sourcebook for Teachers
By Lee R. Summerlin and James L. Ealy, Jr.
192 pp; spiral bound; ISBN 0–8412–0923–5

Phosphorus Chemistry in Everyday Living, Second Edition
By Arthur D. F. Toy and Edward N. Walsh
362 pp; clothbound; ISBN 0–8412–1002–0

Pharmacokinetics: Processes and Mathematics
By Peter G. Welling
ACS Monograph 185; 290 pp; ISBN 0–8412–0967–7

Liquid Membranes: Theory and Applications
Edited by Richard D. Noble and J. Douglas Way
ACS Symposium Series 347; 196 pp; ISBN 0–8412–1407–7

*Design Considerations for Toxic Chemical
and Explosives Facilities*
Edited by Ralph A. Scott, Jr. and Laurence J. Doemeny
ACS Symposium Series 345; 318 pp; ISBN 0–8412–1405–0

*Metal Complexes in Fossil Fuels: Geochemistry,
Characterization, and Processing*
Edited by Royston H. Filby and Jan F. Branthaver
ACS Symposium Series 344; 436 pp; ISBN 0–8412–1404–2

Sources and Fates of Aquatic Pollutants
Edited by Ronald A. Hites and S. J. Eisenreich
Advances in Chemistry Series 216; 558 pp; ISBN 0–8412–0983–9

Nucleophilicity
Edited by J. Milton Harris and Samuel P. McManus
Advances in Chemistry Series 215; 494 pp; ISBN 0–8412–0952–9

For further information and a free catalog of ACS books, contact:
American Chemical Society
Distribution Office, Department 225
1155 16th Street, NW, Washington, DC 20036
Telephone 800-227-5558